P9-DWI-991

FIGHTER

THE WORLD'S FINEST COMBAT AIRCRAFT—1914 TO THE PRESENT DAY

FIGHTER

THE WORLD'S FINEST COMBAT AIRCRAFT – 1914 TO THE PRESENT DAY

JIM WINCHESTER

BARNES
& NOBLE
NEW YORK

This edition published by Barnes & Noble Publishing, Inc.,
by arrangement with Parragon Publishing.

2006 Barnes & Noble Books

M 10 9 8 7 6 5 4 3 2 1

ISBN 0-7607-7957-0

Editorial and design by
Amber Books Ltd

Printed and Bound in China

Contents

Introduction

Ever since the earliest observation aircraft were fitted with a machine gun during World War I, fighter and attack aircraft have been a key weapon in every major conflict.

The definition of fighter has come to mean an aircraft designed primarily for destroying other aircraft in the air, especially other fighters. Fighters began as 'scouts' in World War I, mainly two-seat reconnaissance aircraft sent out to survey the enemy's positions. Soon opposing scouts began to encounter each other and fighting broke out between them. The period of revolvers, rifles and even thrown objects was very brief before fixed and swivelling machine-guns appeared as standard armament.

The first German *Jastas* or hunting squadrons were formed in the summer of 1916. Prior to this, single-seat scouts were issued in small numbers to two-seater units. The *Jastas* were the first air units formed with the purpose of engaging other aircraft in combat, setting the pattern for fighter squadrons worldwide and beginning the struggle for true 'air superiority' over the battlefield.

In the interwar years, the practice of standing patrols partly gave way to the interceptor, able to climb fast to destroy incoming bombers. The Americans developed 'pursuit' aircraft with largely the same mission.

In the early years of World War II, the definition of fighter and bomber blurred somewhat, with most new aircraft and new versions of older ones able to carry bombs and or rockets. Thus the fighter-bomber was born. When air superiority was largely achieved, fighter aircraft could support the troops on the ground.

In the immediate postwar era, fighters once again became interceptors, designed to counter the threat of nuclear bombers. Many of these later gained an air-to-ground role. The same thing happened again in the late 1980s and 1990s, when fighters designed for the air defence or air superiority mission were adapted to carry precision ordnance. Conversely, the Harrier, for example, was designed for close-air support and battlefield interdiction, but variants have evolved with a significant close-in and beyond-visual-range (BVR) air combat capability.

Machine guns to missiles

The core of any fighter is its armament. The true fighter was made possible by the mechanism that allowed machine-guns to synchronize their fire with the passage of propeller blades. Although usually associated with World War I and biplanes, synchronized guns were used on many World War II fighters, such as the Curtiss P-40, Mitsubishi Zero and Focke-Wulf Fw 190.

In World War II, American single-seat fighters had a more-or-less standard armament of six 0.50-in (12.7-mm) machine-guns. Thousands of Mustangs, Hellcats, Warhawks, Corsairs and other fighters were armed with a sextet of 'fifties' and could put about 16lb (7kg) of lead on a target in three seconds of fire. Other nations put much more store in cannon that fired explosive rounds, usually of 0.78-in (20-mm) caliber. Most Focke-Wulf Fw 190s could put 26lb (12kg) of cannon and machine-gun fire onto a target in three seconds. With four 0.79-in (20-mm) Hispano cannon, a Tempest V could lay on 40lb (12kg), and the four 1.18-in (30-mm) MK 108s of the Me 262 a whopping 96lb (44kg) in the same time. The impact of only one or two of these shells could bring down a B-17, but the slow rate of fire and high closing speed lowered the chances of multiple hits.

At the end of the war, the Germans experimented with air-to-air missiles (AAMs), although they had more success with unguided rockets as an anti-bomber weapon, but guns remained the primary armament of most fighters

***Right:** The future of many air arms is represented by the F-35 Joint Strike Fighter, which seems likely to equal the sales success of the F-16.*

Above: The basic tactics of air combat were established during World War I by aces such as America's Eddie Rickenbacker.

Right: By the eve of World War II most nations had replaced their biplane fighters with monoplanes like these Hurricanes of No. 111 Squadron, seen in August 1938.

for the following decade. Aerial rocket systems, unguided but with the launch aircraft guided to the firing point by radar and ground control, entered widespread use, although were probably never fired in anger. A small number of kills were scored in Vietnam and the Middle East with air-to-ground rockets, used when the opportunity arose.

Guided air-to-air missiles were not used in combat until 1958, during tensions between China and Taiwan. The cult of guided missiles, both air- and ground-launched, had already seen gun armament omitted from most new US fighters, and in Britain all new fighter programmes except the English Electric Lightning were cancelled in favor of surface-to-air missiles (SAMs).

The Soviets (and French) retained cannon in their fighters, and most of the dogfights over the Middle East in the 1960s were gun engagements. In Vietnam the rules of engagement (and poor performance of early AAMs) saw the sophisticated American fighters often drawn into close-range dogfights within range of the more agile MiGs.

Today, missile reliability and accuracy has improved exponentially compared to the superficially similar weapons of the 1950s and 1960s. Helmet-mounted sights and thrust-vectoring controls mean that targets can be engaged which are well away from the direction in which the aircraft is pointing, and even over the pilot's shoulder.

The debate about the utility of a gun in fighters continues. The UK decided to do without cannon on most of its Eurofighter Typhoons, but at the same time US Hornets and Tomcats were using their guns in combat for the first time against ground targets in Afghanistan and Iraq. The F/A-22 Raptor and F-35 Joint Strike Fighter will use versions of the Vulcan rotary cannon that was first introduced in the 1950s.

Fighter evolution

The marketing departments of today's few remaining combat aircraft manufacturers identify five generations of postwar fighter aircraft,

L1559
L1560
L1548

although they disagree on the details. The first generation fighters were the early jets such as the F-86 Sabre, Hunter and the MiG-15 and -17. The second generation was usually supersonic and featured integrated electronics and guided missiles. Examples are the F-4 Phantom, MiG-21 and Mirage III. Third generation fighters such as the F-16, Mirage 2000 and MiG-29 introduced digital electronics and integrated systems. Many had 'fly-by-wire' control systems. The fourth generation encompasses the new fighters such as the Gripen, F/A-22 and Typhoon. These are characterized by some degree of stealth and totally integrated weapons, controls, displays and sensors. A term for this is 'sensor fusion'. Russian manufacturers in particular say that their latest prototypes represent a fifth generation, incorporating all of the above, plus thrust-vectoring engines. Despite these technological advances, the world's air forces still field large numbers of second generation and quite a few first generation jet fighters.

Increasing complexity

Fighter aircraft once took months to develop. Looking at some recent programmes, an observer might assume that a modern fighter takes nearly twenty years to move from drawing board to squadron flight line. This is not always for reasons of increased technical complexity and sophistication. Wartime urgency gives way to peacetime budgetary crunches. Today's governments tend to balk at large-scale procurement of fighters costing from $30 to $100 million each in any given fiscal period. This can be illustrated by looking at the time between first flight of the prototype and entry into service of some of the aircraft in this book. The Albatros D.I took under a month from factory to front line, the Hawker Fury, 27 months; the Supermarine Spitfire 17 months; the Focke Wulf Fw 190, 27 months; the MiG-21, about three years; the F-16, five years and the Dassault Rafale, eight or 15 years depending on which

__Below:__ By the end of the 1950s, supersonic missile-armed fighters such as the Convair F-106 were in service.

Above: Air combat was revolutionized by the development of guided air-to-air missiles such as the AIM-120 AMRAAM carried by this F-16.

prototype you choose as the starting point. In relative terms, the Eurofighter Typhoon makes the Rafale look urgent.

The role of the fighter pilot

With increasing computerization of weapons and sensor functions, it was once largely thought that the two-crew fighter had had its day. All of the current generation of superfighters were originally intended as single-seaters, with a two-seat version procured in low numbers as a less capable model for conversion training. The decreased numbers and types of fighters in most air forces' inventories has seen increasing adaptation of "pure" fighters for the strike role. The Rafale, Super Hornet, Gripen, Sukhoi Su-27 'Flanker' and now the Typhoon and MiG-29 all now have mission-capable two-seat versions. The proportion of the two-seaters ordered has been increased from original estimates in most cases, and they have taken on such extra roles as airborne command and control of other aircraft and UAVs. The exceptions to this trend are the F/A-22 and the Joint Strike Fighter, which have been designed with no dual place version at all. It remains to be seen how these aircraft will evolve in the future.

The next generation of fighters may have no crews at all, being unmanned (or in the current parlance, uninhabited) and controlled from the ground by video and satellite link. The 2003 Iraq war was notable for the complete lack of air-to-air combat, Saddam's air force preferring to hide under the sand. In the run-up to the war, however, a little-noticed first occurred when a USAF Predator unmanned aerial vehicle (UAV) fired a Stinger AAM at an Iraqi MiG-29 over the southern "no-fly zone". Unfortunately for the Predator's operators and for history, the MiG's missile arrived first. The day of the first pilot to make ace while sitting in a converted shipping container in another country, or even continent, will have to wait.

Fokker E.I—E.III

Anthony Fokker's E.III began the cycle of fighter development that saw the warring nations produce design after design in an attempt to win air superiority over the Western Front.

FOKKER E.III

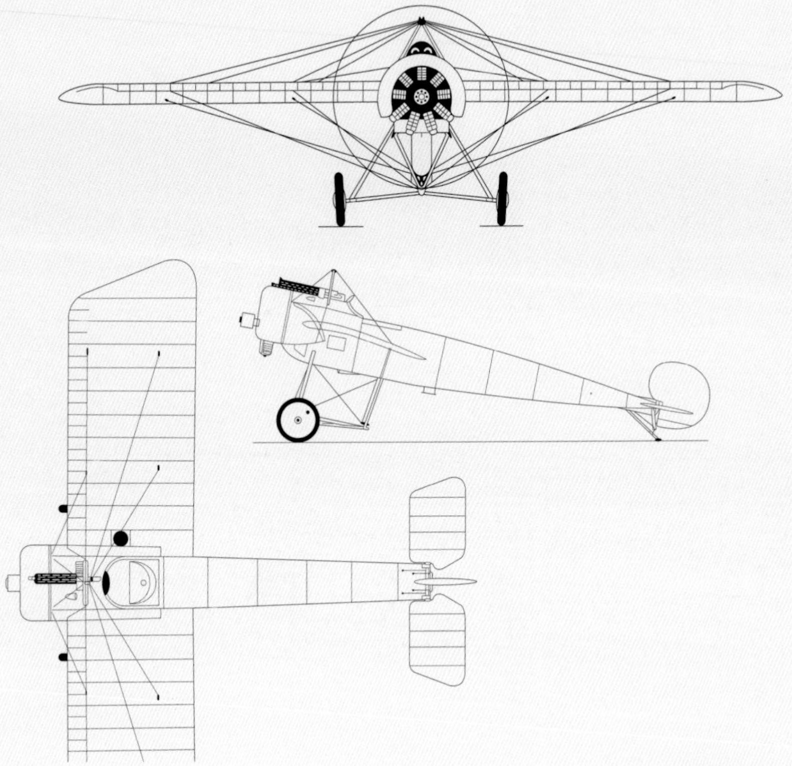

Crew: one

Powerplant: one 100-hp (74.6-kW) Oberursel UR.1 rotary piston engine

Maximum speed: 93mph (150km/h)

Combat radius: 75 miles (120km)

Service ceiling: 11,810ft (3,600m)

Weight: 770lb (349kg) loaded

Armament: one LMG 08/15 synchronized machine gun

Dimensions: span 32ft 11in (10.04m); length 23ft 11in (7.3m); height 8ft 2in (2.49m)

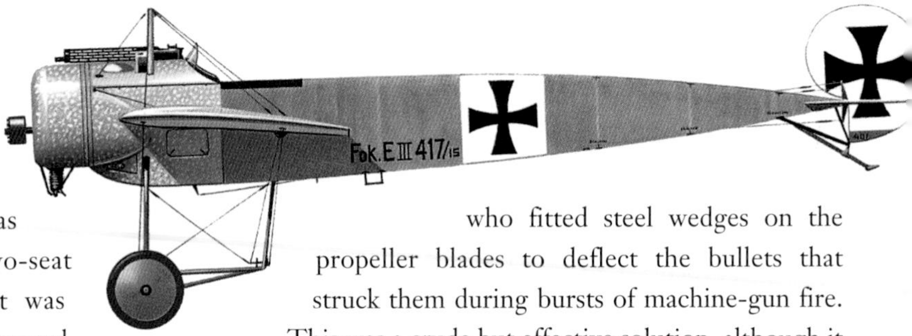

Right: *Built to a 1915 contract, this E.III was delivered in January 1916. Damaged in service, it was repaired at the factory and reissued in August.*

Far right: *Bruno Loerzer, one of the top 10 German aces of World War I with 41 victories, poses with the twentieth production E.III.*

The first aircraft that could really be called a fighter in the classic sense was the French Morane Saulnier Type L of 1915. This was actually a parasol-wing two-seat reconnaissance aircraft, but was adapted to have a fixed forward-facing armament so that a single pilot could aim the aircraft at the enemy, rather than try to fly and shoot a flexible or free weapon at the same time. The problem of not shooting one's own propeller off was partially solved by French pilot Roland Garros and aircraft designer Raymond Saulnier, who fitted steel wedges on the propeller blades to deflect the bullets that struck them during bursts of machine-gun fire. This was a crude but effective solution, although it was difficult to test on the ground—ricochets killed at least two bystanders during ground trials of a previous design.

During April 1915, Roland Garros surprised and shot down three German fighters with his Morane Saulnier Type L, but he and his aircraft

PILOTING THE EINDECKER

Above: *Max Immelmann, the "Eagle of Lille," poses proudly with the wreckage of one of his victims, a two-seat BE.2 scout.*

Some of the first E.Is were issued in ones and twos to various frontline units and flown only by experienced pilots. The first to score in an Eindecker was Lieutnant Kurt Wintgens. His first confirmed victim was a Voisin downed on July 15, 1915, although he had previously claimed two Morane Saulnier parasol fighters. Two other early recipients were Lieutenants Max Immelmann and Oswald Boelcke of *Feldflieger Abteilung 67*. They scored their first victories on August 1 and 19, 1915, respectively. Enemy single-seat scouts were no easy meat, so they preferred to attack two-seat reconnaissance aircraft. One pilot stayed above and to the side to protect the attacking fighter from being "bounced" by an enemy aircraft.

Not all successful combat flights were made as pairs. Max Immelmann wrote of a dogfight with a British BE2c two-seat scout. On September 21, 1915, he took off from Douai, near Lille, at 9 a.m. in his E.III to escort a two-seat artillery spotting machine. Failing to meet his charge, he circled for an hour at the arranged rendezvous point, mainly looking to his right. Something made him look left, and there "...quite close behind me is a Bristol [sic] biplane which is heading straight for me. We are still 400 meters apart. Now I fly toward him; I am about 10–12 meters above him. And I streak past him, for each of us has a speed of 120 kilometers an hour. After passing him I go into a turn. When I go round again, I find he has not yet completed his turning movement. He is shooting fiercely from the rear. I attack him in the flank, but he escapes from my sights for a while by a skillful turn. Several seconds later I have him in my sights once more. I open fire at 100 meters, and approach carefully. But when I am only 50 meters away, I have troubles with my gun. I must cease fire for a time.

The death of the "Eagle of Lille"

"Meanwhile I hear the rattle of the enemy's machine gun and see plainly that he has to change a drum after every 50 rounds.... Aiming carefully, I give him another 200 rounds from close quarters, and then my gun is silent again. One glance tells me that I have no more ammunition left. I turn away in annoyance, for now I am defenceless." The other machine flies off westward, and Immelmann loses sight of him, but circles the battlefield, finally spotting the enemy 3,300 ft (1,000 m) below, falling like a dead leaf. "He gives the impression of a crow with a lame wing. Sometimes he flies a bit; sometimes he falls a bit. It seems as if he wants to land. And now I see plainly that he is falling. A thick cloud rises from the spot where he crashes." Immelmann landed beside the wreckage to find the wounded observer in the hands of German soldiers and the pilot, killed by one of the Eindecker's last bullets, "burnt to a cinder" under the wreckage. This was Immelmann's third victory out of an eventual total of 17. His victim was a Royal Aircraft Factory B.E.2c of No. 10 Squadron, Royal Flying Corps (RFC).

Immelmann was killed on June 18, 1916, in combat with F.E.2bs of No. 25 Squadron while flying an E.III. The RFC credited one crew with his destruction, but it is usually stated that a failure of the interrupter gear had caused him to shoot his own propeller off. His plane broke up and he fell near Lens. He is remembered today not only by the name of a wing in the modern *Luftwaffe,* but also by the maneuver he invented to regain altitude and reverse direction, known as an "Immelmann."

***Left:** This E.III was one of those converted from an unarmed E.I trainer to become one of the first true fighter aircraft.*

force-landed and were captured on the 18th. Contrary to popular belief, he did not shoot off his own propeller due to failure of the plates, but was probably brought down by damage to a fuel line from a single shot from the ground. The Germans soon copied the steel-wedge idea; however, because their own ammunition was steel-jacketed, rather than copper-jacketed as were French bullets, the wedges tended to shatter, followed quickly thereafter by the blades themselves. The German High Command sought a better solution and asked a number of aircraft designers to improve on the deflector idea. The best came from Java-born, German-based Dutchman Anthony Fokker. He had established an aircraft factory in Berlin in 1912, building several fairly primitive types including the *Spinne* (Spider), which were bought by the German army and used mainly for training. Fokker adapted an untested patent design by Franz Schneider of the LVG company dating from 1913 that interrupted the stream of bullets as the propeller blade passed in front of a machine-gun muzzle to work with a standard Parabellum 08/14 7.92-mm weapon. This was fitted to his M.5 scout monoplane, or *Eindecker*, an aircraft heavily influenced by the Morane Type H. The High Command ordered 30 as the Fokker E.I, which were delivered from June 1915.

The Fokker E.I was a mid-winged monoplane with externally braced wings and a tapered box-

***Left:** Despite the aircraft's role in the development of the fighter, few replica Fokker E.IIIs have been produced.*

Above: *The British replica, built by well-known film pilot Doug Bianchi, was first flown in this authentic, but basic, factory color scheme.*

section fuselage. There was no rudder or elevator as such, the entire fin and tailplane being moveable surfaces. There were no ailerons, lateral control being effected by wing warping. External cables that ran through a king post in front of the cockpit moved the controls. The basic structure was steel, but there was no armor protection for the pilot or the fuel tanks. Power came from an 80-hp (59.7-kW) nine-cylinder Oberursel rotary engine. A total of 54 E.Is was produced for the German army, navy, and the Austro-Hungarian army by June 1916. The E.I was quickly followed by the refined and strengthened E.II, which was slightly longer and heavier, even though it had shorter wings. The E.I and E.II were built in both armed and unarmed versions, and mainly used for training, before the armed versions were re-engined with a 100-hp (74.6-kW) Oberursel rotary and redesignated as the E.III. They also had lengthened wings, could carry more fuel, and had greater ammunition capacity.

One E.III was part of trials of an early "stealth" concept. The fabric covering was replaced with a transparent Cellon material, allowing all the internal structure to be seen, but otherwise reducing the visibility of the aircraft from a

Above: *This E.III, possibly pictured at Fokker's Schwerin factory, has an unusual pointed propeller spinner.*

Right: *RFC riggers evaluate a captured E.III, which has been restored to flight. Only one genuine E.III, possibly this one, survives today.*

***Left:** Anthony Fokker (back to camera) discusses the E.III with the German Crown Prince. This image gives a good view of the 9-cylinder Oberursel rotary engine.*

distance. Although it was a relatively effective camouflage, the material itself lost its tautness when wet, thus affecting the flying qualities. The Cellon, which was an early form of Cellophane plastic, would also tear severely following minor damage, and so it was not used in service.

The final production version of the Eindecker was the slightly larger E.IV. Despite its more powerful (but unreliable) 160-hp (119.3-kW) engine and having twin machine guns as standard, the slightly larger E.IV was by now facing better Allied designs and only 49 were delivered, the last in July 1916. It was the first fighter aircraft to employ the two-gun configuration, which was to become standard until the eve of the next world war. One often-illustrated E.IV had three machine guns, but is not believed to have seen combat in this form.

Of the 409 examples of the Fokker Eindeckers produced, only a single E.III has survived. Captured by the RFC in April 1916, it has hung for many years without covering in the Science Museum in London. The Eindecker has not been a popular subject with replica builders, and only a very small number have been built to an airworthy standard.

***Below:** A replica of one of the last E.IIIs shows all the salient points of the Eindecker design, such as the king post through which the control wires passed.*

SPAD VII—XIII

The SPAD series of fighters were used by many French aces, as well as many British, Italian, and other Allied pilots. In particular, the SPADs are associated with Eddie Rickenbacker, Frank Luke, and other American Air Service aces.

SPAD S.XIII

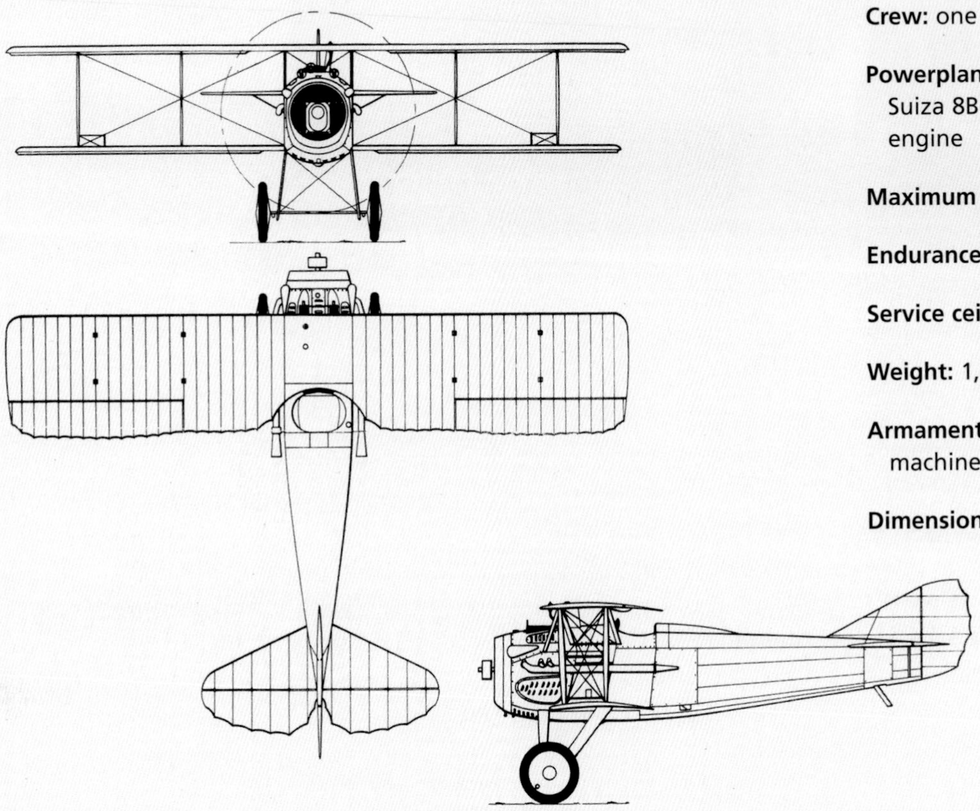

Crew: one

Powerplant: one 164-hp (220-kW) Hispano-Suiza 8Be eight-cylinder inline piston engine

Maximum speed: 135mph (218km/h)

Endurance:1 hour 40 minutes

Service ceiling: 21,820ft (6,650m)

Weight: 1,888lb (856kg) loaded

Armament: two Vickers 0.303 cal. (7.7-mm) machine guns

Dimensions: span 27ft 1in (8.25m); length 20ft 6in (6.25m); height 8ft 6.5in (2.60m)

Right: *The louvered cowl is one of the most distinctive features of the SPAD fighters. The SPAD served into the mid 1930s in Czechoslovakia, and this example has been preserved in the Czech Republic.*

In 1910, entrepreneur and silk magnate Armand Deperdussin founded the French company SPAD. His first airplane was in fact a nonflying attraction for a display of his products in a Paris department store. He was so impressed that he hired its designer, Louis Bécherau, to build a flyable version, and in this unlikely way Deperdussin started an aviation company (Société Provisoire des Aéroplanes Deperdussin, or SPAD), which is remembered today in the designations of French air force fighter squadrons.

Bécherau's early designs were unconventional two-seaters with tractor propellers, but a gunner's position mounted ahead of the engine. By late 1915, Bécherau had turned to more conventional designs and produced the SPAD 5, which was first flown in April 1916 by a company test pilot named Bequet. This was designed to a French General Headquarters requirement for a scout based around the Hispano-Suiza V-8, a 150-hp (112-kW) engine derived from a successful racing-car engine. The *Aviation Militaire* ordered a version of this design with a greater wing area as the Spa.VII, or S.VII, in May.

***Above:** This view of a US squadron in France shows several S.VIIs and a single Nieuport 17, at right.*

Deperdussin himself had many business problems (he was eventually convicted for his part in a massive fraud), and he sold the company in 1916 to a group of investors headed by Louis Blériot. It was reorganized as the Société Pour Aviation et ses Dérivés, retaining both the SPAD appellation and the talents of Louis Bécherau. Delivery of the 268 S.VIIs to the original order was delayed by engine and gun synchronization problems. A few early aircraft were delivered to French fighter squadrons in September 1916, but full-scale operations did not begin until early 1917, usually replacing Nieuport 17s in the Escadrilles de Chasse or fighter squadrons. The SPAD dived better than the Nieuport and was much stronger, although slightly less maneuverable.

The S.VII was constructed around a fabric-covered wooden frame, with louvered metal panels covering the engine area. Vertical struts made of duralumin tubes faired with spruce separated the two wings, which were of essentially equal area. They were also of exceptionally thin

***Above:** This restored SPAD was flown by US ace A. Raymond Brooks. It flew for many years with the Old Rhinebeck collection in New York.*

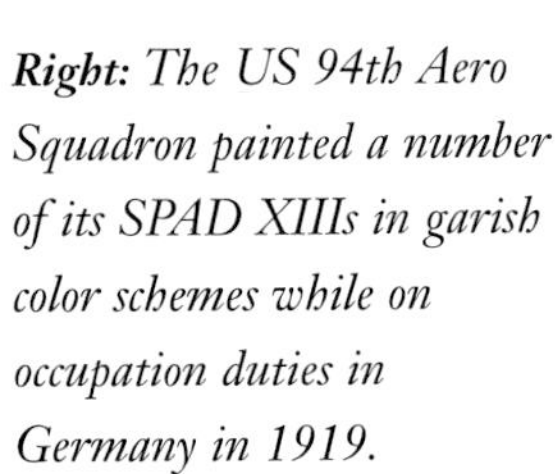

***Right:** The US 94th Aero Squadron painted a number of its SPAD XIIIs in garish color schemes while on occupation duties in Germany in 1919.*

PILOTING THE SPAD

Above: "Balloon buster" Frank Luke of the 27th Aero Squadron poses by his Blériot-built SPAD XIII. In August and September 1918 he destroyed 14 observation balloons and four aircraft.

As with the French, the Americans replaced their Nieuports with S.XIIIs, of which they accepted 893. Balloon-buster Frank Luke brought down four aircraft and 14 balloons in S.XIIIs, and the leading US ace of the war, Edward "Eddie" Rickenbacker, scored all of his 26 victories in the S.XIII. On September 25, 1918, Rickenbacker, newly promoted to the rank of captain and to the command of the 94th Aero Squadron, was on patrol when he spotted two German LVG two-seaters on a photo-reconnaissance mission, escorted by five Fokker D.VII scouts.

"Climbing for the sun for all I was worth, I soon had the satisfaction of realizing that I had escaped their notice and was now well in their rear. I shut down my engine, put down my nose, and made a beeline for the nearest Fokker." Catching the D.VII by surprise, Rickenbacker fired a long burst and reported that it crashed just south of Étain. "It had been my intention to zoom upwards and protect myself against the expected attack from the four remaining Fokkers as soon as I had finished the first man, but when I saw the effects of my attack on the dumbfounded Boches, I instantly changed my tactics and plunged straight through their formation to attack the photographing LVGs ahead." The two-seaters supported each other well, thwarting several attempts until Rickenbacker "... decided upon one bold attack, and if this failed I would get back to my own lines before it was too late.

"Watching my two adversaries closely, I suddenly found an opening between them. They were flying parallel to each other and not 50 yards apart. Dropping down in a sideslip until I had one machine between me and the others, I straightened out smartly, leveled my SPAD, and began firing. The nearest Boche passed directly through my line of fire, and just as I ceased firing I had the satisfaction of seeing him burst into flames." Then, as the regrouped Fokkers dived on him, Rickenbacker said, "I put on the gas and headed for my own lines."

With 26 victories, Eddie Rickenbacker was to be the greatest American ace of World War I. He was eventually to be awarded the Medal of Honor for his actions of September 25, 1918. The SPADs were well regarded by the Americans, and more than 430 S.XIIIs were taken to the United States at the Armistice. Others were exported to Spain, Poland, Czechoslovakia, and even Japan. The type served in France as late as 1923. Production had amounted to more than 7,000 S.XIIIs.

cross-section for their day. The fuselage tapered back to a fin of acute triangular shape and a large tailplane and elevator. Long exhausts ran along each fuselage side from the engine past the cockpit. Armament was a single synchronized 0.303 cal (7.7-mm.) Vickers gun.

Even before the SPAD had entered French service, the Royal Flying Corps (RFC) had taken notice of the high performance of this new fighter and received its first evaluation models in September 1916. An initial order for 30 S.VIIs was made the following month. Deliveries were also delayed, but No. 19 Squadron was fully equipped by February 1917. A production line was opened at Brooklands to make further S.VIIs for the RFC, but British-built SPADs were generally found to be slower and not as well built as the French-made

Left: This was one of several SPADs flown by Francesco Baracca of the 91st Squadriglia. The crest contains his personal emblem of a prancing horse.

Above: *A view of a SPAD S.VII shows its extremely complicated structure. Original SPADs were covered with cotton muslin fabric and flammable cellulose nitrate dope.*

models, and most were retained for training or sent to the Middle East. In all, two British firms built 220 and France supplied another 185 to the RFC.

By August 1917, there were nearly 500 S.VIIs in French service, equipping more than 50 units. The practice of designating squadrons for their equipment arose. For example, the famous *Cigonges* (Storks) escadrille was SPA3. The designation remained even after the units re-equipped, and remains to this day with the flights of the modern *Armée de l'Air's Escadres de Chasse*. Later model S.VIIs had a 180-hp (134-kW) Hispano-Suiza 8Ab motor. The SPADs gained fame by becoming the mount of some of the great French aces, including Nungesser, Fonck, and Guynemer. The leading Italian ace Francesco Baracca was also a SPAD VII exponent. When they were superseded by later models, French S.VIIs were used as trainers, and remained in this role as late as 1928.

S.VIIs were supplied to (and built in) Russia, and nearly 200 were issued to the squadrons of the American Expeditionary Force, some of which were still in use in October 1918. Altogether, seven firms in France, two in Britain, and one in Russia built a total of about 5,820 S.VIIs. After the war, examples served with a number of European and South American air forces.

One problem with the S.VII was its single gun. By the time it appeared, most German aircraft had twin guns. With the encouragement of Georges Guynemer, Louis Béchereau developed the slightly larger S.XII (SPAD 12), with a 1.45-in (37-mm) Hotchkiss cannon that fired through the propeller hub, being mounted between the cylinders of the new 200-hp (149-kW) Hispano-Suiza 8C. Wing and tail surfaces were slightly rounded off, and the lower wing was staggered slightly backward. Guynemer himself scored

Right: *A trio of SPAD XIIIs of the US Air Service is seen after the war. The post-war US national insignia can be seen under the wing of the nearest aircraft.*

several kills in the prototype, but effective use of the cannon (which was hard to aim and required reloading after each shot) was beyond the skills of most ordinary pilots. Most of the few S.XIIs to see service were issued only to experienced pilots, such as René Fonck and Georges Madon. The S.XII was also nose-heavy and difficult to fly. With the cannon breech intruding between the pilot's knees into the space where a conventional control column would normally be, control had to be effected by a pair of levers, as used on some very early Deperdussin aircraft.

The definitive S.XIII appeared in March 1917 and flew on April 4. It was larger and heavier again than the S.XII, with a larger fin and rudder, and a pronounced hump behind the cockpit. The wings had no stagger. Most importantly, the armament was increased to two Vickers guns that had 400 rounds of ammunition each. The cannon was deleted, but the same 200-hp (149-kW) V-8 engine was used. The *Aviation Militaire* ordered a preproduction batch of 20, and then 250 more, but once again deliveries were delayed by engine problems. This was mainly due to excessive vibration, which caused damage to the radiators. The RFC ordered 160 S.XIIIs to follow on from S.VII orders. Deliveries were slow, however, and many aircraft were diverted to French squadrons. Only No. 23 Squadron RFC operated the SPAD XIII in combat.

The French made great use of the SPAD XIII when its teething troubles were over. More than 80 escadrilles used them, and the great aces all increased their scores. Fonck was eventually to become the leading Allied ace, with 75 victories. Guynemer scored the first victory for a French S.XIII in August 1917, but it was to be his last, as he was killed in air combat on September 11 and his body lost in no-man's-land. The legendary ace had a total of 53 victories at the time of his death.

***Above:** A SPAD S.VII flown by Francesco Baracca, the top Italian ace, is preserved at a museum in Ravenna.*

***Below:** Georges Guynemer is seen pointing out features of his SPAD XII to a French general in July 1917.*

Albatros Fighters

The Albatros D-series fighters were good basic designs hampered by weak details. The final D.Va model cured the faults of its predecessors. It became the most numerous German fighter in service and the mount of many aces.

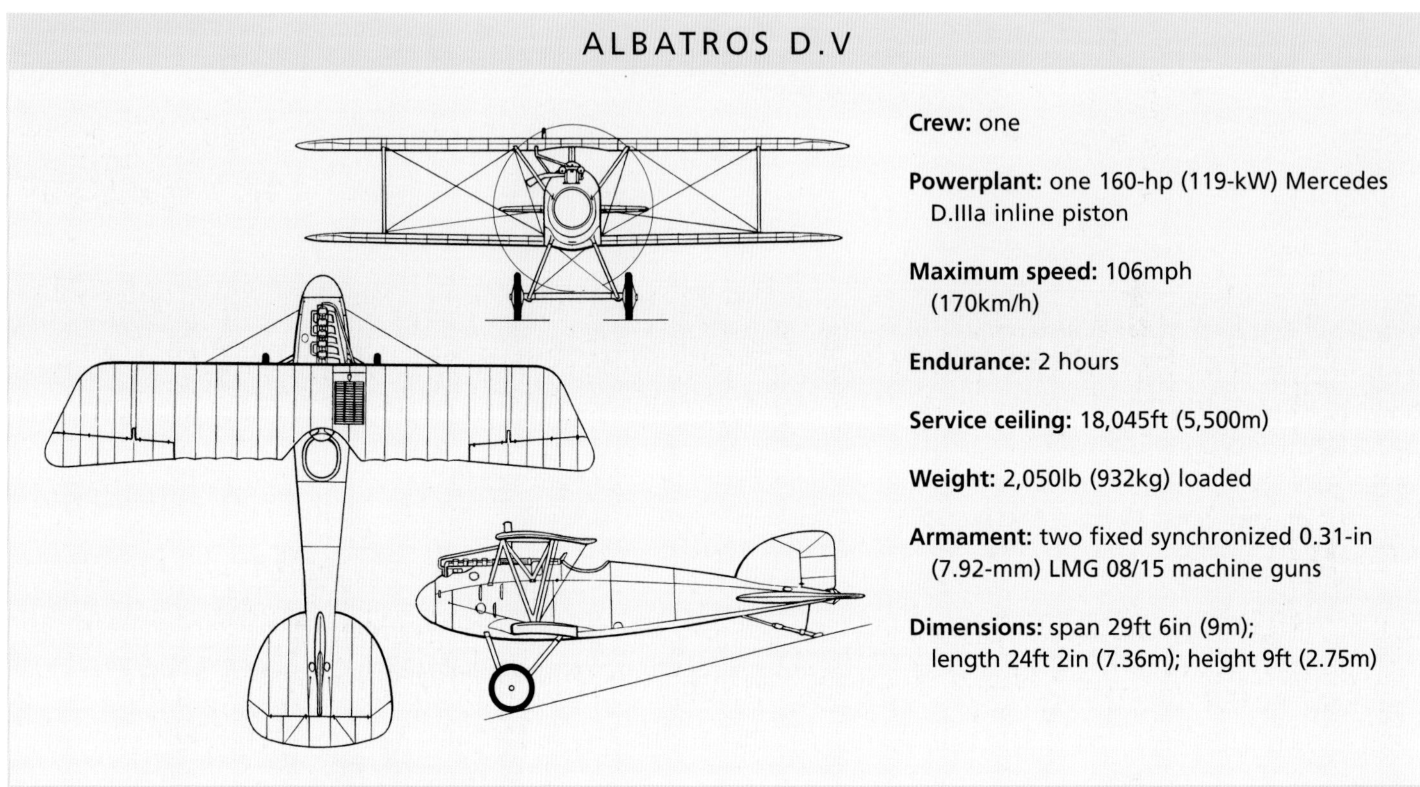

The sharklike Albatros fighters of World War I were among the most distinctive aircraft of that conflict. They appeared in rapid succession from the middle of 1916, but early models suffered from structural weaknesses and were largely obsolete within a year.

The streamlined plywood fuselage originated in a design for a racing aircraft that was not built due to the outbreak of the war. In 1916 its designer, Robert Thelen, who was now the design supervisor of the Albatros Flugwerke, dusted off the plans and incorporated many of the same principles in a new biplane fighter called the D.I. The aim was to counter the new maneuverable Nieuport 11 and Airco DH.2 fighters that had reached the front in the latter half of 1915.

The D.I first flew in August 1916, 50 examples having been ordered the previous month. Production was given priority and deliveries began to Jasta 2 by early September. Engines were either a 150-hp (112-kW) Benz or 160-hp (119-kW) Mercedes water-cooled inline engine. The D.I was almost immediately superseded by the D.II, which had a lowered top wing and other differences to improve pilot visibility. Its greatest innovation was to have twin machine guns, a pair of LMG 08/15s of 0.31-in (7.92-mm) caliber, making it one of the first fighters with two guns. This advantage, when combined with rapid production that saw more than 210 in service with frontline squadrons by January 1917, meant that the Albatros D.II gave Germany both qualitative

***Right:** Propped up for a firing session on the range, this D.V displays the characteristic asymmetric exhaust of the Albatros fighters.*

and quantitative air superiority.

The D.II and its successors had a streamlined plywood fuselage with a tapering oval cross-section. The domed spinner contributed to the sleek appearance. The tailplane had a distinctive curved leading edge, and the wings had squared-off tips on the D.II, but later Albatros D-series fighters mainly had curved upper wingtips.

The next stage in the evolution of the Albatros single-seaters was again developed rapidly and was in particular response to the Nieuport fighters and their unequal area wings, which conferred a tight turning radius. The new D.III was also a sesquiplane, having a lower wing of the same span, but half the chord and thus the area of the upper wing. The two wings were joined by V-shaped struts, which became one of the main recognition features of the most important Albatros scouts. Unfortunately, the single bracing points allowed the lower wing to twist in flight.

PILOTING THE ALBATROS

Above: With a mostly red D.V in the background, officers of Richthofen's Jasta 11 gather at Kortrijk (Courtrai) in Belgium during a visit by General Ludendorff.

In his partial autobiography *The Red Air Fighter*, Richthofen wrote of a combat that took place at the end of "Bloody April" 1917. The pilots of Jasta 11 had come to believe that the British had established an "anti-Richthofen unit" in his sector of the front. The "aggressive activity" of the RFC seemed to be principally directed against the red-painted German aircraft:

"We flew up to the Front, hoping to find the enemy. After some 20 minutes the first arrived and really pounced on us.

"There were three Englishmen in SPAD single-seaters, who thought themselves superior to us because of the excellence of their machines. [Kurt] Wolff, my brother [Lothar von Richthofen], and I were flying together. We were three against three. That was as it ought to be.

"Immediately at the beginning of the encounter the aggressive became a defensive. Our superiority became clear. I tackled my opponent and could see how my brother and Wolff handled each their own enemy. The usual waltzing began. We were circling around one another. A favorable wind came to our aid. It drove the fighting away from the Front in the direction of Germany.

"My man was the first who fell. I suppose he had smashed up his engine. At any rate, he made up his mind to land. I no longer give pardon to anyone. Therefore I attacked him a second time and the consequence was that his whole machine went to pieces. His planes dropped off like pieces of paper and the body of the machine fell like a stone, burning fiercely. It dropped into a bog. It was impossible to dig it out and I have never discovered the name of my opponent. He had disappeared. Only the end of the tail was visible and marked the place where he had dug his own grave.

"Simultaneously with me, Wolff and my brother had attacked their opponents and had forced them to land not far from my victim."

Richthofen's conquest was Lieutenant Richard Applin of No. 19 Squadron, based at Vert Gallant. He was flying a SPAD S.VII. Applin was aged just 23 and only had 75 hours total flying time. One of the other pilots brought down by the three Dr.1s died of wounds, while the other was taken prisoner.

Manfred von Richthofen took command of D.III-equipped Jasta 11 in January 1917 and immediately had his aircraft painted overall bright red. His men said that this would single him out to the enemy, so he suggested that they all paint red on their aircraft, along with some other color as a personal marking. The brightly painted fighters were soon noticed by the Royal Flying Corps (RFC), and the legend of Richthofen's Flying Circus began.

Richthofen himself scored the D.III's first victory, over an F.E.8, on January 23, 1917, and the next day brought down an F.E.2b. During this combat, however, the lower wing spar on the Red Baron's D.III cracked, and he was forced to land near his victim. As a result of this and other wing failures, restrictions were put on the diving speed of the D.III, which was hardly satisfactory for a high-performance combat aircraft. Another serious fault was that the radiator was located under the center of the top wing, where any battle damage would cause the pilot to be sprayed with boiling water. Wing-strengthening modifications and a relocated radiator were features of later production D.IIIs.

While the deficiencies of the D.III were being sorted out, Richthofen switched to an older but more trustworthy Halberstadt D.II, in which he scored 11 victories before returning to the (modified) D.III in March 1917.

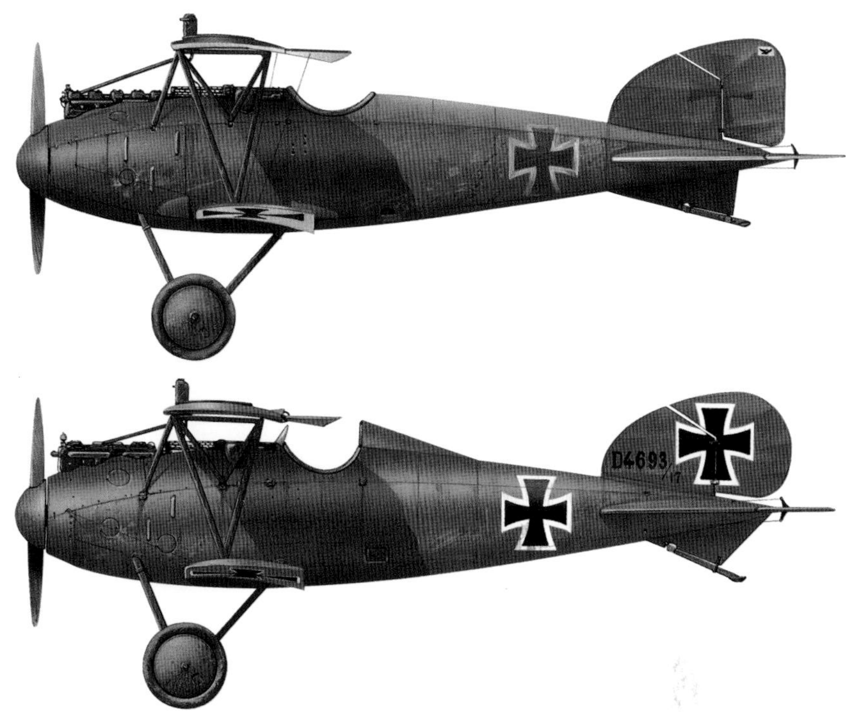

Even as Richthofen was enjoying success with the D.III, development of the series continued. The D.IV was a unique model based on the D.II airframe with a geared Mercedes engine. It was tried out with two-, three-, and four-bladed propellers, but persistent vibration problems were never cured, and development ended shortly after it began in mid-1916.

The final significant model was the D.V, which was essentially a lightened and improved D.III.

Top: *Not all scarlet fighters of World War 1 belonged to the "Red Baron." This one was the mount of fellow Jasta 11 pilot Karl Allmenröder in 1917.* ***Above:*** *Manfred Von Richthofen did fly this aircraft, and added a further half-dozen victories to his total score of 80 while flying D.Vs.*

Left: *This D.Va of Jasta 29 is one of two Albatros D-series fighters to survive today. It can be seen at the Australian War Memorial in Canberra.*

Right: Groundcrew run alongside as a D.I moves to its takeoff point. The D.I was the first of the breed, with a shorter wingspan than its successors.

The fuselage of the D.IV was married to the wings and tailplane of the D.III and a new, larger fin. The upper wing was further lowered to improve visibility, and power came from a 180-hp (134-kW) Mercedes D.IIIA with large cylinders that somewhat blocked the forward view. Although about 12 mph (19 km/h) faster than the D.III, the D.V was not a great improvement and suffered from the same structural weaknesses as the D.III, and it also had its share of failures. Nonetheless, the D.V and the strengthened D.Va were the most widely produced of the Albatros fighters, with an estimated 2,200 plus being produced, the majority of them D.Vas. German Air Service use peaked in May 1918, with almost all of the 80 Jastas having at least some on strength.

Albatros continued fighter development after the D.V, but never achieved the same success as it had with the D.II and D.III. Excluding an abortive triplane version of the D.V and one other model,

Below: The Western Front was not the only theater of the air war. This D.Va was captured in Palestine and put into service by the British.

***Left:** Curious British infantrymen inspect this D.Va, brought down intact behind their lines. Note the "lozenge" camouflage pattern on the wings.*

the succeeding Albatros fighters deviated from the streamlined plywood fuselage formula used in the D series. None was ordered in quantity before the war's end.

Manfred von Richthofen scored 48 of his 80 victories in Albatros fighters, 17 in the D.II, 23 in the D.III, 6 in the D.V, and 2 in the D.Va. After the war, his D.Va was preserved in the Deutsche Luftfahrt Sammlung aeronautical collection in Berlin. According to some sources, this was one of the many aircraft destroyed by Allied bombing during World War II. An alternative story is that it was removed to a safe location, as yet undiscovered. Whatever the truth, only two genuine examples of the D-series Albatros fighters, both D.Vas, are known to exist today, one in Washington D.C. and the other in Canberra, Australia. Very few D.III or D.V replicas have been flown, possibly because of the reputation for structural failure.

***Below:** Bad weather usually prevented flying operations in World War I, but the pilot of this D.V looks eager to get airborne from his snow-covered base.*

Sopwith Camel

The Sopwith Camel was one of the most maneuverable fighters of all time, but had handling characteristics that made it difficult to master. Nearly as many Camel pilots were lost in accidents as fell to enemy fighters.

***Far right:** A replica Camel painted in the elaborate markings of Lieutenant L. S. Breadner, a Canadian pilot of No. 3 Squadron, Royal Naval Air Service.*

***Right:** A Camel of "Naval Ten," No. 10 Squadron RNAS, which flew from land bases in Belgium.*

By the end of 1916, the Sopwith company of Kingston-on-Thames had produced several important aircraft for the Royal Flying Corps (RFC) and the Royal Naval Air Service (RNAS). Notable among these were the Pup, the 1½ Strutter, and the Triplane. The Strutter was more commonly employed as a light bomber, and the Triplane was exclusively used by RNAS squadrons. Although a successful fighter and delightful to fly, the Pup was perhaps too stable to take on the maneuverable German scouts that were in service by mid-1916. It was also underpowered, with only an 80-hp (60-kW) Le Rhône nine-cylinder radial, and underarmed, with only a single 0.303-cal. (7.7-mm) Vickers machine gun.

Even as the Pup and Triplane were just entering service in December 1916, the talented design team at Kingston, led by Herbert Smith, had completed the prototype of a new biplane fighter with more power and more armament than the Pup. This aircraft, known as the Sopwith F1, was similar in layout to the Pup, but had a sloping rear deck and the mass (engine,

SOPWITH CAMEL

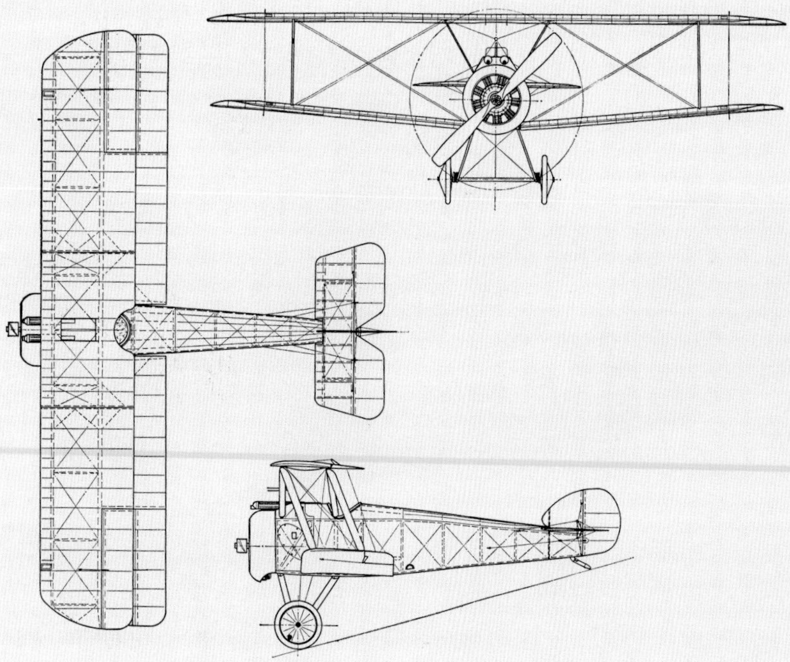

Crew: one

Powerplant: one 130-hp (97-kW) Clerget 9B nine-cylinder rotary piston engine

Maximum speed: 115mph (185km/h)

Endurance: 2 hours 30 minutes

Service ceiling: 17,300ft (5,273m)

Weight: 1,453lb (659kg) loaded

Armament: two .303-cal. (7.7-mm) Vickers machine guns

Dimensions: span 28ft (8.53m); length 18ft 9in (5.71m); height 8ft 6in (2.59m)

B6401

Above: The 2F1 Camel was the first British carrierborne fighter. This example, with an overwing Lewis gun, gets airborne from the carrier HMS Pegasus.

pilot, fuel, ammunition) was concentrated in a much smaller space. The two Vickers guns were mounted well forward, with a curved fairing behind that directed turbulent airflow away from the pilot. Someone likened this "hump" to that of a camel, and the name "Camel" stuck. Famed test pilot Harry Hawker flew the first F1 from Brooklands on December 16, 1916. The following month, the first order of 50 F1s was made for the RNAS. In all, more than 5,700 F1s were to be built, many of them under subcontract.

Below: Taking off from a towed lighter like this in 1918, Lieutenant Stuart Culley shot down a German airship.

The Camel was a conventional biplane with wings of equal area and span, and moderate backstagger. A cutout in the trailing edge of the upper wing and a transparent panel gave the pilot a degree of upward view. Different engines were available for the Camel without a change of designation. Initial deliveries had the 130-hp (97-kW) Clerget 9B nine-cylinder rotary, while others had the 150-hp (112-kW) Bentley B.R.1 or the 110-hp (82-kW) Le Rhône. Later a 140-hp (104-kW) version of the Le Rhône became available. Many Clergets and Le Rhônes were license-built in England. Pilots preferred the Le Rhône-engined Camels to the Clerget-powered ones. The Le Rhône was regarded as more reliable, and French-production examples of both were better regarded than the English-built models.

The first RFC Camels arrived in France in late May 1917, equipping No. 70 Squadron at Boisdinghem, a former 1½ Strutter unit. Deliveries to further RFC units were delayed due to the need to hold back aircraft for Home Defence duties following Gotha bomber raids on London. All deliveries until the end of the year were of Clerget-engined Camels, and priority for the Le Rhône-engined variants was given to Home Defence squadrons. It was an RNAS unit that was to introduce the Camel to combat. Flight Commander Alexander Shook of No. 4 (Naval) Squadron destroyed one enemy scout and sent another down out of control near Ostend in the first week of June 1917. The bomber threat to London had vanished almost as soon as it appeared, but the Gothas were still active over the Western Front, and, on July 4, five "Naval 4" pilots attacked 16 Gothas northwest of Ostend. At least four were badly damaged and the formation broken up for no losses.

The powerful rotary engines and the short wingspan contributed both to the Camel's exceptional maneuverability and to its reputation as a difficult machine to fly and killer of inexperienced pilots. The torque effect of the engine and propeller would allow exceptionally tight turns to the right. On takeoff, full right rudder was needed to counteract the tendency of the Camel to roll to the left and dig a wingtip into the ground. In flight, the gyroscopic effect of the rotary engine would cause rapid right turns with nose drop and gentler left turns with a climbing tendency. A poorly made right turn could easily develop into a spin, which would invariably be fatal at low level.

Following attachment of some US pilots to the

PILOTING THE SOPWITH CAMEL

Left: *These RNAS Camels are armed with an overwing Lewis gun as well as the standard twin Vickers guns.*

Australian Flying Corps (AFC) pilot Arthur Cobby was the top-scoring Camel pilot from that country, with 29 victories. On July 15, 1918, he and fellow No. 3 Squadron AFC pilot H.G. Watson encountered some German Pfalz scouts over Armentiéres. "They were flying in company southeast from the line toward that much battered town at 6,000 feet and my partner and I climbed above the clouds from farther east and flew toward them. The clouds were scattered cumulus, and when he had gone far enough we put down our noses and went through them flat out—Wattie's wing tip was almost up against mine. We came out a little to the east and slightly above the Germans and immediately attacked. There was a crowd of other enemy scouts about at the time, including some 'Tripes'—a type we had not seen for some time, but they couldn't have noticed us. We were almost behind the Pfalz, and turning slightly while diving, came down on the tails of the two rear ones, and with my first burst sent my opponent down in flames. Wattie's fire must have been accurate, as his man went up nose first until the machine stalled, then went down in a spin.

"I did not watch it for long, as I went on through to the next machine on my side, opening fire as I came up on him. He half-rolled at once and I zoomed up over him and turned to fire again, but it was unnecessary, as the right-hand wing had collapsed and the machine fell to pieces. I was startled by the familiar pop-pop-pop of machine guns from above, and glancing over my shoulder saw the 'Tripe' formation coming down on us. Wattie also shot past me on a 'split-arse' turn, firing his guns to attract my attention to the danger, and pointing upward. I shook my head and pointed downward, indicating 'nothing doing,' then kicked my bus into a half-roll, pulled the stick back into my tummy, and went into the clouds in a vertical dive and kept it in for about 4,000 feet before easing it out. This manoeuvre was not as dangerous from an attack point of view as it may seem, as the [Fokker] Triplane was notoriously weak structurally, and would break up at excessive speeds."

Below: *Famous film pilot Frank Tallman, dressed as an RFC officer, inspects the oil-soaked cowlings of his Camel on a postwar movie set.*

Right: *This is one of the few genuine Camels still airworthy, and the only one built by Sopwith themselves. It served with No. 10 Squadron in 1917.*

RFC Camel squadrons for training, several units of the American Expeditionary Force, notably the 17th Aero Squadron, were equipped with Camels from mid-1918. The top American Camel ace was Elliot Springs of the 148th Aero Squadron, with 12 victories, 10 of them against the Fokker D.VII, widely regarded as the best fighter of the war.

Above: *Now resident in the US, the same Le Rhône-engined Camel has been valued at over $1.6 million.*

Naval orders included 150 of the Camel 2F1 variant, which had shorter wings, a detachable rear fuselage, and was usually powered by the Bentley BR.1 It was operated from shore bases, but also from lighters, cruisers, and the new carriers HMS *Argus*, *Pegasus*, and *Eagle*. On August 11, 1918, Lieutenant S.D. Culley flew off a lighter towed by a destroyer to attack and destroy the German naval airship L53. His aircraft is preserved at the Imperial War Museum in London.

Although the threat of day bomber attacks diminished as the Camel appeared, raids by night continued, and a number of home-based Camels were adapted for night-fighting duties. The flash from the Lewis guns would dazzle the pilot, so twin Vickers guns above the upper wing often replaced these. In order for the pilot to reach the guns and clear jams, his position was moved further back. An additional Lewis gun was sometimes mounted at a 45-degree angle alongside the starboard side of the cockpit. Night-fighter Camels were also used successfully in France, but usually with standard armament.

The Camel was credited with more victories over enemy aircraft than any other Allied fighter, but losses in combat and to accidents were also heavy. It took a heavy toll of its own flyers. During World War I, 413 Camel pilots died in combat, while 385 pilots died from noncombat related causes, often spin-related accidents. A total of 1,294 enemy aircraft were credited to Camel pilots, the highest scoring of which was Canadian Donald MacLaren of No. 46 Squadron, with 54 victories.

One attempt to reduce training losses was by creating a two-seat variant. The first dual-control Camels were created unofficially at the unit level, but later models had official sanction, although there was no standard conversion. The guns were

Left: *This view of an F1 Camel of No. 44 Squadron shows how the pilot, engine, and armament were all confined to a small space, boosting the turning ability.*

removed, and a much smaller tank replaced the original gravity fuel tank to make way for a new forward cockpit. As such, the converted machines had an endurance of only about 20 minutes. Only a handful saw service.

Although controversy remains to this day over who brought down Manfred von Richthofen, the "Red Baron," his death came on April 21, 1918 in a dogfight with Camels of No. 209 Squadron RAF (the Royal Air Force having been formed by amalgamation of the RFC and RNAS on the first of that month). Richthofen had scored 80 victories, nine of them—and all of the last five—being Sopwith Camels. He was on the brink of adding Lieutenant Wilfred "Wop" May to his tally when fellow Canadian Captain Roy Brown and Australian machine-gunners on the ground both fired on him at close range.

Left: *Visible here are the "humps" that gave the Camel its name. These were aerodynamic fairings beside the guns that smoothed the airflow around the cockpit.*

Fokker Dr.I Triplane

The famous Fokker Triplane was only built in small numbers and had a brief combat career. In the hands of the most experienced pilots it was deadly to the enemy, but its weak structure made it hazardous to its own side as well.

Right: *Triplane 425/17 was the machine in which the "Red Baron" scored his final victories in April 1918.*

Far right: *The Fokker Dr.1 was built in Germany in response to the brief but spectacular career of the Royal Navy's Sopwith Triplane.*

Although regarded as the archetypal German fighter of the Great War, the Fokker Triplane was nearly obsolete when it entered service in strength. Its fame stems from its association with several of the top-scoring pilots, supreme above them being Manfred von Richthofen, the "Red Baron."

After the success of the Eindecker monoplanes, Anthony Fokker turned his hand to biplane designs to meet the High Command's requirements for higher performance fighters. None of the resulting designs was a great success. Some were used in reasonable numbers by the

Austrian and Turkish air services, but crashes of the inline-engined D.I due to poor quality control (a perennial Fokker problem) led to a ban on Fokker types being used for combat, and most saw out their service as trainers. Fokker, who had no formal engineering qualifications, rejected the need for stress calculations and bought and used the cheapest materials he could find. Almost all his

FOKKER DR.I

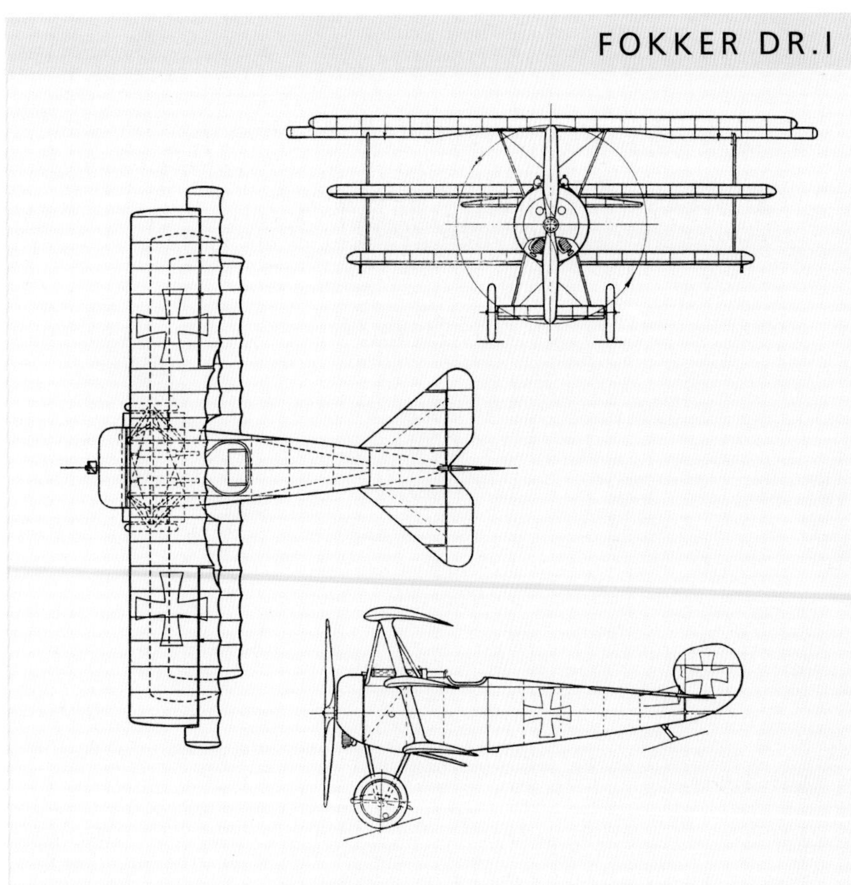

Crew: one

Powerplant: one 110-hp (82-kW) Oberursel UR.II, nine-cylinder rotary piston engine

Maximum speed: 115mph (185km/h)

Endurance: 1 hour 30 minutes

Service ceiling: 20,013ft (6,100m)

Weight: 1,292lb (586kg) loaded

Armament: two synchronized 0.31-in (7.92-mm) LMG 08/15 machine guns

Dimensions: span 23ft 7in (7.19m); length 18ft 11in (5.77m); height 9ft 8in (2.9m)

PILOTING THE FOKKER TRIPLANE

By the spring of 1918, the Dr.I's heyday was over, and most pilots were swapping them for D.VIIs and other superior biplane types. A few leading pilots kept their Triplanes, including Josef Jacobs, commander of Jasta 7, who was still flying one as late as October 1918. On July 19, he wrote in his diary: "I left with my *Kette* [flight] for the front, where I saw through the light haze two-seaters and single-seaters coming from Bailleul just below the clouds at an altitude of hardly more than 1,500 meters, being fired at by German flak. My red warning flare had just been fired when a flight of SEs [SE.5as] came out of the clouds firing furiously. Right away I turned toward one SE, but was attacked from behind by three of them. At the same time I also saw three Bristol Fighters shooting as they passed me, so I dived. In the meantime, a second SE formation came to their assistance, as did two German *Jastas*. All engaged in the whirlwind battle.

Above: *With the aid of a smoke generator, this replica Dr.1 simulates being shot down for the camera.*

Below: *Airmen guide the F.1 of Werner Voss across a muddy airfield. Voss used it to shoot down 10 British aircraft in 1917.*

"One moment I held this enemy in sight, and the next moment shook that enemy (from my sights) without being able to shoot properly myself. Suddenly I watched another opponent going after a Fokker. I fired, and the Englishman gave up. A second one came to his aid, and I quickly had him 'wrapped up' and did not let him loose.

"I followed 50 meters behind him, and when he wanted to straighten out I shot him full of holes so that he turned toward Germany and prepared to land. He glided very slowly across a road, pulled his airplane up a little and then it turned over on its head. He immediately jumped out and ran into a deserted trench, followed by some soldiers.

"When I came home I at once took my car and drove to the landing site. It was a brand new SE.5a with an American 1st Lieutenant as pilot. His name was A.M. Roberts (of No. 74 Squadron). He had been at the front for three months, and was astonished at the speed of my triplane. He much regretted the death of Richthofen. He gave me his zippered map case."

Josef Jacobs was to become the most successful Dr.1 pilot, surviving the war with approximately 47 kills, up to 30 of them scored on Dr.1s. Other notable aces who scored some or all of their totals on the Triplane were Werner Voss, Hermann Göring, and Ernst Udet.

designs went through a period in which they were grounded due to serious structural defects.

Reinhold Platz was the chief designer at the Fokker factory, translating his boss's ideas into hardware, but having no direct contact himself with the military authorities. He had been working on advanced plywood designs, designated V.1 to V.3 ("V" standing for *Versuchmaschine*, or "experimental machine"), when Fokker instructed him to build a more conventional lightweight biplane called the V.4. This had a fuselage structure of alloy tubing covered by fabric. The wings were fabric-covered wood with an upper wing of much greater span than the lower and distinctive overlapping ailerons on the top wing.

Fokker visited the front and met the great Manfred von Richthofen, who had recently narrowly escaped from a combat with a Sopwith Triplane. By the time of this fateful meeting, *Rittmeister* (cavalry captain) von Richthofen had scored almost 60 victories in Albatros and Halberstadt biplanes. The maneuverability of the Sopwith Triplane, which was actually built in very small numbers and only in service with a few units of the Royal Naval Air Service (RNAS), had deeply impressed the Red Baron. During this visit Richthofen urged Fokker to develop a similar machine. Fokker was also able to watch Triplanes in action from a forward observation post and view a captured example. Immediately on his return to Berlin in July 1917, he told Platz to abandon the V.4 as a biplane and to develop a triplane with many of the same components. At the same time, the Inspectorate of Military Aviation, or *Idflieg*, commissioned Siemens-Shuckert and Pfalz to build triplanes. All in all, the Sopwiths caused something of a "triplane frenzy" among German manufacturers, although only one fighter design (Fokker's) was to see series production.

Platz modified the V.4 to make it a triplane with three slender wings. These were stepped back and diminished in span and chord from the top to the bottom. The large tailplane had a movable elevator, but the rudder was of the "comma" type as used on the E.III. As such, the modified aircraft was redesignated the V.5, and, after successful test flights, Fokker ordered two more to be built.

***Left:** This replica built in the US in the 1960s was one of the first of many to represent the Dr.1 flown by the "Red Baron". It is pictured without an engine, and the wheels are somewhat on the large size.*

In late August 1917, the two "preproduction" V.5s were sent to the front for evaluation under the military designation F.I. They were issued to Richthofen at Jasta 11 and Werner Voss of Jasta 10. Jasta was an abbreviation of *Jagdstaffel*, or "fighter squadron." The Red Baron scored his first victory (his 60th overall) on September 1 against an R.E.8. The crew of the R.E.8 probably thought the approaching triplane was a Sopwith. He scored one further victory in the F.I, but Voss was to score 10 in his, distinctively painted with a fearsome face on the front of the cowling. On September 23, Voss was involved in combat with a large group of SE.5as of Nos 56 and 60

***Below:** These triplanes of Jasta 11, Richthofen's Flying Circus, need a helping hand to overcome the Flanders mud.*

***Above:** This Dr.1 replica lacked an engine when photographed. Many flew with either fixed radial or rotary powerplants.*

Squadrons. Despite scoring hits on many of his opponents, he was eventually hit by Second Lieutenant Arthur Rhys-Davids of No. 56 Squadron and crashed near Frezenberg. At the time of his death, he was credited with 48 victories.

While Richthofen was on leave in Germany, Lieutenant Kurt Wolff was killed in Jasta 11's F.I on September 15, having scored 33 victories. He was shot down by a Sopwith Triplane of 10 (Naval) Squadron. This was one of the few combats between triplane fighters, as the RNAS had begun to phase out the type in August in favor of the Camel.

The first production batch of 20 Triplanes, now known as the Dr.I (for *Dreidecker*), were handed over during September 1917 and began to enter service with the new *Jadgeschwader* 1 (JG 1) in October. JG 1 was the first German Army Air Service fighter wing and was put in the command of Manfred von Richthofen. It was a formal recognition of the success of the "Flying Circus" of four Jastas, which had been flying together informally in an attempt to win local air superiority.

The Dr.I was essentially the same as the V.5/F.1, but with longer wingspans and skids under the wingtips. The powerplant was an 110-hp (82-kW) Oberursel UR.II 9-cylinder rotary. The strong box structure created by the three wings, two of which were attached directly to the fuselage, eliminated the need for almost all the bracing wires found on other contemporary types. The undercarriage also featured an aerofoil section, which contributed to the lift.

Although the ban on combat use of Fokker products had ended, the structural problems affecting the aircraft had not. The commander of Jasta 15, Heinrich Gontermann (38 kills), was demonstrating the maneuverability of his new Dr.I to his pilots when the top wing came off. He was fatally injured in the ensuing crash, as was a Jasta 11 pilot two days later in similar circumstances. The examination of many other Triplanes found evidence of poor workmanship, and all aircraft were ordered stripped for inspection. A program to modify all Dr.Is was ordered, and the type was grounded until this was

***Right:** The red Dr.1s flown by Manfred Von Richthofen are among the all-time most recognizable aircraft ever.*

Left: *Only relatively few Dr.1s reached the front, but they had an impact out of proportion to their numbers.*

carried out and all wings were rigorously inspected. There were further instances of structural failure in the Fokker Triplane's career, but no further known fatalities as a result.

Both German and Allied pilots soon became aware of the Dr.I's agility and excellent climbing ability. The Triplane could climb to 3,380ft (1,000m) in less than three minutes, and dive faster than most of its opponents. It was, however, slower than the latest Allied scouts, with a lower maximum ceiling. The gyroscopic effect of the rotary engine took a bit of getting used to for pilots accustomed to inline engines as found on Albatros and many other fighters. Landing was one of the hardest parts of flying the Triplane. The effect of gusts on the slab-sided fuselage tended to make the rudder ineffective, and the center wing blanked out the elevator in the landing attitude.

Returning from leave, Richthofen scored two more victories in an Albatros D.Va before receiving his own Dr.I. In all, he was to fly five production Dr.Is, only two of which were painted overall red. Richthofen scored his 16 final victories in the various Dr.Is, reaching a total of 80 by the time of his death on April 21, 1918, the victim of a single bullet fired either by Sopwith Camel pilot Captain Roy Brown of No. 210 Squadron or Australian machine-gunners on the ground.

In total, only 323 Fokker Triplanes were built. Several Dr.Is were captured in various states of repair before the end of the war. One was later exhibited in London, but appears to have been scrapped some time afterward. The last known genuine Dr.I was Richthofen's last aircraft—although souvenir hunters had damaged this where it fell, and pieces purporting to come from it exist in various museums around the world. This machine was displayed in Berlin, but was destroyed by Allied bombs in 1944. Enthusiasts have built many full-scale, airworthy replicas.

Below: *The markings of this all-black Dr.1 approximate those of Josef Jacobs, the most successful Fokker triplane pilot.*

Hawker Fury

The beautiful inline-engined Hawker biplanes epitomized the RAF between the wars. The Fury fighter was one of the best-loved warplanes of all time and taught many of the RAF's pilots and leaders the skills they needed in combat.

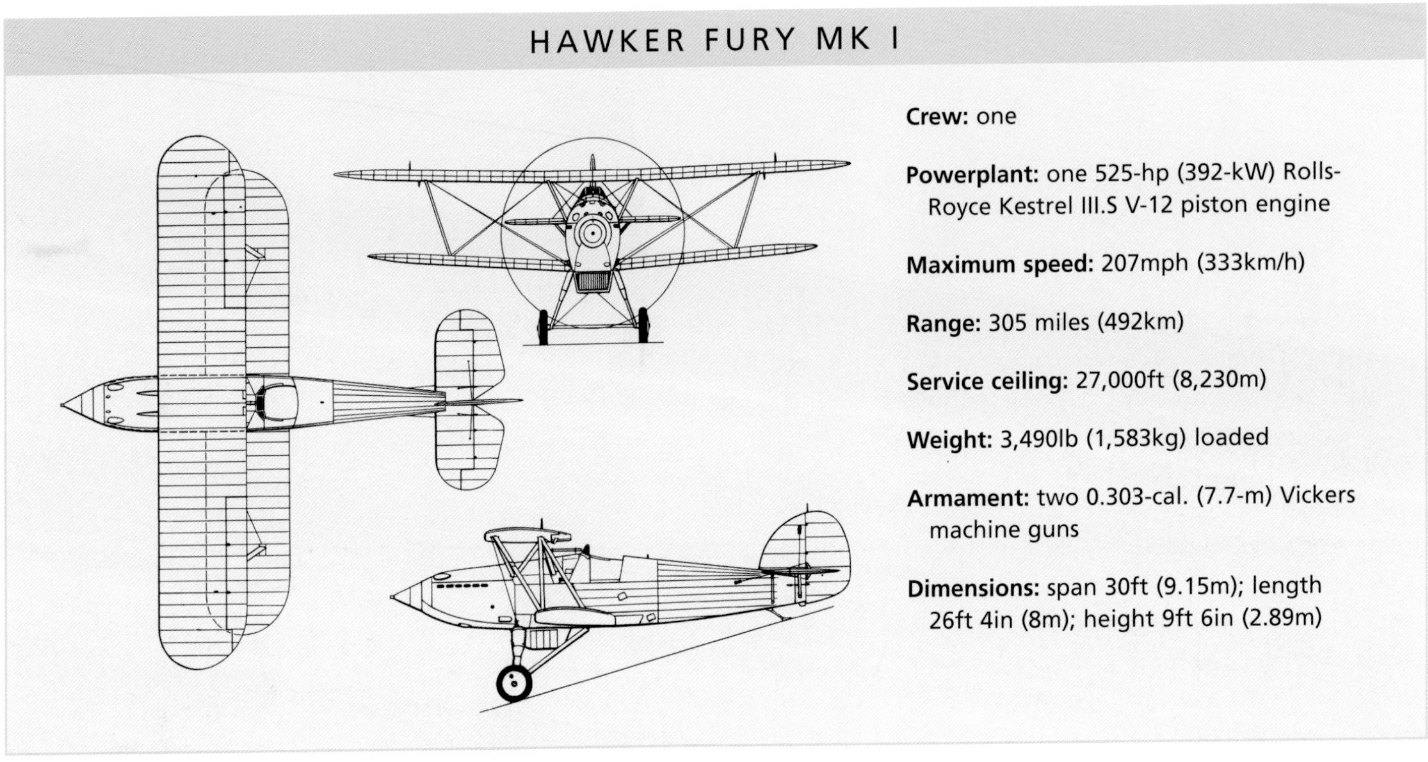

HAWKER FURY MK I

Crew: one

Powerplant: one 525-hp (392-kW) Rolls-Royce Kestrel III.S V-12 piston engine

Maximum speed: 207mph (333km/h)

Range: 305 miles (492km)

Service ceiling: 27,000ft (8,230m)

Weight: 3,490lb (1,583kg) loaded

Armament: two 0.303-cal. (7.7-m) Vickers machine guns

Dimensions: span 30ft (9.15m); length 26ft 4in (8m); height 9ft 6in (2.89m)

Far right: *Fury I K1926 was the first production aircraft, delivered to No. 1 Squadron at Tangmere in 1932. Note the ring-and-bead gunsight.*

Right: *A Hawker Fury II of No. 41 Squadron at Catterick in the early 1930s.*

Hawker's sleek Fury fighters represented the zenith of biplane development. They helped the Royal Air Force (RAF) retain expertise in fighter operations through the lean interwar years. Many prewar Fury pilots rose to high rank in the RAF during World War II and later. Others were to achieve fame with world speed and altitude records before and after the war.

The Fury fighter was one of a number of successful Hawker aircraft to stem from the Hart bomber of 1928, all based around the Rolls-Royce Kestrel V-12 engine. The Kestrel was the first reliable lightweight inline engine. It had been used in the Hart, which, although not the first RAF bomber able to outrun its contemporary fighters, was more than 30mph (50km/h) faster than the aircraft that held that honor, the Fairey Fox. The Kestrel allowed the forward fuselage of the Hart and its derivatives to be streamlined, contributing to a higher speed than radial-engined aircraft of similar power output.

To meet a 1927 RAF requirement, Hawker's Sydney Camm developed a single-seat fighter of the same basic configuration as the Hart in competition with the similar-looking Fairey Firefly IIM. The prototype was flown in March 1929 (the actual date and pilot

K
1926
K1926

Right: *After the Munich crisis in September 1938, the markings of the RAF's Furies disappeared under drab earth and green tones.*

seem to have gone unrecorded) as the Hawker Hornet and selected in 1930 as the Fury. Gerry Sayer flew the first production Fury on March 25, 1931. Despite its looks, the Fury was smaller and structurally different to its progenitor. Of mixed metal, wood, and fabric construction, the Fury had a tightly cowled engine with a radiator slung between the undercarriage legs. The pilot had an open cockpit with a small windshield, through which was mounted a telescopic sight.

PILOTING THE HAWKER FURY

Above: *No. 43 Squadron "Fighting Cocks," seen here with its famous checkered markings, had a rogue Fury in its midst.*

Flight Lieutenant Theodore McEvoy of No. 43 Squadron had a startling experience in a Fury in 1934 at Tangmere. "The Fury was a delightful aeroplane to fly: one could almost say that it had no vices, but one I knew in No. 43 Squadron, though I loved it, was a rogue. According to Group Standing Orders, spinning had to be practised once a month. On 17 December 1935, in Fury K1934, I began my spin at 20,000 feet and let it go for some time. After several turns the propeller stopped (which hadn't happened before) and the nature of the spin changed. The Willesden Green covers on the Vickers guns began to pull off forwards. This, I thought, must be the dreaded 'flat spin,' but I still had thousands of feet in hand and didn't worry much. However when I put on opposite rudder and centralized the stick the spin continued unaffected. I wound the incidence wheel fully forward—no effect. All the controls could have been cut for all the effect they had.

"By the time I passed through 10,000 feet I had tried all the tricks I knew and got ready to bail out. I undid the Sutton harness, disconnected oxygen and R/T [radio] and stood up to jump. As I stood up the Fury's nose dipped and I realised I was recovering. I still had hold of the spade-grip on the control column but as I had wound the tail gear [tailplane trim] forward the Fury went into an increasingly steep dive, tending to throw me out by the centrifugal force. Moreover, as I had left the throttle wide open and the switch on, as the propeller began to turn the engine started.

"At full throttle, the Fury went into an over-the-vertical dive. Had I let go I should have had no problem in clearing the aircraft—I should have been catapulted out with some vigor. I couldn't reach throttle, switch, or tail wheel, nor could I see the altimeter, but the ground, seen over the centre section, looked unpleasantly close. With the strength of despair I managed to pull myself back into the cockpit, got the throttle back and pulled out, with much *g*, before hitting the deck. After that I flew around a bit, calming down.

"We sent the Fury to RAE [Royal Aeronautical Establishment] for testing, where 'Batchy' Atcherley and Pat Fraser found it took them 16 turns to recover from induced stable spins with the propeller stopped, though its measurements and weight distribution were standard. I tried the same trick with the other Furies in my flight, but it was only K1934 that had this strange propensity."

Left: The clean lines of the Fury were marred slightly by the large radiator bath between the undercarriage legs. Note the highly polished engine cowling.

The armament was a pair of .303-cal. (7.7-mm) Vickers guns concealed under the brightly polished cowlings. The Kestrel IIIS gave 525 hp (392 kW) and drove a two-bladed wooden Watts propeller.

Most Kestrels were allocated to Hart production, which restricted Fury numbers. The complicated water-cooled Kestrel contributed to the high cost of the Fury—each cost £4,800, a fortune during the Depression years, and £700 more than the contemporary Bristol Bulldog. The Fury Mk I entered service with No. 43 Squadron in May 1931. Mk Is equipped only three frontline squadrons, Nos. 1, 25, and 43, for most of their careers, but some were later briefly operated by Nos. 41, 73, and 87 Squadrons. The Fury was operated as an interceptor fighter, replacing the World War I concept of standing patrols.

In 1931, the Hawker Fury was the fastest aircraft in the RAF, with a maximum speed of 207mph (333km/h). At the same time, the civilian Schneider Cup seaplanes had reached more than 403mph (650km/h). The Fury was the first production warplane able to exceed 200mph (330km/h) in level flight.

Like other RAF fighters of the era, the Furies were finished in a "silver" scheme of polished metal and metallic doped fabric, with colorful squadron markings. Those aircraft in service at the time of the Munich Crisis in 1938 were repainted in dark earth and green camouflage. The three remaining Fury squadrons were re-equipped with Hurricanes and Spitfires during 1939.

In order to increase the number of fighter squadrons in the RAF prior to the arrival of the new Spitfire and Hurricane monoplanes, a batch of 99 Fury Mk IIs were delivered in July 1936. The Fury II had a Kestrel VI engine of 640 hp (477 kW) and greater fuel capacity. Speed increased to 223mph (357km/h). The first batch

Below: K3586 was the "high-speed Fury," fitted with a tapered lower wing and faired wing struts. It was mainly used as an engine testbed.

Above: The Fury II had wheel spats, and in some cases a tailwheel rather than a skid. Under the skin, the Mk II had a stronger engine and larger fuel capacity.

had wheel spats, but these were later removed as they tended to clog with grass and mud. The main distinguishing feature was a tailwheel rather than a skid, and this was only found on some later aircraft. The Fury II entered service in November 1936 with No. 25 Squadron, which was the only unit to receive this version as new, although it later passed its aircraft to No. 41 Squadron.

The Fury was regarded as one of the nicest aircraft to fly ever built, and the prewar RAF was thought of by many as something of a gentleman's flying club. It was not the most stable gun platform, but was superb at aerobatics. The Furies were the stars of the annual Hendon Air Displays from 1931 to 1937. The 1933 display saw the debut of formation aerobatics with the Furies' wingtips tied together. Nine aircraft took off all connected by ropes fixed to the wingtips before splitting into three flights of three and conducting maneuveres including loops and rolls.

Right: The Hawker PV.3 was an advanced derivative of the Fury using the Goshawk steam-cooled engine.

Like other RAF fighters of the era, the Furies were finished in a "silver" scheme of polished metal and metallic doped fabric, with colorful squadron markings. In September 1938, the Furies and other RAF warplanes were hastily camouflaged in dark green and earth colors in response to the Munich Crisis and the imminent threat of war.

Six countries bought Furies. Small numbers went to Portugal, Spain, and Norway. Some of the 24 Iranian Furies had Bristol Mercury and others Pratt & Whitney Hornet radials. The 10 Spanish Furies had Hispano-Suiza 12Xbr engines and unbraced cantilever undercarriage.

At the time of the German invasion in April 1941, the Royal Yugoslavian Air Force flew a mixed bag of aircraft made in Britain, France, Italy, and Germany. After deliveries of 10 Fury IIs with cantilever undercarriage to Yugoslavia, local manufacturers Ikarus and Zmaj built a further 43 under license. By 1941, two squadrons were each equipped with 15 Fury IIs. Although they had enough warning to take off before the German attacks started on the morning of April 6, they were overwhelmed by Messerschmitt Bf 109Es and Bf 110s. Eleven Furies were destroyed with the loss of seven pilots, effectively seeing one squadron wiped out. Two Bf 110s were brought down, one of them rammed by a Fury.

The other Yugoslav squadron lasted a little longer, flying a number of strafing missions as it moved from base to base ahead of the German advance. Some planes were lost to ground fire and one to an Italian Cr.42. Many others were burnted when they became unserviceable and at the time of the armistice on the 15th. A couple of surviving aircraft were tested by Italy.

South Africa bought seven Furies with Kestrel VI engines in 1935. Initially used for training, they were the most modern fighters available to the South African Air Force (SAAF) at the outbreak of war. In May 1940, six of the Furies were shipped to Mombassa as part of the South African campaign against Italian forces in East Africa. Despite their obsolescence, the SAAF accepted 22 more ex-RAF Fury Is between August 1940 and January 1941. In August 1940, they first saw action against Italian bombers, destroying a Caproni Ca.133. Several successful attacks on airfields were made and Italian aircraft destroyed by strafing Furies. One other Caproni was shot down in October 1940. In April 1941, the surviving Furies were returned to South Africa and were finally retired from service in mid-1943.

The RAF retired its Furies from frontline duties as the Spitfire and Hurricane entered service. More than 140 were issued to the RAF's flight training schools. These yellow-painted trainers were the first fighters that many of the top wartime pilots were to fly. A few were still in use during 1940.

Above: *The Fury was regularly displayed in aerobatic performances at the Hendon Air Pageant, in the UK, and other air shows.*

Below: *Some nations received Furies with a variety of powerplants. Portugal bought three examples, equivalent to the RAF's Fury I.*

Polikarpov I-16

Subject to disparaging nicknames such as "rat," "mule," and "fly," the Polikarpov I-16 was advanced for its day, maneuverable and popular with pilots. Thousands were built and maintained by semiskilled personnel in the early war years.

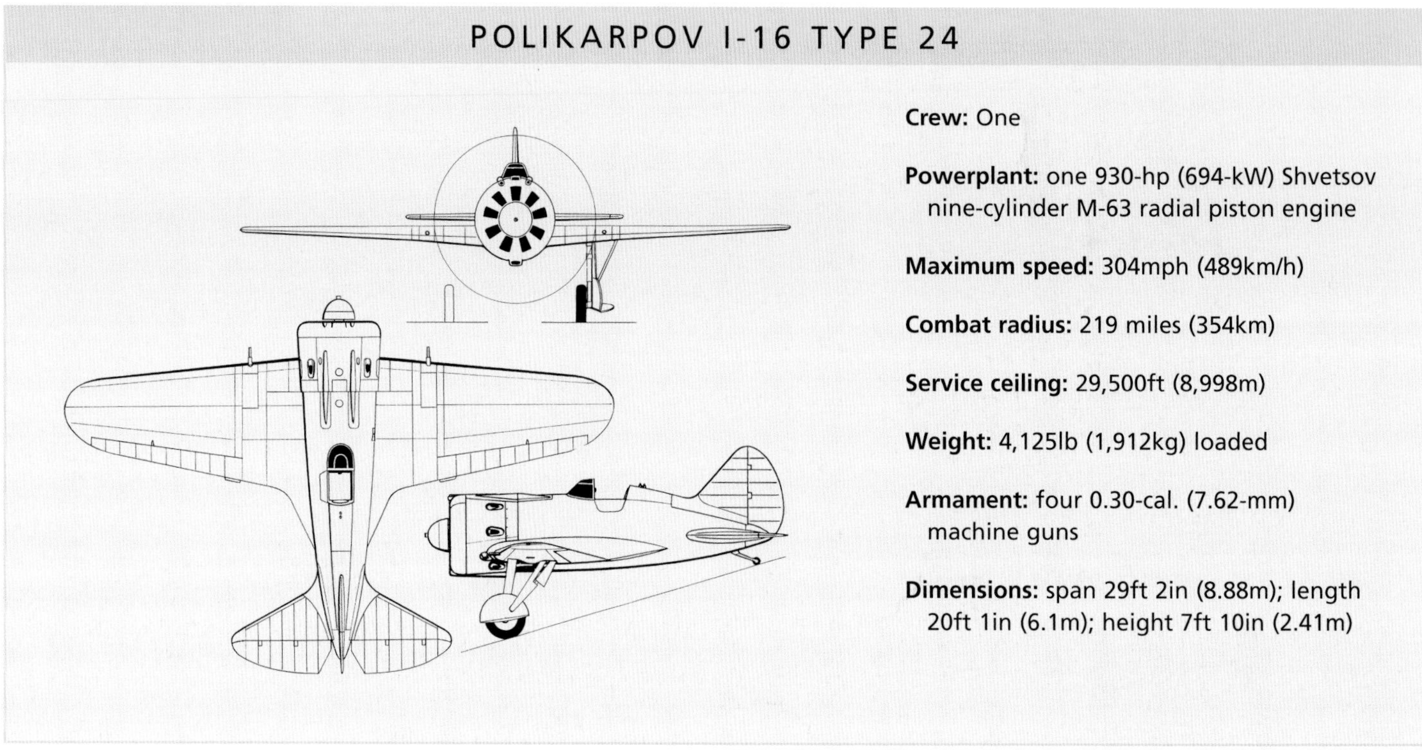

POLIKARPOV I-16 TYPE 24

Crew: One

Powerplant: one 930-hp (694-kW) Shvetsov nine-cylinder M-63 radial piston engine

Maximum speed: 304mph (489km/h)

Combat radius: 219 miles (354km)

Service ceiling: 29,500ft (8,998m)

Weight: 4,125lb (1,912kg) loaded

Armament: four 0.30-cal. (7.62-mm) machine guns

Dimensions: span 29ft 2in (8.88m); length 20ft 1in (6.1m); height 7ft 10in (2.41m)

Far right: *This winter-camouflaged I-16 suffered a landing accident and was found in this embarrassing state by Finnish troops.*

Polikarpov's stubby little I-16 today looks completely old-fashioned, even compared to other fighters of the late 1930s. At the time of its appearance over the battlefields of Spain and China, however, the "Rata" (rat), as it was disparagingly known, was the first cantilever monoplane fighter with retractable undercarriage in service anywhere. Despite its open cockpit and wooden construction, the basic layout of the I-16 was to serve as the template for fighters throughout the world conflict to follow and beyond.

The Polikarpov I-16 was the end result of conceptual studies begun by Andrei Tupolev in 1932. Together with Nikolai Polikarpov, head of the Central Construction Bureau (TsKB), Tupolev developed the ANT-31 or I-14 biplane. Polikarpov was then sent to Factory No. 36 to oversee the I-15, also a biplane, but wanted to apply some of the lightweight features of the I-14 in a new monoplane, and this was first flown on 30 December 1933 as the TsKB-12, with Valery Tchakalov as test pilot. The powerplant was a Shvetsov M-22 9-cylinder radial of 480 hp (358 kW), this being derived from a French version of the Bristol

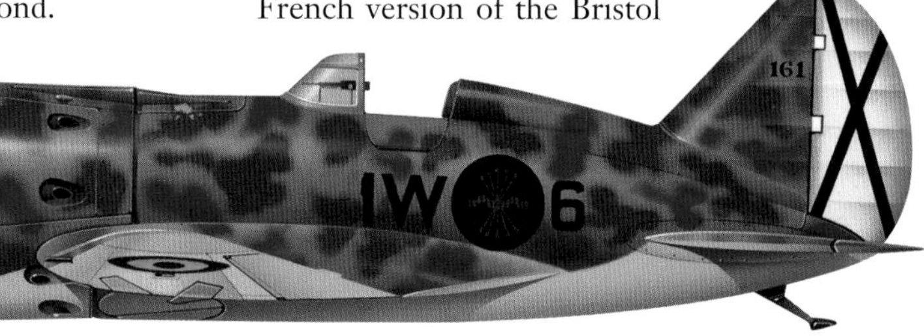

Right: *An I-16 Type 10 captured by Spanish Nationalist forces at the end of the Civil War.*

Above: *Some I-16s were captured from the Russians during the Winter War and put into Finnish service. Skis allowed ice operations.*

Below: *Most I-16s were powered by the Shvetsov M62 engine. Produced later as the ASh-62, many remain in service today.*

Jupiter engine. The TsKB-12 was later renamed the I-16, "I" standing for *Istrebitel*, or "fighter," and a small preseries batch of Type 1 models entered service in early 1935.

The basic structure of the I-16 was a laminated wooden monocoque fuselage attached to metal wings with fabric-covered control surfaces. The radial engine was enclosed in a metal cowling, which extended to cover the forward surface, with moveable louvers allowing cooling air to reach the cylinders. A two-bladed metal propeller was mounted behind a huge domed boss. The blunt and unaerodynamic appearance disguised a very clever bit of design work. The jet effect from the ring of exhaust ports exiting around the cowl actually produced enough thrust to cancel out the drag of its flat-front face. Armament usually consisted of four 0.30-cal. (7.62-mm) ShKAS machine guns. Two machine guns were mounted in the forward fuselage, firing through the propeller arc, and two in the wings. Some models had two 0.79-in (20-mm) ShVAK cannon in the wings, and these were the most powerfully armed fighters in service anywhere in 1939.

The simple instrument panel lacked an artificial horizon, and the pilot controlled the aircraft with a spectacle-type control grip. The undercarriage was manually retracted and lowered using a chain drive, which required 44 turns on a crank to bring it up or down. Although there was no canopy, the pilot was afforded protection of armor plate behind his head.

The preseries I-16 Type 1 was followed by the Type 4 with a longer chord cowl. The I-16 Type 5 introduced the license-built 700-hp (522-kW) M-25 (Wright Cyclone) engine and added the two 0.30-cal. (7.62-mm) machine guns in the wings. A small number I-16s were built in Spain as the Type 10. The Type 12 and the Type 17 had a pair of 0.79-in (20-mm) ShVAK cannon in the wings and 750-hp (560-kW) M-25V engines. By 1939, the I-16 was becoming heavier and more power was needed. This came in the form of the 800-hp

Right: *The "Zveno" connected a pair of I-16s to a TB-3 bomber, and allowed long-range attack missions by fast and nimble aircraft.*

PILOTING THE POLIKARPOV I-16

Above: The restored open-cockpit I-16s have given some lucky modern pilots a whole new warbird flying experience.

The last airworthy I-16s, probably all single-seaters, were to be found serving at the Spanish Air Force's fighter school in 1952, and that would have been the end of the story but for the efforts of a New Zealand businessman and his contacts in Russia. Sir Tim Wallis organized the rebuilding of six Type 24s from wrecks recovered from wartime crash sites. All new wooden parts were needed, but as many original parts as possible were retained during the rebuilding, which took place in modern aircraft plants. The first rebuilt aircraft flew in September 1995, powered by the ASH-62 engine used in the An-2 biplane, of which there are many in service in Russia and elsewhere.

The late Mark Hanna offered his thoughts on flying one of the restored examples. "How does she feel? We're holding a slight push force on the stick (remember no elevator trim)—roll rate is excellent and very positive—about 100–120 degrees per second. Pitch is also very effective and the Rata is delightful in aerobatics—although as speed increases in the dive, passing 400km/h the push force on the stick reduces to zero and then as 430km/h is reached, a very slight pull force is required—something that needs a little care running in low level for the start of a display. The aeroplane accelerates very quickly in the dive and, when seen from the ground, appears extremely fast. Stalling in manoeuvre gives plenty of warning with pronounced tail buffeting before she drops the left-hand wing quite progressively and definitely not violently. The aeroplane delights in reversing from a maximum rate turn in one direction rapidly to the other. You can see that this is a superb close-in dogfighter.

The delightful handling characteristics, plus the open cockpit, vibrations, and noise, provide a very exciting ride. Rolling requires little rudder input to stay balanced. I have the feeling that you could snap roll the Rata deliberately very precisely. Vertical performance is excellent and with excess energy pulling up and unloading straight up in to the vertical produces spectacular performance."

Left: With its poor forward visibility in the tail-down position, the I-16 has a reputation for being very difficult to land smoothly.

***Above:** The prototype I-16 looked more like a racing plane than a fighter. Note the cables for raising and lowering the undercarriage.*

(597-kW) Shvetsov M-62 on the Type 18 with four machine guns and the 930-hp (694-kW) M-63 on the Type 24. The Type 24 had two 0.79-in (20-mm) cannon in the wings and the Type 27 had one 0.50-cal (12.7-mm) machine gun in the cowl and two 0.30-cal. (7.62-mm) machine guns in the wings, as well as the capability for underwing rockets.Two two-seat training variants, the Type 4 UTI and the Type 15 UTI, were built to the tune of 1,640 examples.

The Soviet Air Force's I-16s were unveiled publicly in May 1935. Although dismissed by some western observers as nothing more than a refined copy of the Boeing P-26 "Peashooter," the two had little in common. For one thing, even the earliest model I-16s were about 50mph (80km/h) faster than the Boeing.

About 475 Type 5s were supplied to the Spanish Republicans from October 1936. The Nationalists soon gave it the nickname "Rata." Other nicknames included "Mosca" (fly) and "Ishak" (little donkey). Flown largely by Soviet pilots using Spanish *noms de guerre*, the I-16s and I-15 biplanes soon took on the Nationalist Ju 52 bombers and biplane fighters. Despite some early successes, the I-16 pilots soon learned to avoid getting into turning fights with the nimble Fiat C.R.32 biplanes. Both the Russian and Italian pilots learnt to attack from above; however, whereas the Polikarpovs would zoom back up for another attack, the Fiats would try to use their better turning ability in a level fight. The German Heinkel He 51B biplane pilots quickly realized not to tangle with the Polikarpovs at all, and looked forward to the arrival of the new Messerschmitt monoplane in Spain.

China received many I-16s. By 1939, they were in action against the Japanese. Soviet pilots also encountered the Japanese over the disputed Nomonhan region between Manchuria and Outer Mongolia. The only advantage the I-16s had over the Japanese army Ki 27 "Nate" and navy A5M "Claude" fighters was the retractable undercarriage. The Japanese fighters, who were better flyers, were usually victorious. But the Soviets improved their tactics and by the time an armistice was signed in September 1939, actual combat losses were not significantly higher than those of the opposition. In one courageous incident, the deputy commander of a Soviet regiment landed his I-16 on the battlefield. In the face of Japanese gunfire, he rescued his commanding officer, who had just parachuted from his burning I-16, by placing him on his lap in the tiny cockpit of his own fighter.

The Soviet Air Force fighter arm was largely equipped with I-16s and I-153 biplanes at the outbreak of the German-Soviet war in 1941. More than 60 percent of the Soviet fighter force was comprised of I-16s. Although the I-16 was revolutionary in 1936, by 1941 all of the fighting nations had monoplane fighters, almost all of them better armed, faster and with better climbing and diving performance. Several thousand aircraft were lost in the opening days and weeks of the German invasion, but significant numbers of I-16s remained in service until 1943.

The I-16 was used for the extraordinary Zveno mothership and parasite fighter combination, which was used successfully in combat. In the 1930s engineer Vladimir Vakhmistrov explored the idea of a large aircraft carrying smaller ones for defense of bombers or for their own attack missions. His first trials in 1931-32 were with a TB-1 bomber and a pair of I-4 fighters strapped on top of the wing. Experiments continued until the Zveno 6 combination of an ungainly Tupolev TB-3 bomber and a pair of I-16s suspended under the wings on struts. One interesting aspect was that the fighters' engines contributed to the power of the combination and were supplied with oil and fuel by umbilical cords from the bomber. Having proved that uncoupling was possible, the Zveno 6 was approved for production as the SPB composite dive-bomber in December 1936.

The next stage, reattaching in flight using a trapeze system, was to prove too difficult for the average pilot, but the "piggy-back" given by the TB-3 gave enough extra range for the I-16s to perform some significant combat missions in the early part of the war with Germany. The Zvenos, using I-16 Type 5s armed with pairs of 550-lb (250-kg) or 1,100-lb (500-kg) bombs, attacked bridges over the Dnieper and Danube rivers, oil fields, and docks during 1941. In all, the six SPBs flew around 30 combat missions. The destruction of the Zaporozhje bridge by two Zvenos in August 1941 was to have a significant effect on the battle of Stalingrad two years later when this route was not available to the Germans for either resupply or retreat.

Above: *Soviet factory workers, seemingly assisted by a pilot, work on an I-16. The fuselage was mainly built of laminated spruce and the tailfin was fabric-covered metal construction.*

Left: *The I-16's operational career began and ended in Spain. The last examples served until the 1950s alongside the last biplane I-153s.*

Gloster Gladiator

The Gladiator, the RAF's last biplane fighter, entered service just ahead of the Spitfire and Hurricane. Despite its obsolescence, it served in World War II and was active on a number of fronts, including Norway, Malta, and the Middle East.

GLOSTER GLADIATOR MK.I

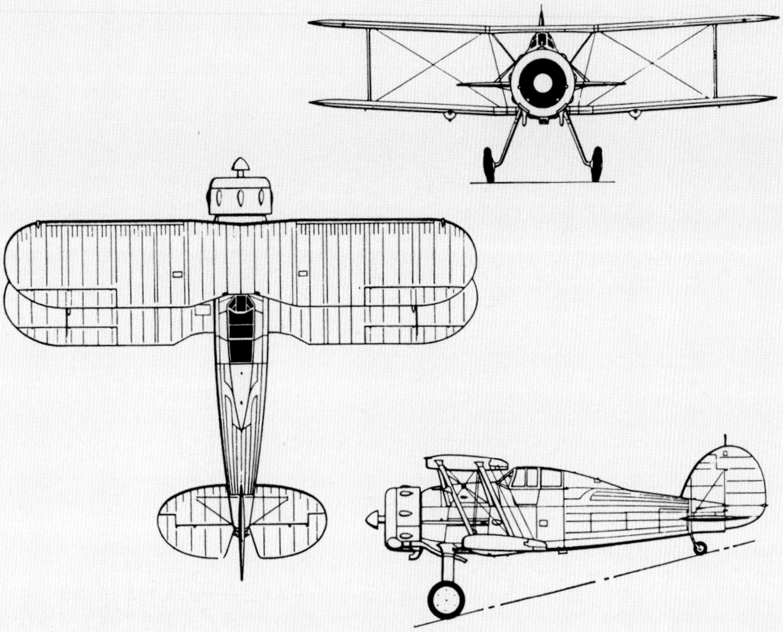

Crew: one

Powerplant: one 840-hp (626-kW) Bristol Mercury IX 9-cylinder radial piston engine

Maximum speed: 253mph (407km/h)

Combat radius: 200 miles (322km)

Service ceiling: 33,000ft (10,060m)

Weight: 4,750lb (2,155kg) loaded

Armament: initially two .303-cal. (7.7-mm) Vickers and two .303-cal. (7.7-mm) Lewis machine guns; later four .303-cal. (7.7-mm) Browning machine guns

Dimensions: span 32ft 3in (9.85m); length 27ft 5in (8.38m); height 10ft 4in (3.17m)

Far right: *An early production Gladiator banks away, showing the fairings for the underwing 0.303-in (7.7-mm) machine guns.*

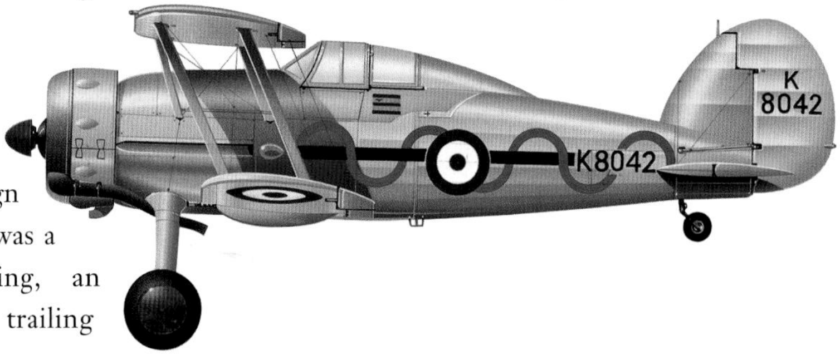

Right: *This Gladiator was flown by the commanding officer of No. 37 Squadron at RAF Debden in 1937.*

The last biplane fighter to enter service with the Royal Air Force (RAF), the Gloster Gladiator was basically obsolete by the time it appeared. Nonetheless, on several battlefronts in the early years of World War II, they were the only fighters available to Britain or its Allies, and they proved surprisingly effective due to their high agility and determined pilots.

In 1934, Gloster Aircraft's designer H.P. Folland made an analysis of the strengths and weaknesses of his previous design for the RAF, the Gauntlet. This was a biplane with a two-bay wing, an undercarriage with cross and trailing braces, and a 640-hp (477-kW) Mercury VIS2 engine. With two fuselage-mounted Vickers guns, the Gauntlet had the same armament as the Sopwith Camel, although it was more than 100mph (160km/h) faster. All that separated the Gauntlet (which flew in 1929, but did not enter service until 1934) from the

K6132
K6132

PILOTING THE GLOSTER GLADIATOR

Above: The cockpit of the Gladiator shows the "blind flying" panel in the center. It had all the instruments necessary for bad weather and night flying.

Three squadrons of RAF Gladiators were based in Egypt when Italy declared war on Britain on July 10, 1940. Within a few days, they were in action against the Regia Aeronautica. The Regia's fighter component in the region consisted of Fiat CR.32 and CR.42 biplanes, the latter having an inline engine of 840 hp (627 kW), a higher top speed than the Gladiator and an armament of only two 0.50-cal. (12.7-mm) machine guns. Flight Lieutenant Marmaduke St. John "Pat" Pattle of No. 80 Squadron based at Amriya made this official combat report after an epic battle between biplanes on August 8, 1940.

"I was leading the top section of three aircraft in a formation of 13 Gladiators which took off from our base at 1740 hours. The formation crossed the [Libyan] border at approximately 1800 hours at Sidi Omar. At 1825 when approaching Bir El Gobi, a large formation of 27 CR.42s were sighted at about 6,000 feet on the starboard beam, flying east.

"Our formation wheeled to attack and approached the enemy formation from the east, the first section approaching within range unobserved. Immediately the first section engaged, the enemy formation split up, and a general dogfight followed. I saw Nos. 2 and 3 sections engage, and before I brought my section into the fight, I saw five aircraft crashed on the ground, three of which were in flames. My own section then engaged those E/A [enemy aircraft] who were attempting to reach their own base, and immediately became engaged in separate combats.

"I engaged a CR.42 and, after a short skirmish, got into position immediately behind him. On firing two short bursts at about 50 yards' range the E/A fell into a spin and burst into flames upon striking the ground. The pilot did not abandon his aircraft. I then attacked three E/A immediately below me. This action was indecisive as after a few minutes they broke away by diving vertically for the ground and pulling out at low altitude.

"Whilst searching for other E/A, I saw two more aircraft crash and burst into flames. Owing to the widespread area, and the number of aircraft involved, it was impossible to confirm what types of aircraft were involved in these crashes or who shot them down. The sky seemed clear of '42s, although several Gladiators were still in the vicinity. I was about to turn for our base when a '42 attacked me from below. With the advantage of height, I dived astern of him and, after a short burst, he spun into the ground in flames. As before, the pilot did not abandon his aircraft. Flying Officer Graham confirms both my combats, which ended decisively."

Pattle's two victories contributed to a total of nine Italian aircraft confirmed and six probably destroyed from the engagement. "Pat" Pattle was eventually to score 15 Gladiator victories, making him the highest-scoring Gladiator pilot, and he eventually became the most successful RAF or Commonwealth ace, with a total of 50 kills.

Below: In the early part of the war in North Africa, the Gladiator was quite effective against Italy's biplane fighters.

Left: Gladiators of No. 72 Squadron RAF in 1937 at Farnborough, in the UK. Later that year, monoplanes would begin to replace them in Fighter Command.

fighters of World War I were the bigger powerplant and higher performance. To meet Specification F.7/30, Folland revised the Gauntlet to have a single bay wing of the same span, an enclosed canopy, a simpler internally sprung cantilever undercarriage, and a revised tail unit. Like the Gauntlet, the private-venture SS.37 prototype, which first flew on September 12, 1934 in the hands of Flight Lieutenant P.E.G. Sayer, had ailerons on all four wings, which helped confer exceptional maneuverability. It demonstrated a maximum speed of 242mph (389km/h). The prototype's Mercury IV engine was actually less powerful at 530 hp (395 kW) than the Gauntlet's, but the production aircraft, ordered in July 1935 as the Gladiator I, had an 830-hp (619-kW) Mercury IX. This had an electric starter and automatic mixture control, and drove a two-bladed wooden Watts propeller. The Vickers guns were supplemented by a pair of 0.303-cal. (7.7-mm) Browning machine guns in pods under the lower wings. The first batch of 23 was followed by another of 186, total Mk I production eventually amounting to 378 airframes.

No. 72 Squadron at Tangmere began to replace its Bulldog IIs with Gladiators in February 1937, becoming the first of nine RAF squadrons to be so equipped. Many future fighter aces flew Gladiators with frontline and auxiliary squadrons in the last years before the war. The Gladiators' silver-doped finish and colorful squadron markings gave way to earth and green camouflage after the Munich Crisis in 1938.

Above: This ski-equipped Gladiator was flown by a Swedish volunteer unit that fought in Finland against the Soviets.

The Watts propellers were blamed for causing rough running of the engine, so the Gladiator II introduced a three-bladed fixed-pitch Fairey-Reed metal unit, which cured the problem. A total of 270 Mk IIs was built before production ended in 1940.

In October 1937, the Chinese Central Government ordered 36 Gladiator Is. The first arrived in late November and the remainder in January 1938, and they were in action against the Japanese by the end of February, following a period of pilot training. John "Buffalo" Wong, commander of the 29th Pursuit Squadron, became the first Gladiator ace, scoring five victories against Japanese navy fighters and dive-bombers to add to two scored on other types.

Export Gladiators also went to Belgium, Egypt, Greece, Iraq, Ireland, Latvia, Norway, South Africa, and Sweden. The Royal Navy ordered 38 more-or-less standard aircraft followed by 60 as the Sea Gladiator, these differing by having an arrester hook, catapult launch points, a naval radio, and an inflatable dinghy stowed in a fairing between the undercarriage legs. In April 1940, the carrier HMS *Glorious* delivered the 18 Gladiators of No. 263 Squadron to support the beleaguered Norwegian forces (whose own 12 Gladiators barely survived one day of fighting). Many of these aircraft were lost in German bombing raids, and *Glorious* returned to collect more aircraft for the squadron and deliver Hurricanes. The Gladiators of No. 263 Squadron and the Fleet Air Arm's No. 802 Squadron fought bravely, the former unit destroying 26 enemy aircraft in 13 days for only two losses in combat. Norway could not be saved, however, and the surviving aircraft (which were not equipped for carrier operations) were flown back to *Glorious* on June 7. Sadly, the following day the carrier was sunk by the German battle cruisers *Scharnhorst* and *Gneisenau*, with the loss of all of the pilots of both squadrons and 1,500 other personnel.

The myth of the defense of the strategic Mediterranean island of Malta being entirely in the hands of three Sea Gladiators named *Faith*, *Hope*, and *Charity* appears to have originated with a local newspaper. This is despite the fact that there were periods in the spring of 1940 when as few as four such aircraft, assigned to the Hal Far Fighter Flight, were available to defend Malta. Although relieved by more modern fighters, these and a handful of other Sea Gladiators had numerous successes against Italian bombers and reconnaissance aircraft, with only one lost in return during air combat.

Above: *The prototype Gladiator flew in September 1934 but lacked the enclosed canopy of production examples. The underwing pods contained Lewis guns.*

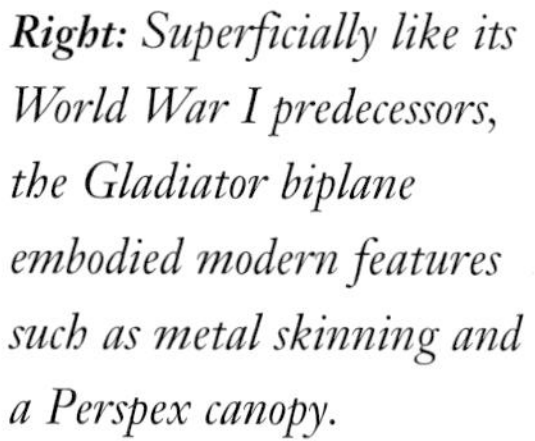

Right: *Superficially like its World War I predecessors, the Gladiator biplane embodied modern features such as metal skinning and a Perspex canopy.*

Left: *The No. 80 Squadron is seen lined up at Ismailia, Egypt, in September 1938. Also visible is the mooring tower for the abandoned Imperial airship service.*

Many of the exported Gladiators also saw action. A unit of Swedish volunteers joined Finland's own aircraft in the Winter War against the Soviet Union. Belgian and Greek pilots also scored victories with Gladiators.

The Gladiator was retired from frontline RAF service in 1942, but served on in such roles as weather reconnaissance until 1944. A Finnish pilot scored the last combat victory by a Gladiator, over a Soviet R-5 biplane in February 1944 during the Continuation War. The Gloster Aircraft company had a Gladiator I restored to flying condition in 1953 and later donated it to the Shuttleworth Collection, which still operates it today. One other Gladiator is under restoration to eventual flight.

Below: *This Gladiator Mk I has been flown by the Shuttleworth Collection for many years and is the only remaining airworthy example.*

Messerschmitt Bf 109

The Bf 109, the mainstay of the Luftwaffe *through the war, was one of the most adaptable fighters ever. Variants of the Bf 109 flew with half a dozen different powerplants and saw service from the 1930s to the late 1960s.*

MESSERSCHMITT BF 109G-6

Crew: one

Powerplant: one 1,475-hp (1,100-kW) Daimler-Benz DB-605A inverted V-12 piston engine

Maximum speed: 387mph (623km/h)

Combat radius: 300 miles (483km)

Service ceiling: 38,550ft (11,750m)

Weight: 6,944 lb (3,150kg) loaded

Armament: two nose-mounted 0.31-in (7.92-mm) MG 17 machine guns, one hub-mounted 1.18-in (30-mm) MK 108 cannon, two 0.79-in (20-mm) MG 151 cannon mounted under wings

Dimensions: span 32ft 6.5in (9.92m); length 29ft 7in (9.02m); height 11ft 2in (3.4m)

Far right: *The "black men" of the* Luftwaffe *kept the aces airborne. Here a crew of JG 53 work on the DB 601 of a Bf 109E.*

Right: *This Bf 109D served with a training unit Flugzeugführerschule A/B 123 at Zagreb, Yugoslavia, in 1943.*

The Messerschmitt Bf 109 was the most produced fighter of all time, with more than 35,000 built. The "109" pilots scored more aerial victories than by those of any other aircraft. Bf 109 development kept pace with Allied fighters until the last year of World War II, but production continued until the final days of the war and beyond.

Wilhelm Emil "Willi" Messerschmitt of the BFW aircraft company entered his four-seat Bf 108A monoplane in an international contest for touring aircraft. Although it won no prizes, the performance of this machine and its many advanced design features impressed the German Air Ministry Reichsluftfahrtministerium (RLM), and Messerschmitt was invited to design a fast "single-seat courier" (a euphemism for fighter) for a *Luftwaffe* competition. The wings and tail of the Bf 108 (which itself was to become the *Luftwaffe*'s main communications aircraft) were retained, but a new fuselage was designed behind a Junkers Jumo 210 inverted-V 12-cylinder water-cooled engine of 507 hp (378 kW). The Jumo was not available when the Bf 109V1 first prototype was completed in May

PILOTING THE BF 109

Above: *One of the* Luftwaffe's *top aces, Werner Schroer scored the first of his 114 victories while flying this Bf 109E-7 in Libya.*

Helmut Wick of I.JG2 claimed the first of his 56 victories in a Bf 109E on November 22, 1939. This was the period of the "Phoney War" when Germany and France faced each other across the border with little combat on land or in the air. "As the French did not cross the German border very often, my wingman and I decided to visit them. A tailwind from the east helped us on our way. Near Nancy I suddenly saw a gaggle of aircraft at an altitude of 6,000 meters. Realizing immediately that they were not German, we began to circle. Two aircraft detached themselves from the bunch above and swooped down on us. Now I could recognize them—Curtiss fighters." These were Hawk 75As (the radial-engined predecessor of the P-40) from GC II/4.

"We dived away and, just as we had anticipated, the two Frenchmen dived after us. I went into a climbing turn with one of the Frenchmen right on my tail. I can still clearly remember how I could see his red, white, and blue roundels when I looked behind me. At first the sight of them was rather exciting, particularly as the Frenchman was firing away with everything he had, but then the realisation that somebody is behind you and shooting at you is very unpleasant.

"I pushed the nose down again and with my superior speed, quickly lost him. When my Frenchman was no longer to be seen, looked up to my left to find the others. Not a thing in sight. I glanced up to my right and I could hardly believe my eyes. I was staring straight at four radial engines all sprouting little red flames. A ridiculous thought flashed through my mind.—'Are they really allowed to shoot at me like that?'

"But then I was all concentration. Should I try to get away again? No! Now's the time to tackle them. One has got to go down. Clenching my teeth, I hauled the stick and rudder to the right and turned into them.

"By the time I had completed my turn the first had already shot past me. The second was right behind him and this one I attacked head-on. It was a nasty moment looking straight down his blazing gun barrels, but we were too close to score any hits. He zoomed over my head and the third one was almost on top of me.

"I maneuvered my aircraft slightly to get him nicely lined up in my sights ... with my first shots I saw some pieces of metal fly off the Frenchman. Then both his wings buckled and gave way.

"Close behind him the fourth Curtiss was also firing at me, but I was not hit. The first pair were now climbing again. I followed suit so that they could not catch me. I was getting low on fuel and it was time to head for home. My wingman, who had returned to base safe and sound, had lost me in the first dive after all the twisting and turning."

Left: *The Bf 109Es of I./JG 27 adopted a highly effective desert camouflage consisting of olive-green patches over the basic sand color.*

1935, and a Rolls-Royce Kestrel VI of 695 hp (518 kW) was substituted in its place.

The exact date of the first flight is lost to history, but senior test pilot Hans-Dietrich "Bubi" Knoetzsch began the test program in late May, following which the V1 was ferried to Rechlin for official testing. The first Jumo-engined aircraft joined the test program in January 1936. A batch of 10 preproduction aircraft was ordered, as was one of the Messerschmit's rival, the Heinkel He 112.

The Bf 109 embodied for the first time many advanced features in one fighter airframe. These included a retractable undercarriage, an enclosed cockpit, and stressed-skin monocoque construction. The first prototypes had two-bladed propellers, as did the first batch of Bf 109B production aircraft. The third, fourth, and fifth prototypes were despatched to Spain in December 1936 for operational evaluation. Although they achieved no combat victories, much valuable data was gathered that was applied to the Bf 109B, which made its first appearance in the Spanish Civil War in March 1937. The Messerschmitts soon turned the tables on the nimble Polikarpovs flown by the Republicans, as much because of their better tactical employment as any great technical superiority.

The tenth prototype was fitted with a 900-hp

Above: *These Bf 109E fighter-bombers served with III./JG 27 based on Sicily for operations over Malta during May 1941.*

Left: *Bf 109G-1s wearing their factory radio code letters await delivery to frontline units. The G entered service in mid-1942.*

***Above:** The principal late-war version was the "Gustav." II./JG 53 moved its Bf 109G-2s from Sicily to Tunisia and back again in 1942.*

(716-kW) Daimler-Benz DB 600Aa, and the thirteenth with a DB 601. In its production form, the DB 601 gave 1,175 hp (876 kW), but using a special boosted version, the Bf 109V13 broke the landplane absolute speed record at 379.38mph (611km/h) on November 11, 1937. In 1938, BFW was renamed Messerschmitt AG.

During 1939, the Jumo-powered Bf 109B, C, and D were replaced in frontline units by Bf 109E with a fuel-injected DB 601. The E's armament varied by subtype, but usually comprised two cowl-mounted 0.31-in (7.92-mm) MG 17 machine guns and two 0.79-in (20-mm) MG FF cannon in the wings. Later "Emils" had a 1.18-in (30-mm) MK 108 cannon firing through the propeller hub. The Bf 109E–equipped fighter units swept the skies during the German blitzkrieg on Poland and, later, against France, Holland, and Belgium.

Based on French and Dutch airfields, the Bf 109E was the principal German fighter in the Battle of Britain. It was closely matched to the Spitfire and Hurricane, but was somewhat hampered by its short endurance, which gave it only 20 minutes of combat time over England. In combats with Royal Air Force (RAF) fighters, it scored slightly better than even.

The Bf 109F, which first flew in late 1940, had a revised nose shape and other refinements, including a DB 601E rated at 1,350 hp (1,007 kW). The "Freidrich" was regarded as the best variant to fly and was mainly used in the Mediterranean and North Africa from 1941. The engine-mounted 1.18-in (30-mm) cannon was fitted to all Fs, and it or a 0.79-in (20-mm) model armed subsequent 109s alongside cowl machine guns. The cannon mounted within the wings was deleted.

The Bf 109G series introduced the DB 605 engine of 1,475 hp (1,100 kW). With water/methanol boost, maximum output went up to 1,800 hp (1,342 kW). The final German production version was the Bf 109K, which had a DB 605AS engine capable of 2,000 hp (1,491 kW) with boost.

Despite its growing obsolescence, many of the most experienced *Luftwaffe* pilots preferred the 109 to newer types and racked up incredible scores on them. The highest scoring ace of all time, Erich Hartmann, scored 352 victories and

***Right:** The successors to Messerschmitt AG converted a Spanish Buchón to Daimler-Benz power in the 1980s, replicating a Bf 109G-6.*

kept the 109 until the end of the war. Less experienced pilots disliked the cramped cockpit, poor view, and narrow track undercarriage, which caused many takeoff and landing accidents.

Bf 109Es were supplied to Spain and Switzerland. Later models served with Italy, Finland, and Switzerland, as well as Germany's wartime puppet states Romania, Croatia, Hungary, and Bulgaria. After the war, Czechoslovakia developed the Avia S.199 from uncompleted Bf 109G airframes with a 1,350-hp (1,007-kW) Jumo 211F engine. Twenty-five of these were supplied to Israel and used in the War of Independence with some success, despite their horrible handling characteristics, which led to the nickname "Mule."

In 1942, Spain received 25 Bf 109Gs, but no engines. They were completed from 1945–48 with 1,300-hp (970-kW) Hispano-Suiza 12Z engines as the Hispano Ha-1109J, followed by 65 new-build Ha-112-K1Ls. The main Spanish version was the HA-112-M1L with a 1,610-hp (1,200-kW) Rolls-Royce Merlin 500. The *Buchón* (a type of fat-breasted pigeon) served from 1956 to 1967 and saw ground-attack action in some of Spain's colonial wars in North Africa. The retirement of the *Buchón* coincided with the production of the film epic *Battle of Britain*, and many of the airworthy examples had a role in it, representing Bf 109Es. Subsequently a number of *Buchóns* have been re-engined with DB 605s to represent Bf 109Gs. An original Bf 109G flew in the United Kingdom for most of the 1990s, but today only one genuine Messerschmitt 109, an E restored from an example found in Russia, is currently airworthy.

Above: *The British rebuilt a Bf 109E-7, which crashed in Kent in 1940, and conducted extensive evaluations of it.*

Below: *The Bf 109E was the main early war version. In 1941 in North Africa they were replaced by the Bf 109F.*

Hawker Hurricane

Hawker's Hurricane, the Royal Air Force's first monoplane fighter, owed much to the technology of the biplane era. The most important fighter of the Battle of Britain, the Hurricane served in all theaters where British forces were engaged.

Far right: *The Hurricane was less maneuverable than the Spitfire or Bf 109 but made a more stable gun platform and could absorb a lot of damage.*

Right: *This early Hurricane of No. 111 Squadron at Northolt set a speed record between London and Edinburgh before the war.*

Like the Spitfire, the Hawker Hurricane, which did more than any other aircraft or defense system in 1940 to save Britain from Nazi invasion, began as a private-venture project. Sydney Camm, chief designer at Hawker Aircraft, had been interested in monoplanes since at least 1925, but did not propose a monoplane fighter to the company until 1933. This began literally as the Fury Monoplane, based on the biplane Fury fighter and powered by a steam-cooled 660-hp (492-kW) Rolls Royce Goshawk engine. The availability of the new Rolls-Royce PV 12 (later to evolve into the famous Merlin) gave extra impetus to the project, and it was redesigned around the PV 12, which offered around 900 hp (671 kW). The Air Ministry wrote Specification F.36/34 around Hawker's proposal, and construction of a prototype took place in the Hawker factory at Kingston-on-Thames on the southwestern fringe of London.

The first flight of the Hurricane took place on November 6, 1935 at Brooklands, in Surrey, in the hands of Flight Lieutenant P.W.S. "George" Bulman, Hawker's chief test pilot. The prototype was finished in silver-doped fabric with polished natural metal cowls, inner leading edges, and

HAWKER HURRICANE MK IIC

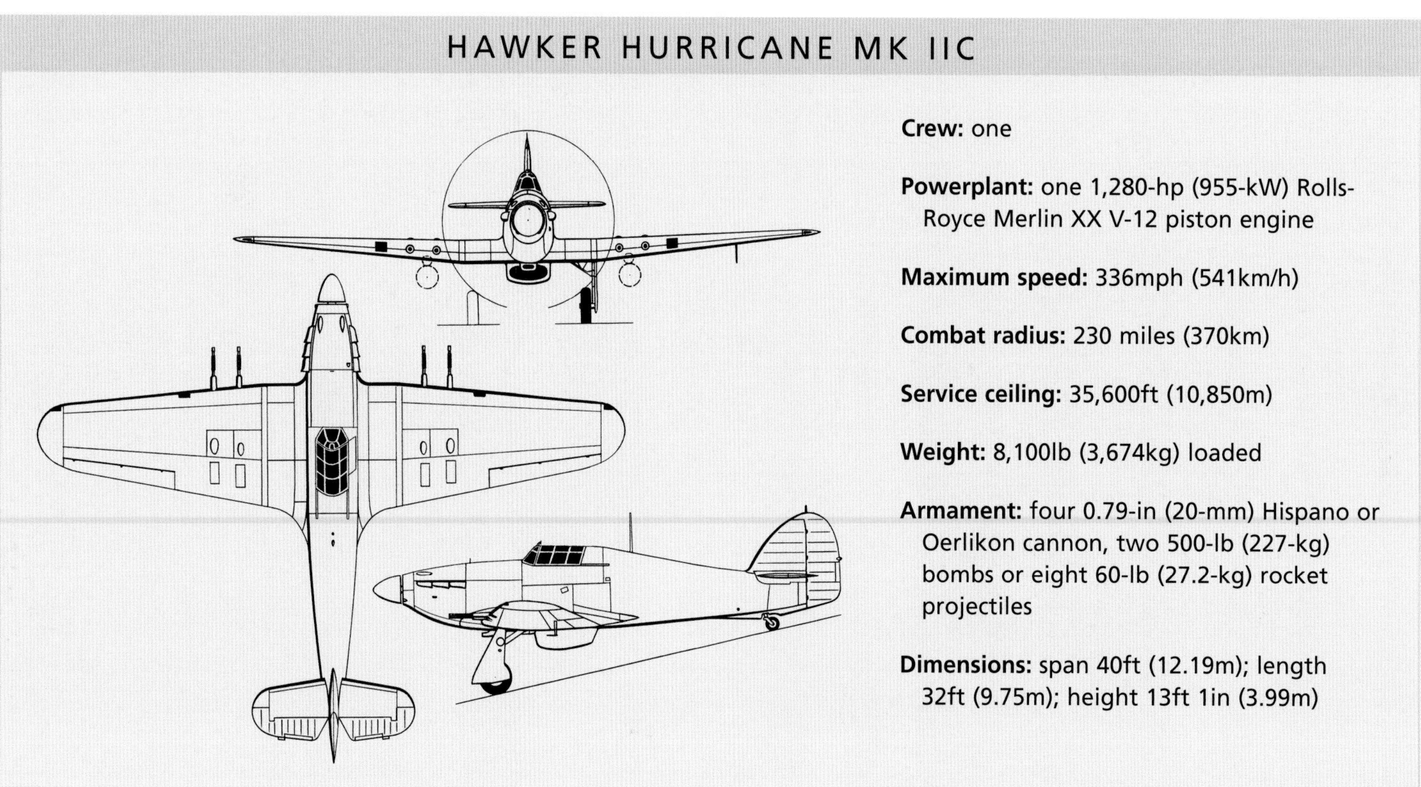

Crew: one

Powerplant: one 1,280-hp (955-kW) Rolls-Royce Merlin XX V-12 piston engine

Maximum speed: 336mph (541km/h)

Combat radius: 230 miles (370km)

Service ceiling: 35,600ft (10,850m)

Weight: 8,100lb (3,674kg) loaded

Armament: four 0.79-in (20-mm) Hispano or Oerlikon cannon, two 500-lb (227-kg) bombs or eight 60-lb (27.2-kg) rocket projectiles

Dimensions: span 40ft (12.19m); length 32ft (9.75m); height 13ft 1in (3.99m)

radiator bath. The engine was now known as the Merlin C. Like the prototype Spitfire, the propeller was a two-bladed fixed pitch Watts wooden unit. The name "Hurricane" was bestowed in June 1936, the same month that the Air Ministry announced an initial order for 600.

The initial Hurricane Mk I model, now with the 1,030-hp (768-kW) Merlin II and armed with eight .303-cal. (7.7-mm) machine guns in the wings, entered service with No. 3 Squadron at Northolt in December 1937. These were the first monoplane fighters to enter Royal Air Force (RAF) service. By the time of the outbreak of war in September 1939, 467 Hurricanes were in service with 17 squadrons.

The Hurricane was of fabric-covered metal and wood construction, with many similarities to the earlier Hawker biplanes. It has been said that British fighters were designed to be assembled by craftsmen and American ones by high-school graduates. The Hurricane is a case in point, having almost no interchangeable parts and many complex ones such as tubes constructed from rolled strips and pressed into square sections at the ends. All of these needed special equipment to produce.

The primary structure was a box section of metal tubes, rounded out by a complex pattern of wooden formers and stringers, covered in doped fabric. The wings on early aircraft were also a fabric-covered wooden structure, but by May 1940 almost all had stronger metal wings, which were retrofitted to earlier aircraft. Many of the first Hurricanes also had wooden propellers, which were set at a compromise position that gave adequate but not ideal takeoff and altitude performance. When these were replaced by de Havilland or Rotol constant-speed (variable-pitch) units during the second production batch, the performance difference between the

***Above:** The first Sea Hurricanes were launched by catapult from converted merchant ships to defend convoys against German patrol bombers.*

***Right:** Later Sea Hurricanes were fully fledged carrier aircraft. Although they lacked folding wings they were suitable for the shipboard role.*

Left: The last Hurricane built, this Mk IIC named "Last of the Many" has flown in civilian hands for more than 50 years.

PILOTING THE HAWKER HURRICANE

Above: This Hurricane wears the colors of No. 615 Squadron based at Kenley during the Battle of Britain.

At the height of the battle, on 18 August, Flight Lieutenant Frank Carey led No. 43 Squadron into action against Junkers Ju 87 Stuka dive-bombers off the south coast of England. 'I took the nine Hurricanes head on into a large formation of Ju 87s midway between Chichester and Selsey Bill. After turning around to get behind some of them I found myself in the middle of some Ju 87 formations. I fired at one ahead of me – it stood straight up on its nose with flames coming out of it – when I was hit in the right knee by cross fire or a stray burst by a Hurricane. It must have been an almost-spent round, for if the bullet had been anything else, I shouldn't have had a knee left! Handing over the squadron to someone else, I had to drop out of the fight as my knee seemed to be locked and I wasn't feeling too well. My wound made it awkward to control my aircraft, and although one did not use the rudder all that much in the Hurricane, there were times when one needed to waggle it a bit. I called Tangmere but they advised me to stay away with the reply, "There are a lot of bombers heading this way and it looks as if they are going to give us another thumping!" I headed north and flew around for a time, but eventually had to crash land at Pulborough.'

Carey's victim was one of 16 Ju 87Bs destroyed that day attempting to attack the radar station at Poling, effectively wiping out a whole *Gruppe* (equivalent to a squadron). Thereafter, the Stuka was essentially withdrawn and played almost no further part in the battle. Frank Carey was to become the RAF's second-ranking Hurricane ace, with 25 confirmed victories, plus several others shared, unconfirmed and damaged. Robert Stanford-Tuck was the RAF's top Hurricane ace with 29 kills.

Right: *Engineers work on the Merlin XX powerplant of a Hurricane IIC. Many aircraft owed their success largely to this adaptable powerplant.*

Below: *The Hurricane had its origins in the Hawker Fury biplane. One Hurricane was given a jettisonable top wing to extend its range for delivery flights.*

Hurricane and Spitfire largely disappeared, at least at lower altitudes.

Conversely, the old-fashioned construction made it more suitable for mass production in the British aircraft industry of the 1930s, which was used to wood and fabric aircraft. The RAF's maintenance troops, the riggers and fitters, had also learnt their trade on the earlier generation of aircraft. As such, production of Hurricanes outstripped the all-metal Spitfire; by July 1940, 28 of Fighter Command's 46 squadrons were Hurricane equipped, compared to 19 that had Spitfires. The remainder flew the largely worthless Blenheim and Defiant day-fighter variants. In No. 11 Group, responsible for London and southeastern England, the Hurricane was even more dominant, equipping 17 squadrons versus seven of Spitfires and five of Blenheims.

After suffering heavy losses against Messerschmitt fighters in the Battle of France, the Hurricanes were withdrawn to the United Kingdom. In the Battle of Britain, the Hurricane, although less maneuverable than the Spitfire, proved a more stable gun platform and more effective in destroying the Heinkel, Dornier, and Junkers bombers. Its thick wing gave its best performance at medium altitudes. Despite this, the actual ratio of victories in combats between Hurricanes and Me 109s has been estimated at 272 to 153. In the final reckoning, Hurricanes destroyed more enemy aircraft during the battle than all other defenses (fighters, antiaircraft guns, and barrage balloons) combined.

By the end of 1940, there were 43 Hurricane squadrons in service in the United Kingdom. After this, the policy became to equip home-based day-fighter squadrons with Spitfires and supply Hurricanes to units in the Balkans, Middle East, and Far East. In Egypt, for several months prior to the Italian declaration of war in June 1940, a single unarmed Hurricane was flown from base to base to convince the enemy that the type was available in strength there. Only a handful were available in all of North Africa until September 1940, when reinforcements were shipped out by aircraft carrier.

After the Battle of Britain, Hurricanes remained in use as night-fighters, intruders, and trainers in the United Kingdom. The Hurricane was vital in the defense of Malta, but was unable to do much against the Zero and other maneuverable Japanese Army and Navy fighters. Several variants followed the Mk I, differing relatively little in outward appearance. The Hurricane Mk II had a Merlin XX with two-stage supercharger and spawned many subvariants, differing mainly in their armament. The Mk IIB had 12 machine guns and could carry light bombs, while the Mk IIC had four 0.79-in (20-mm) cannon. The Mk IID with two underwing 1.6-in (40-mm) Vickers "S" cannon and two machine guns operated mainly in the Western Desert in the anti-armor role.

With its wide track undercarriage and good endurance, the Hurricane made a better naval fighter than the Spitfire/Seafire. The first naval version was the Sea Hurricane Mk I and was fired from a merchant ship's catapult on one-way trips as a convoy defender. These "Hurricats" had to make for the nearest land base or bale out or ditch in the sea after tackling the enemy patrol bombers. The Sea Hurricane IB was a tail-hooked version without wing folding for the smaller escort carriers. All were converted from existing Mk Is and IIs, and Canadian-built aircraft. The Sea Hurricane IIC had the 1,280-hp (955-kW) Merlin XX and four cannon.

Unusual versions included a biplane (or "slip wing") with a jettisonable upper wing tested as a means of extending the ferry range. Two two-seat trainers were delivered to Persia (Iran) in 1947. These had open cockpits, although a canopy was later fitted to the rear position. Other two-seat versions were created in Russia.

Above: *The first prototype shows the mixture of metal-skinned and fabric-covered construction used on Hurricanes.*

Hurricanes were also exported to Belgium, Yugoslavia, Finland, India, Turkey, Ireland, and Portugal. The Canadian Car and Foundry (CCF) built 1,451 Hurricanes, beginning with the Mk X. They were used in Canada for training and by frontline RAF and Royal Canadian Air Force (RCAF) squadrons in Europe and elsewhere. The last Hurricanes were retired by Portugal in about 1954. Total production amounted to 14,323 Hurricanes in the United Kingdom, Canada, and Belgium.

Hawker retained the very last Hurricane built, suitably inscribed as "The Last of the Many" as a company communications aircraft. In 1972, it was passed to the Battle of Britain Memorial Flight (BBMF) and for many years was one of only two Hurricanes still airworthy. Recent years have seen more restorations, and now about eight remain flyable today.

Below: *A growing number of Hurricanes have been restored to fly. This Canadian-built Mk XII is one of the most recent and wears mid-war markings.*

Supermarine Spitfire

The development of the Spitfire, probably the most famous fighter ever, kept pace with the opposition from the late 1930s until the war's end. The Mk 24 had almost no common parts with the Mk I, yet retained its thoroughbred lines.

***Far right:** One of the most famous of the surviving Spitfires is Mk IX MH434, which has a distinguished wartime record and a long career in civilian hands.*

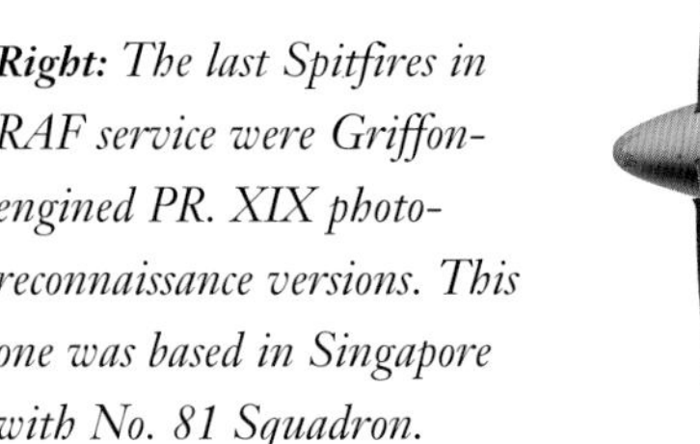

***Right:** The last Spitfires in RAF service were Griffon-engined PR. XIX photo-reconnaissance versions. This one was based in Singapore with No. 81 Squadron.*

Probably the most famous fighter of all time, the Supermarine Spitfire bridged the period between biplanes and jets; with 22,000 built, it became the most numerous fighter produced in Britain or the United States. As the plane was constantly developed, later versions had almost nothing in common with early Spitfires except the name, having two and a half times the weight and almost twice the power, and being 100mph (160km/h) faster.

During the 1920s and 1930s, Reginald (R.J.) Mitchell of the Supermarine company designed a series of high-speed floatplanes. His S.5 design won the Schneider Trophy in 1927, as did the S.6 in 1929 and the S.6B in 1931, with a world-record speed of 407mph (635km/h). In the latter year, Supermarine offered its Type 224 designed by Mitchell for the Royal Air Force's (RAF's) new fighter specification F.7/30, which emphasized climb rate and speed above 15,000 ft (4,573 m). The Type 224 was one of three monoplanes among the eight contenders from seven firms, and it flew in early 1934. It was an ungainly fixed-gear, open-cockpit aircraft and lost out to the faster

SUPERMARINE SPITFIRE MK IX

Crew: one

Powerplant: one 1,720-hp (1,283-kW) Rolls-Royce Merlin 61 V-12

Maximum speed: 408mph (657km/h)

Combat radius: 450 miles (724 km)

Service ceiling: 43,000ft (13,105m)

Weight: 9,500lb (4,309kg) loaded

Armament: two 0.79-in (20-mm) Hispano cannon and two 0.50-cal. (12.7-mm) Browning machine guns in wings

Dimensions: span 36ft 10in (11.23m); length 31ft 1in (9.47m); height 12ft 8in (3.86m)

SZ
G
MH4

PILOTING THE SUPERMARINE SPITFIRE

Above: Flt. Lt. Jan Zumbach, commander of the No. 303 "Kosciusko" Squadron flew a series of Spitfires with his personal Donald Duck emblem.

The arrival of the Focke Wulf 190 saw the balance tip greatly in favor of the *Luftwaffe*. In his 1959 autobiography, *Nine Lives,* Battle of Britain ace Squadron Leader Al Deere recalled a major battle between a dozen Spitfire Vs and 30 Fw 190s on June 2, 1942.

"Shortly after we crossed the French coast on the way in, the controller reported enemy activity to the raid ... but there was no sign of enemy fighters until about 20 miles from Le Touquet on the way out. At this point 'Mitzi' [Flight Lieutenant Edward Darling of No. 403 Squadron] reported a formation of about a dozen Fw 190s directly behind, at the same height and closing fast. I picked them up immediately and warned the rest of the squadron to prepare for a break. We had practised a manoeuvre to cope with just this contingency; one section would break upwards in the opposite direction from the other two which would turn in to the attacking fighters.

"'They're getting close Toby Leader,' a breathless and worried Mitzi urged some action.

"'OK Blue One, I see them. Wait for the order to break.'

"When I judged that the Huns were about the right distance away to suit the manoeuvre I intended to carry out, I gave the order.

"'Toby squadron, break left!'

"On my right, Yellow section broke upwards and away while, with Blue section outside me, I turned hard into the closing enemy fighters. About halfway around the break I looked for Yellow Section above and to my left and was startled to see another formation of Fw 190s about 2,000 feet above and on our beam.

"'Watch out Red Leader, more of them coming down from above and to our right.'

"Savagely I hauled my reluctant Spitfire around to meet this new attack and the next moment I was engulfed in enemy fighters, above, below and on both sides. Ahead and above I caught a glimpse of a Fw 190 as it poured cannon shells into the belly of an unsuspecting Spitfire. For a brief second the Spitfire seemed to stop in mid-air, and the next instant it folded inwards and broke in two, the pieces plummeting earthwards.

"I twisted and turned my aircraft in an endeavor to avoid being jumped and at the same time to get myself in a favorable position for attack. There was no lack of targets, but precious few Spitfires to take them on. I could see my number two, Sergeant Murphy, still hanging grimly on to my tail, but it was impossible to tell how many Spitfires were in the area, or how many had survived the unexpected onslaught. Break followed attack, attack followed break and all the time the determined Murphy hung to my tail until finally, when I was just about short of ammunition and pumping what was left into a Fw 190, I heard him call.

"'Break right Red One, I'll get him.'

"As I broke I saw Murphy pull up after a Fw 190 as it veered away from me, thwarted in its attack by his prompt action. My ammunition expended, I sought a retreat from a sky still generously sprinkled with hostile enemy fighters, but no Spitfires that I could see. In a series of turns and dives I made my way out until I was clear of the coast, and diving full throttle I headed for home."

In this sharp encounter, a total of seven Spitfires was lost (including that of Flight Lieutenant Edward Darling), for no casualties among the Fw 190As of I. and II.JG 26.

Left: *Wearing a full set of D-Day stripes, this No. 453 (RAAF) Squadron Mk XVI was photographed on the eve of the Allied invasion of Europe.*

Gloster SS.37, which became the Gladiator. The Type 224 experience taught Mitchell a great deal, however, and he was able to persuade his bosses to fund a new project based on the Rolls Royce PV.12 (later named the Merlin). The Air Ministry drew up a new specification for a prototype of this promising design, and the prototype F.37/34 was completed in February 1936.

On March 5, 1936, with J. "Mutt" Summers at the controls, the F.37/34, soon named Spitfire by Vickers, Supermarine's parent company, flew at Eastleigh near Southampton. The Spitfire was all-metal, with a stressed-skin monocoque fuselage and distinctive elliptical wings. The radiator was in a square fairing under the starboard wing and the oil cooler in a cylindrical unit beneath the port

Above: *The Mk XIV was the first mass-produced Griffon-engined variant. The increased power required a five-bladed propeller.*

Left: *This PR. Mk XIX built in 1945 belonged to the Battle of Britain Memorial Flight for many years, but now is owned by the Rolls-Royce company.*

Right: *The Spitfire's instrumentation featured the standard RAF blind-flying panel with a large horizontal compass between the pilot's knees.*

wing. The canopy had a central blown Perspex section, which gave a better view than the heavily framed units on most contemporary fighters.

The Spitfire Mk I, powered by the Merlin II or III of 1,060 hp (790 kW) and armed with eight 0.303-cal. (7.7-mm) machine guns in the wings, entered service with No. 19 Squadron at Duxford in August 1938. The first 78 Mk Is had a Watts fixed-pitch two-bladed wooden propeller; however, by the outbreak of World War II, most had three-bladed metal variable-pitch de Havilland or Rotol airscrews.

By August 18, 1940, 510 Spitfires had been delivered to the RAF—some of them the Mk II with an extra 110 hp (82 kW)—and 348 remained. Of these, 276 were serviceable with 19 Fighter Command squadrons. Production at three factories barely kept up with attrition during the Battle of Britain. The Spitfire squadrons were credited with 521 victories and suffered 403 losses between July and the end of October 1940. Hurricanes scored 655 for 631 for a slightly poorer kill/loss ratio.

Below: *The prototype Spitfire, K5054 first flew in March 1936. Later painted in camouflage colors, it was wrecked in an accident the day after the outbreak of war.*

The Mk V was powered by the Merlin 45 of 1,515 hp (1,130 kW), and most were equipped with a pair of 0.79-in (20-mm) cannon and four machine guns. Many pilots regarded the Mk V as the preferred version to fly. Like the Messerschmitt 109, later versions were heavier and less well balanced, although faster and better climbing. Entering service in 1941, the Mk V was used on various types of sweep and fighter-escort mission over occupied Europe.

One-sided battles such as these were the stimulus for development of a new variant using the Merlin 61 with a two-stage supercharger. This was to be the Mk VIII, but development problems saw the Mk IX, essentially a MK V with minimum changes made to allow acceptance of the Merlin 61, become operational first, in July 1942. The MK XVI partnered the Mk IX and was essentially identical but for its Packard-built Merlin. The Mk IX was in fact to become the most important version, regaining performance parity with the Fw 190 and supplanting the "definitive" Mk VIII. The latter was sent to Australia, New Guinea, and the Mediterranean, and supplied to two United States Army Air Force (USAAF) groups, as well as the Royal Australian Air Force (RAAF).

At the peak of deployment in mid-1944, slightly more than 100 RAF squadrons operated the Merlin-engined Spitfire. Added to this were RAAF and South African Air Force (SAAF) squadrons and an unknown number of Soviet units, operating some of the 1,200 Spitfires sent to the Soviet Union from 1943.

The Mk XII was the first production Spitfire variant to have the new Rolls-Royce Griffon of 1,735 hp (1,294 kW). This engine had been tried out in late 1941 on the Mk IV, but the Mk XII did not enter service until early 1943. Other "Griffon

Spits" included the Mk XIV, which was especially suited to combating V-1 flying bombs, and the Mk XVIII, capable of 442mph (707km/h). The Mk XII was an interim model before the Mk XVI, with a two-charge supercharged Merlin 61, a larger fin and rudder, more fuel capacity, and a five-bladed propeller. In 1944 trials against a captured Bf 109G and an Fw 190A, the Spitfire XIV proved superior in all respects to both except that the Focke-Wulf had a faster rate of roll. The Mk XIV was the only model fast enough to chase down V-1 flying bombs, and the first units so equipped were despatched to Britain's south coast to deal with this threat in June 1944. The Spitfire pilots specialized in the dangerous business of flying alongside the V-1s and "tipping" them with their wingtips.

Some of the Mk XIVs were built as fighter/reconnaissance FR.XIVs with vertical and oblique camera mountings. The later production Mk XIVs and XVIs had a cut down "clear view" rear fuselage and bubble canopy, as did the Mk XVIII, which equipped overseas-based squadrons postwar. The Spitfire F.21 (mark numbers became Arabic numerals above 20) had a stiffer wing of revised profile, an even bigger fin and rudder with split trim tabs, and a four-cannon wing. The Mk 21 saw a little wartime service, but the Mk 22, which was essentially identical except for its bubble canopy, entered service after the war and mainly equipped Royal Auxiliary Air Force squadrons. Some Mk 22s had a contra-rotating propeller, which eliminated the torque effect, being particularly strong on Griffon Spitfires and working in the opposite direction to that of the Merlin.

Many RAF units retained Merlin Spitfires until the end of the war (the last were not retired until 1951), and only seven squadrons were equipped with Griffon-engined models in May 1945, although more formed before the war against Japan ended in August. The very last RAF Spitfires were Mk XIX reconnaissance models flown by a weather unit and retired in 1957.

The Spitfire was supplied to many nations after the war and used in various conflicts, including both sides in the Israeli War of Independence and in the Greek Civil War. French Seafires (a maritime variant) were used in Indochina. Postwar users included Australia, Belgium, Myanmar (Burma), Czechoslovakia, Denmark, Egypt, France, Greece, India, Ireland, Israel, Italy, the Netherlands, Norway, Portugal, South Africa, Southern Rhodesia, Sweden, Syria, Thailand, Turkey, and Yugoslavia.

A number of two-seat Spitfires were converted for use as trainers. Some appeared in Russia during the war, but most were converted by Vickers in the late 1940s to Tr.9 configuration with a raised second cockpit and a large bubble canopy for use by Egypt, India, Ireland, and the Netherlands.

A healthy population of about 50 Merlin- and Griffon-engined Spitfires still fly today in Britain, the US, Canada, Australia, and New Zealand.

***Above:** Several Spitfires, including this Mk IX, were tested on floats. The huge floats greatly reduced performance, however, and the concept was abandoned.*

***Below:** As Supermarine works reached capacity, "shadow factories" were set up, such as this one at Castle Bromwich. It is seen here with Mk IIs almost complete.*

Dewoitine D.520

The nimble Dewoitine D.520 was France's best fighter of World War II. It fought on both sides in the conflict but without the constant development of other fighters was increasingly outperformed by newer adversaries.

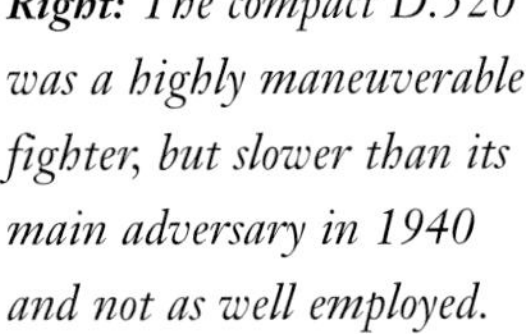

***Right:** The compact D.520 was a highly maneuverable fighter, but slower than its main adversary in 1940 and not as well employed.*

In the 1920s, Emile Dewoitine had designed a range of parasol-wing monoplane fighters. These were followed from 1932 by a series of low-wing cantilever monoplanes with fixed landing gear and open cockpits. The most numerous of these was the D.510, with which three *Groupes de Chasse* were still equipped in 1939. Dewoitine's first enclosed-cockpit fighter with retractable gear was the D.513, built for a 1934 contest. This proved inferior to the Morane-Saulnier MS.405, of which nearly 1,100 were built as the MS.406 up to March 1940. Emile Dewoitine ordered his chief designer, Robert Castello, to design an all-new fighter using the Hispano-Suiza 12Y21 V-12 engine of 900 hp (671 kW) to reach a top speed of 300mph (500km/h). Dewoitine in fact left the firm he founded (Société Aéronautique Française—Avions Dewoitine, or SAF-AD) in June 1936 and set up his own design office to work on this project.

The original design that Dewoitine submitted to the French Air Ministry for the A23 fighter competition was rejected because the ministry's detailed specification (which had been secret) called for a top speed of 322mph (520km/h). The team literally went back to the drawing board and revised its design, making provision for the Hispano-Suiza 12Y engine, then under development. They designated it the D.520 for the new specified maximum speed. The wing incorporated Handley Page leading-edge slots for

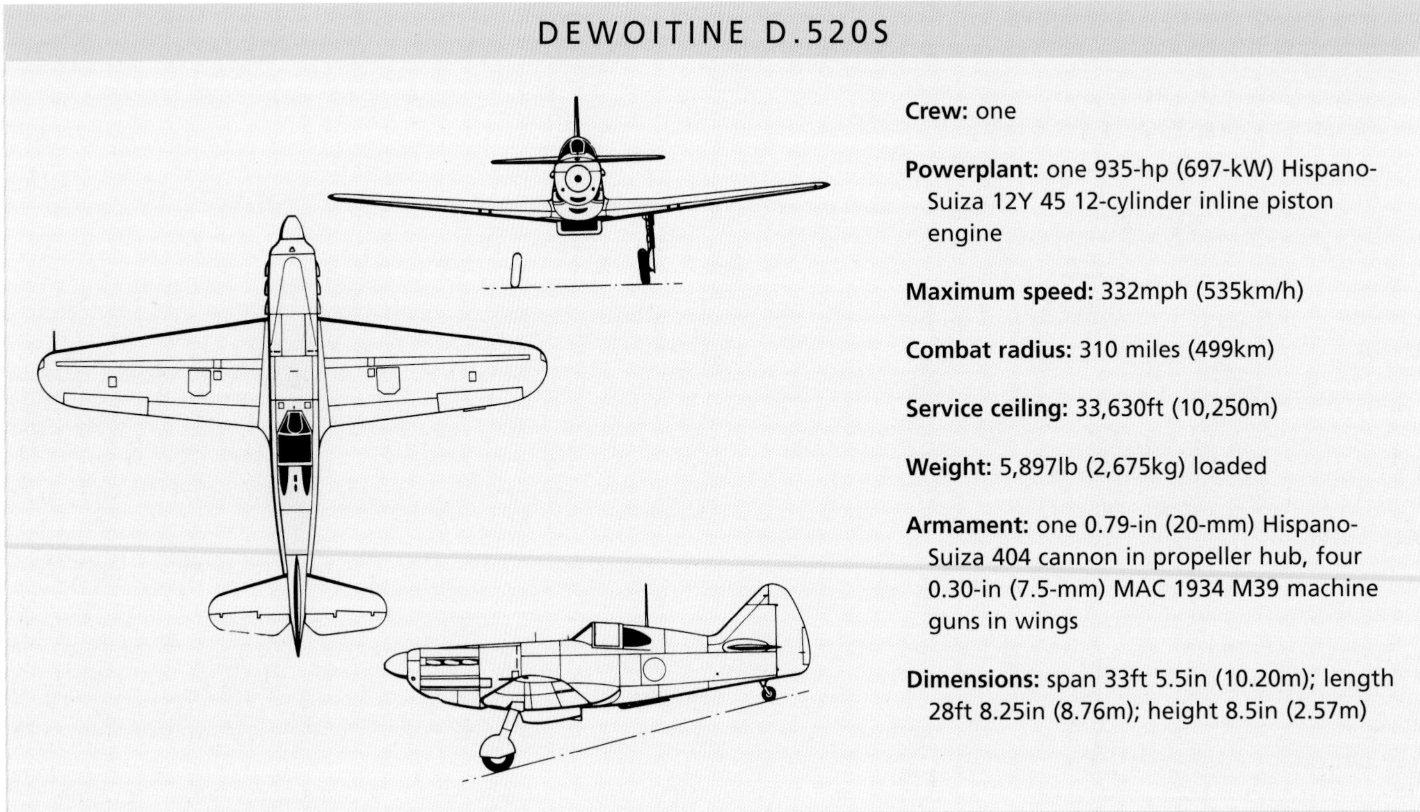

DEWOITINE D.520S

Crew: one

Powerplant: one 935-hp (697-kW) Hispano-Suiza 12Y 45 12-cylinder inline piston engine

Maximum speed: 332mph (535km/h)

Combat radius: 310 miles (499km)

Service ceiling: 33,630ft (10,250m)

Weight: 5,897lb (2,675kg) loaded

Armament: one 0.79-in (20-mm) Hispano-Suiza 404 cannon in propeller hub, four 0.30-in (7.5-mm) MAC 1934 M39 machine guns in wings

Dimensions: span 33ft 5.5in (10.20m); length 28ft 8.25in (8.76m); height 8.5in (2.57m)

D520

PILOTING THE DEWOITINE D.520

Above: A D.520 of the Free French "Saintonge" fighter group, based at Cognac in late 1944.

One of the most remarkable flying careers of the war was that of Pierre Le Gloan, born to a peasant family in 1913. Obsessed with flying, he was awarded a state scholarship that allowed him to enter flight training in 1931. After graduation as *Adjutant* (Warrant Officer), he soon proved the best shot in his unit and was rated as a flight leader and a career NCO. By the time his unit, GC III/6, was re-equipped with the D.520 at the end of May 1940, Le Gloan had destroyed several German bombers while flying the Morane Saulnier MS.406. Italy joined the war on June 10, 1940 and three days later Le Gloan destroyed three Fiat BR.20 bombers over southwestern France.

At midday on June 15, Le Gloan and two senior pilots, Capitaines Jacobi and Assolant, were on ground alert at Coulommiers when the alarm was sounded—many fighters were headed toward Toulon. Le Gloan's regular aircraft became unserviceable and he took another, leaving his parachute behind. After takeoff, Jacobi's propeller control failed and he was forced to turn back, but the other two pilots climbed rapidly at full throttle in their new D.520s. Above Saint- Raphaël, they saw 12 CR.42 inline-engined biplanes heading toward the southwest, "sailing in a straight line like tourists" without checking their backs.

Le Gloan and Assolant attacked the trailing group of Fiats. With their first burst, the left-hand Fiat fell in flames toward Beauvallon. The two others tried to escape by breaking away; one of them burst into flames following hits by both Frenchmen and the pilot bailed out. Then Assolant's guns jammed, leaving only Le Gloan, who moved toward flak bursts he could see above Hyères. He spotted three more CR.42s and shot down the right-hand one. At that moment, a formation of eight others Fiats emerged from the clouds firing on him. Le Gloan dived away from the Fiats, leaving them far behind.

Le Gloan was told by radio of a French base under attack by Fiats and arrived in time to destroy another CR.42. He orbited overhead to protect the base until he saw a BR.20 bomber flying a reconnaissance mission 1,640ft (500m) above him. Although out of cannon shells, he had enough machine-gun ammunition to destroy that, too. When he landed, after only 40 minutes' flight time, he had become only the second pilot of the war to score five victories in one mission. The following day he was promoted to *Sous Lieutenant* (Second Lieutenant).

At the armistice with Germany, GC III/6 withdrew to North Africa, and fell under control of the Vichy regime who cooperated with the Germans and governed southern France and the French colonies. In May 1941, Le Gloan's unit was sent to Syria to support German action against Free French and British forces. In a short campaign, *Sous Lieutenant* Le Gloan destroyed six Royal Air Force (RAF) Hurricanes and a Gladiator to bring his score to 18 confirmed and three probable victories. Pierre Le Gloan was unique in being an ace against the Germans, the Italians, and the British.

Following the Allied victory in North Africa and the German occupation of southern France, GC III/6 became part of the Allied forces again and was re-equipped with Bell P-39 Airacobras. On September 11, 1943, while most of the pilots of the 3rd Escadrille were commemorating the anniversary of the death of World War I ace Georges Guynemer, Le Gloan and a wingman took off on an escort mission. The wingman spotted smoke pouring from Le Gloan's P-39 and the two returned to base. Unable to lower his undercarriage, Le Gloan attempted a belly landing, but forgot about or was unable to jettison his auxiliary fuel tank, and the Airacobra exploded on touchdown, killing him instantly.

***Left:** The last airworthy D.520, No. 408 (marked as No. 90), was lost in an accident in the 1980s. The three remaining examples are in French museums.*

better low-speed handling. The first prototype was unpainted, had a two-bladed propeller, no spinner, a tailskid, and a shallow fin. Marcel Doret flew it for the first time on October 2, 1938.

Production aircraft had a three-bladed variable-pitch propeller, a tailwheel, and the 820-hp (612-kW) HS 12Y45 supercharged V-12 engine with a 0.79-in (20-mm) HS 404 cannon firing between the cylinders. Two 0.30-in (7.5-mm) MAC-1934 machine guns were fitted in the wings. The D.520's top speed reached 332mph (534km/h) at 18,045ft (5,500m).

Despite the approach of war in Europe, French fighter development had moved and continued to move at a glacial pace. Several rearmament plans were drawn up, abandoned, and replaced with new plans. Political instability and the nationalization of the aircraft industry meant that aircraft were not ordered in sufficient quantity; when they were, the airframe, engine, and component manufacturers could barely coordinate themselves so as to produce a fighter with armament, an engine, and a propeller all at the same time. Almost as soon as he had left SAF-AD, Emile Dewoitine found himself in charge of it again, as the nationalized SNCAM (Société Nationale de Construction Aéronautique du Midi). This in turn was later dissolved and absorbed by SNCASE (*Sud-Est*). Eventually orders for 2,250

***Above:** An* Armée de l'Air *D.520 prepares to get airborne during the Battle of France.*

***Far left:** The Germans continued to build D.520s after the fall of France. This one served with JG 105 at Chartres in May 1944.*

***Left:** D.520 No. 48 was owned by GC I/3 at Cannes in the spring of 1940.*

Above: Groundcrew prepare a D.520 of GC I/3 for a flight in April 1940, during the "Phoney War" period.

Below: The D.520Z was an aircraft built only once. It had a new undercarriage and "jet" exhaust stacks.

D.520s were placed for the *Armée de l'Air*, plus another 120 for the *Aéronavale*, but the first unit, *Groupe de Chasse* (GC) I/3, was not equipped until November 1939, two months after the outbreak of World War II. Only 79 of the 246 D.520s built had been accepted for service by the end of the "Phoney War" in May 1940, when Germany launched its assault on France and the Low Countries. The remainder were parked outside the Toulouse factory awaiting propellers and other components.

In April 1940, the second production aircraft was test flown against a Bf 109E that had landed intact behind French lines. The more powerful Messerschmitt was 20mph (32km/h) faster, but the Dewoitine was much more maneuverable. Despite this there was little that could be done to prevent the inevitable and, although they fought well, the undertrained French pilots and their bases were eventually overwhelmed by the German blitzkrieg. Nevertheless, the few D.520s in service were credited with 108 "kills" versus 54

air combat losses in the Battle of France.

After the armistice, the Germans ordered the completion of unfinished D.520s and for production to continue. This finally ended in the summer of 1944 with completion of the 905th aircraft. Many were issued to Vichy units, and others used as trainers by the *Luftwaffe*'s fighter schools. Sixty were supplied to Italy and saw some combat use with this country. Bulgaria received 96 surplus D.520s and used them to defend against US Ninth Air Force raids against the Romanian oil industry, which crossed Bulgaria en route. Without the development that contemporary fighters had undergone, the Dewoitines were unable to compete with the escorting P-38s and P-51s, and most were lost in combat. Some survived to fly ground-attack missions following Bulgaria's September 1944 communist-led coup and declaration of war on Germany.

After the invasion of southern France in July 1944, a group led by Marcel Doret, the original D.520 test pilot, fought the retreating Germans. The various Free French and pro-Allied ex-Vichy Dewoitines were amalgamated into one unit in February 1945. At the war's end, only 10 were still airworthy in mainland France, but more were repaired or brought back from overseas to equip postwar training units. Thirteen were converted to two-seat trainers as the D.520DC (*double commande*). The last D.520 was retired in 1953.

One D.520 was restored to fly in 1980, but was later lost in an accident. Otherwise, only three examples survive in museum collections in France.

Above: *Photographed at the Toulouse factory, this Vichy French D.520 was issued to GC II/5 in March 1942.*

Below: *The second prototype D.520 first flew in late January 1939.*

Curtiss P-40 Warhawk/Kittyhawk

As the most numerous US Army fighter at the time of Pearl Harbor, the P-40 bred a generation of fighter pilots and won fame with General Chennault's "Flying Tigers," who took it to the limit against superior Japanese forces.

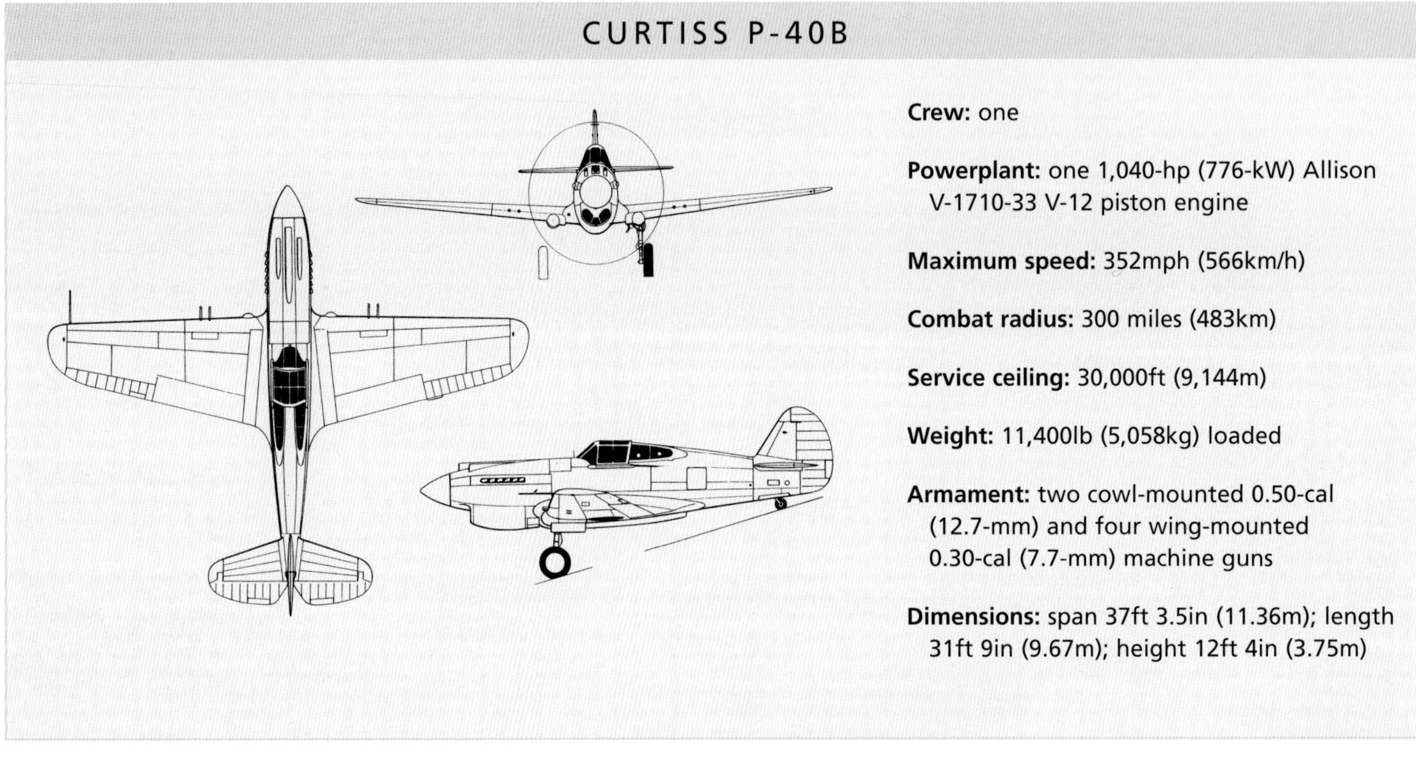

CURTISS P-40B

Crew: one

Powerplant: one 1,040-hp (776-kW) Allison V-1710-33 V-12 piston engine

Maximum speed: 352mph (566km/h)

Combat radius: 300 miles (483km)

Service ceiling: 30,000ft (9,144m)

Weight: 11,400lb (5,058kg) loaded

Armament: two cowl-mounted 0.50-cal (12.7-mm) and four wing-mounted 0.30-cal (7.7-mm) machine guns

Dimensions: span 37ft 3.5in (11.36m); length 31ft 9in (9.67m); height 12ft 4in (3.75m)

Far right: *P-40s were often found in the peripheral theaters of war, but still saw plenty of action. This USAAF P-40K was based in Alaska's Aleutian Islands.*

Right: *A Kittyhawk Mk I of the famous No. 112 "Shark" Squadron based in the Western Desert, flown by the ace Neville Duke.*

The Curtiss Aircraft Company of Buffalo, New York, was successful in the lean years of the 1920s and 1930s with the P-1 and F6C series of Hawk biplane fighters for the US Navy and the US Army Air Corps (USAAC). The definitive P-6E variant was delivered from 1931 with a metal-skinned fuselage and was the last biplane fighter ordered by the USAAC, but still represented a bygone era. By 1934, the company realized that the future lay in retractable-gear metal monoplanes, and Donovan (Don) Berlin designed the Curtiss Model 75 around a Wright R-1670 radial engine of 900-hp (671-kW) output. It lost out in a 1935 competition with the Seversky IXP (P-35); however, after being modified as the Model 75B, it was ordered to the tune of 210 examples designated the P-36A. The last 30 of these were delivered as P-36Cs with more powerful engines and four machine guns instead of two. Although underarmed and underpowered, the P-36 Hawks gave the USAAC much useful experience and helped them to develop tactics for high-performance fighters. At the outbreak of the Pacific war in December 1941, some of the few P-36s still in service in Hawaii got airborne and destroyed four of the 29 Japanese attackers lost in the Pearl Harbor attack.

PILOTING THE CURTISS P-40

Above: The "Flying Tigers" disbanded in 1942 but the P-40 continued to serve with the US 14th Air Force. Here they have staged a "scramble" for the photographer.

Royal New Zealand Air Force (RNZAF) pilot Squadron Leader Guy Newton, commander of No. 17 Squadron, led his unit on a sweep to the island of Rabaul alongside other RNZAF P-40s and US fighters on Christmas Eve 1943. Two large groups of Japanese fighters could be seen taking off and Newton led his squadron against one of them.

"I picked a 'Zeke' near the front of the very loose formation and opened fire at 300 yards in a stern quarter attack, continuing firing as I followed the fighter around in a turn until I was dead astern. The Zeke exploded at the wing roots and started to burn, with bits of the aircraft flying off. He tumbled over and went down in flames.

"I saw a Zeke on my left at the same level doing a left-hand turn. I turned, closing in astern, and fired a one-second burst at 250–300 yards. He did a complete flick roll to the left and when he pulled up I was still astern at 200 yards. I fired a two- to three-second burst and got hits all round the fuselage. He fell off in a lazy roll to the right and went straight down, apparently out of control."

Newton found another group of P-40s dogfighting with A6Ms and shot down one into the sea. He was set upon by six more and joined another P-40 down at low level, and they scissored together for protection. The A6Ms broke away, and the P-40s turned back toward the fight, meeting up with four others. Almost immediately, the group was bounced by six to eight more A6Ms and split up. Newton saw one P-40 shot down. "His aircraft trailed smoke and went into the sea ten miles north-west from Cape St. George. I went right down to the water at full throttle with two Zekes behind shooting. I skidded violently and most of the tracer went over my head and into the sea. The Zekes broke off five miles from Cape St. George, where I joined five or six P-40s and set course for Torokina. We pancaked [landed] there at 1300 hours." In this battle, the Kiwi pilots destroyed 12 Japanese fighters for seven losses. Newton was credited with two victories and one probable.

Right: The RNZAF operated nearly 250 P-40s in New Zealand and the Pacific Islands. They destroyed 99 Japanese aircraft in air combat.

The P-36/Hawk 75 was widely exported to European, Asian, and South American air forces, and the foreign sales potential of an improved version was one reason that Curtiss tested a P-36A with a turbocharged version of the new Allison V-1710 V-12 engine as the XP-37. A revised, non-turbocharged installation with an underwing radiator was flown as the XP-40 (Model 75P) on October 14, 1938. Following testing, the oil cooler was moved to a chin position beneath the spinner, giving the new fighter its characteristic pugnacious appearance. In April 1939, the US Army ordered 524 P-40s, one of the largest aircraft orders ever made by the United States to that time. They were to be powered by the 1,040-hp (746-kW) V-1710-33 engine and armed with only two machine guns, mounted on the cowling and firing through the propeller arc. From the firewall back, the P-40 was essentially the same as the earlier Hawk 75s, but had increased, if not stunning, performance and better handling.

The P-40 was a conventional all-metal monoplane, largely distinguished by its chin scoop and its rounded fin and wingtips. The leading edge of the wing was perpendicular to the fuselage, and the trailing edge tapered toward the tip. Fuel tanks were housed in the fuselage behind the cockpit and in the wing center section. The main landing gear retracted backward and rotated to lie flat inside the wing, leaving the wheels uncovered.

Deliveries to the USAAC began in June 1940, but only 199 of the initial P-40 model (no suffix) were built as such. The French made a large order of these as Hawk 81As, but with the fall of France in June 1940 the 130 built were diverted to the United Kingdom as the Tomahawk I. The Royal Air Force (RAF) also took large numbers of basically identical aircraft as the Tomahawk IIA. One change needed before the French-ordered aircraft could enter RAF service was to reverse the direction of throttle operation. Since the invention of the variable throttle, the French had worked on the basis that pulling back the lever increased the power, and vice versa—the opposite of the practice in most other nations.

The RAF's Tomahawks were largely used in North Africa, where they were effective until the Italian fighters, which had similar performance, were replaced with much better *Luftwaffe* aircraft. The most famous unit was No. 112

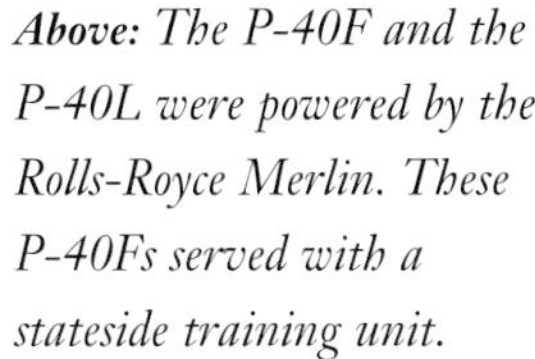

Above: *The P-40F and the P-40L were powered by the Rolls-Royce Merlin. These P-40Fs served with a stateside training unit.*

Above: *The design of the P-40 lent itself particularly well to the "shark's-mouth" marking as seen on this restored example.*

Left: *After the war, many P-40s were converted to take a passenger, such as this "short-tailed" P-40 in pseudo-RAF markings.*

Above: A lineup of P-40Es at a Stateside training base. Although outclassed by the mid-war period, the P-40 made a useful trainer for pilots destined for more effective fighter types.

Below: The 8th Pursuit Group at Langley, Virginia, was equipped with P-40Cs in late 1940. The USAAC had many of these early models in service in 1941.

Squadron, soon known as the "Shark Squadron" because of its habit of painting fearsome sets of teeth on the chin cowls of its aircraft.

The "shark's-mouth" design was noticed by pilots of the American Volunteer Group (AVG), a unit of "civilian" pilots recruited to provide air defense for the Chinese government against the advancing Japanese. The AVG soon applied a similar decoration to its Hawk 81A-2s and adopted the name "Flying Tigers." Contrary to popular belief, the AVG did not see action before the Japanese attacks on Hawaii and the Philippines, but in their brief existence created nearly 20 ace pilots and won eternal fame for the P-40. Its main opposition was against medium bombers and the Ki-43 "Oscar" fighter, and it did not meet any of Japan's best fighter, the A6M "Zero."

The early P-40B and C models were the most numerous fighters in US Army service at the time of Pearl Harbor, but were soon replaced by the new P-40E. This featured the longer "F-series" V-1710 engine with a single-stage supercharger and saw the nose lengthened and deepened. Cowl guns were dispensed with, the armament consisting of six 0.50-cal. (12.7-mm) machine guns in the wings. The British called this new model the Kittyhawk, as did the Commonwealth nations who procured it in large numbers, including Canada, Australia, and New Zealand. The Kittyhawks were called Warhawks by Curtiss and the US Army.

The P-40F Kittyhawk II was unusual in that it used the Rolls-Royce Merlin, which gave better high-altitude performance. The P-40L was a lightweight Merlin-powered version with only four guns. The longer and more powerful engines were causing longitudinal stability problems on takeoff and landing, so later P-40Fs, Ls, and subsequent models had lengthened rear fuselages. Some P-40Fs made aircraft-carrier takeoffs (but not landings) as part of the Operation Torch landings in North Africa. Further developments included the P-40K and P-40M Kittyhawk III with developed Allisons that gave even better altitude performance, and the P-40N Kittyhawk IV, the best and most widely produced version. The N was mainly distinguishable by the cut-down fuselage structure beneath the rear canopy, which gave much better rearward visibility. The lightweight XP-40Q with a bubble canopy, reprofiled nose, and four-bladed propeller was an attempt to match the performance of the P-51D Mustang, but no orders were forthcoming.

The continuing US Army orders for successive

batches of only slightly improved P-40s was the subject of an inquiry by the Truman Defense Committee, led by the future president Harry S. Truman. Although the committee criticized the US Army for ordering too many, particularly after better competing designs came along, and not insisting on greater performance improvements, it was cleared of favoritism toward the company.

A total of 13,739 Curtiss P-40s were built, and many of these went to smaller air forces, such as Australia, New Zealand, the Free French, the Netherlands East Indies, and Brazil. Several thousand P-40s were supplied to the Soviet Union, where they were used largely as ground-attack fighters. The Russians were not particularly impressed, preferring the P-39 Airacobra and its ability to absorb more battle damage. About the only place that the P-40 did not serve was the European theater, but they proved effective against most contemporary fighters before 1943, particularly in the Pacific and Mediterranean.

After the war, the P-40 quickly faded away, with only a few serving on in training roles or used for such things as cloud-seeding experiments and air racing. A relatively small number were to be found on the warbird circuit until the recovery of wrecked airframes from the former Soviet Union in the 1990s allowed more to be restored. More than 20 Warhawks and Kittyhawks are currently airworthy.

Below: *Although by no means a naval aircraft, P-40Fs were delivered to North Africa by aircraft-carrier during Operation Torch in November 1942.*

Lockheed P-38 Lightning

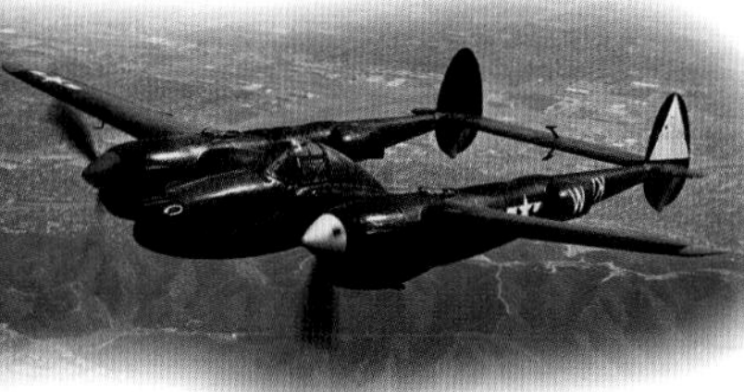

Lockheed's P-38 Lightning had the longest range and was one of the fastest and best-armed fighters of its day, but it was costly and complicated to maintain. In the hands of the best pilots it was a deadly adversary, particularly in the Pacific.

***Far right:** The might of US industry can be seen in these Lightnings. They were built outside while a new production line was installed at the factory in Burbank.*

***Right:** This P-38H served with the 79th Fighter Squadron of the 20th Fighter Group at Kingscliffe, Norfolk, in England.*

The P-38 was America's only production twin-engined single-seat fighter of World War II. Despite a lengthy development and a troubled early history, it was the mount of America's top aces, and its range allowed bombers to have protection across the expanses of the Pacific.

The P-38 emerged from a 1936 specification for a long-range fighter, which called for a speed of 360mph (579km/h) or greater at 20,000ft (6,100m) and a full-throttle endurance of at least one hour at this altitude. At Lockheed in Burbank, California, a design team led by Hall Hibbard and Clarence "Kelly" Johnson came up with a most unusual layout to meet this requirement. The only twin-engined contender for the requirement, Lockheed's Model 22 was unlike any previous US aircraft, although the Dutch Fokker G.I, which was unveiled in mid-1936, was similar in having a podded crew and weapons compartment and twin tail booms and fins joined by a tailplane. (The model 22's twin booms provided space for the turbo superchargers and their radiators. The main undercarriage was also located here, retracting backward to lie

LOCKHEED P-38L LIGHTNING

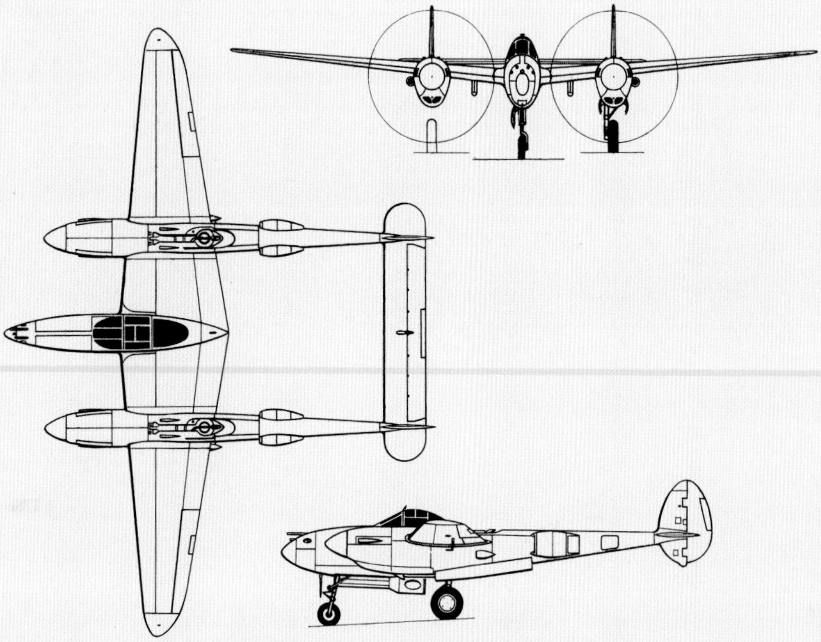

Crew: one

Powerplant: two 1,475-hp (1,100-kW) Allison V-1710-111/113 V-12 piston engines

Maximum speed: 414mph (666km/h)

Combat radius: 1,130 miles (1,818km)

Service ceiling: 44,000ft (13,410m)

Weight: 21,600lb (9,798kg) loaded

Armament: one 0.79-in (20-mm) cannon, four 0.50-cal. (12.7-mm) Browning machine guns in nose, and up to two 1,600-lb (726-kg) bombs

Dimensions: span 53ft (15.85m); length 37ft 10in (11.52m); height 9ft 10in (2.99m)

PILOTING THE LOCKHEED P-38 LIGHTNING

Above: *A P-38F of the 1st Fighter Group's 91st FS is seen in Algeria in late 1942. The 1st FG's Lightnings spent over a year in North Africa.*

Flying a P-38F with the 27th Fighter Squadron of the 1st Fighter Group was Lieutenant John Wolford. On December 3, 1943, he scored the first of an eventual five victories near Bizerte airfield in Libya, and submitted the following combat report, which shows the value of a good wingman. "Lt. Sullivan and I turned left into two Me 109s, which were diving from about 4 to 5,000 feet above us. Lt. Sullivan had completed his turn and I was about 100 yards behind him still turning. One Me 109 made a quick turn from his altitude, at this time about 1,000 to 2,000 feet above us, to Lt. Sullivan's right and behind, and cut between Lt. Sullivan and myself. I saw the E/A (enemy aircraft) give Lt. Sullivan one burst before I could bring my sights into line. When I had turned sharply enough to bring my sights to bear, I gave the E/A a wild burst to try and turn him from Lt. Sullivan. Time did not permit me to line my sight carefully, because of the short distance between the E/A and Lt. Sullivan, now about 50 yards.

"As I fired, my cannon ran out of ammunition and two machine guns jammed. Tightening my turn as much as possible, I slipped over the E/A to the right side, from which I took another shot with the two good guns. As I shot, Lt. Sullivan started a turn to the right and the E/A followed. I observed the tracers entering the cockpit of the E/A [which] shook slightly and entered a gentle turn to the right, nosing down gradually. No evasive action was taken by the E/A and the last I saw him, he was headed straight down through the clouds. I could not follow him down because of the crippled condition of Lt Sullivan's ship, behind which I weaved to fend off any further attack. During my attack on the first E/A, the second E/A evidently got a shot at me as I had a hole in my right wing tip, severing the navigation light wire, a glancing shot off the left-hand wheel door and a clean hole through one blade of the left propeller. I claim this E/A destroyed."

Right: *The P-38F was the first model that could carry drop tanks for increased range. Later, modified tanks were used as weapons.*

***Left:** With a search radar in an undernose pod, the P-38M was the fastest US night-fighter. P-38Ms only saw limited service in the Pacific at the end of the war.*

between the engines.) The P-38 was the first US fighter to have a tricycle (nosewheel) landing gear. The twin-engined configuration left the nose heavy for the time but free for armament, consisting of four 0.50-cal. (12.7-mm) machine guns and a cannon. This was originally to be a 0.90-in (23-mm) Madsen gun, but was later changed to a 1.45-in (37-mm) Oldsmobile cannon and a mix of two 0.50-cal. (12.7-mm) and two 0.30-cal. (7.62-mm) machine guns. Most production aircraft actually had four "fifties" and a 0.79-in (20-mm) Hispano cannon.

The engines were a pair of the new 1,090-hp (813-kW) Allison V-12s, designated the V-1710 after their configuration and cylinder capacity in cubic inches. The engines had General Electric superchargers and turned three-bladed propellers, which operated in opposite directions to counteract torque. Having "handed" engines and props complicated logistics, but made handling better and takeoff and landing safer, particularly compared to aircraft with powerplants that rotated the same way, such as the Mosquito.

On June 23, 1937, the US Army awarded a contract for one XP-38 prototype. Detail design and tool-making took a year and construction only five months. The first flight came on January 27, 1939 at March Field, California, made by Army test pilot Benjamin Kelsey. The silver-finished XP-38 prototype was unarmed and performed well in initial tests, but an attempt to set a transcontinental flight record before delivery to Wright Field, Ohio, for army testing ended in disaster. With two refueling stops, the XP-38 made it to Mitchell Field, New York, in a record

***Below:** Reconnaissance models included the F-5E, with no armament but with cameras fitted in the nose section. Many were painted in an overall blue color.*

***Above:** When the war against Japan ended, this newly completed P-38 was painted orange and named Yippee to celebrate the event.*

time of seven hours and two minutes, but lost power on the landing approach. Like the prototype F4U Corsair, the prototype crashed on a golf course; however, unlike the Corsair, it was wrecked beyond repair. The pilot (Ben Kelsey again) was not injured in this accident on February 11, 1939, but it was not until September 16 the following year that a P-38 flew again. The government had ordered an evaluation batch of 13 YP-38s in April 1939, followed soon after by 66 production P-38s and then 607 more.

Not only was the US Army prepared to buy large numbers of a barely tested fighter, but Great Britain was also desperate for modern fighters as well and paid cash for 667 Lightning Mk Is in March 1940. Although the British gave the P-38 its name, soon adopted officially in the United States, the Royal Air Force (RAF) actually flew very few of them. Testing at Boscombe Down revealed many deficiencies, and the orders were canceled. This was largely because the United States refused to allow export of superchargers, thus severely limiting the high-altitude performance. The first batch was returned to the United States and used for training or modified to become P-38Fs (with superchargers), while later ones were rebuilt and then delivered to the USAAF as P-38Gs.

***Right:** The twin-boom made the Lightning one of the most distinctive fighters of the war. The superchargers can be seen above the rear of the engine nacelles.*

The first Lightnings in service were of the first combat-capable version, the P-38D, and joined the 1st Pursuit Group at Selfridge Field, Michigan, in August 1941. By the time of the attack on Pearl Harbor in December, fewer than 50 Lightnings had been issued to Air Corps squadrons. The first deployment to a combat zone was to Alaska and the Aleutian Islands. In June 1942, Japan occupied parts of the Aleutians, and it was here that the first combats and combat victories were scored by P-38s, over Kawanishi HK64 "Mavis" flying boats.

By July 1942, P-38F Lightnings were on their way to Europe to join the Eighth Air Force. The P-38F had 1,388-hp (988-kW) V-1710-49/53 engines, and provision for two 1,000-lb (454-kg) bombs or, more importantly, two 165-gallon (588-liter) drop tanks, which gave a maximum range of up to 1,750 miles (2,816km), making the Lightning a much more useful bomber escort. In practical terms, the bombers could be protected up to 450miles (720km) from home base, allowing for combat and other maneuvering. There were numerous teething troubles with the early P-38s in the European theater. Cockpit heating was inadequate, leading to frozen pilots; parts would fall off at high speed; and a diving P-38 could soon reach its structural limits due to "compressibility" as airflow around parts of the airframe approached the speed of sound. The large size and unmistakable shape of the Lightning made it easy to detect at long range, and engine and supercharger problems often forced them to fly at medium altitudes where their performance was no better than the German fighters. All models of P-38 served in Europe, although some, such as the P-38G, were quickly sent on to North Africa and the Twelfth Air Force.

The next major model was the P-38H, with uprated engines and improved superchargers, followed by the P-38J, which had relocated the supercharger intercooler intakes from the wing leading edges to an enlarged chin scoop under each engine. This allowed larger fuel tanks to be installed there, increasing range by 100 miles (160km). Problems continued, however, with excessive oil loss leading to engine failures, and high-altitude performance remained inadequate. Eventually, in mid-1944, the decision was made to replace all Lightnings in the Eighth Air Force with P-51 Mustangs.

The P-38 fared much better in the war against Japan. The first unit to take the Lightning into combat—in late 1942—was the 39th Fighter Squadron, based in New Guinea. One of the squadron's pilots, Richard I. (Dick) Bong was to become the top-scoring American ace of all time, destroying 40 Japanese aircraft while flying various models of P-38. The second-highest scorer, Thomas B. McGuire (38 victories) also flew P-38s. Both received the Medal of Honor.

Although designed as a daylight interceptor, the need to combat Japanese night intruders saw several types of hastily converted, radar-equipped night-fighter created. These included the P-38M, with a radar operator crammed into a tiny compartment behind the pilot. In Europe, a number of P-38s were fitted with a nose compartment for a bomb aimer to act as a navigator/leader for standard Lightnings. The most important nonfighter variants were the F-4 and F-5 photoreconnaissance Lightnings with armament replaced by a battery of cameras. The P-38J and the P-38L—the most numerous model with 3,810 built of a total of 10,037—had "combat flaps" that could be lowered to an intermediate eight-degree position. This gave better lift in combat, allowing tighter turns, and could also be used to slow the aircraft in a dive.

A few reconnaissance Lightnings were supplied to Australia and to Free French forces. After the war, France continued operating F-4s and F-5s until 1952. Honduras and Cuba operated a small number of P-38s into the 1950s, and civilians used the others for photo-survey work and air racing. Seven P-38s are currently airworthy, including one that was recovered from beneath many yards of accumulated ice on the Greenland ice cap.

Above: *This P-38L is fitted with 0.49-in (12.7-mm) rockets for ground attack. An arrangement of 10 rockets mounted on two "trees" was usually used in combat.*

Left: *This Lightning was a "pathfinder" conversion of the P-38L. The nose contained both a BTO ("bombing through overcast") radar and a seat for its operator.*

Grumman F4F Wildcat

The Wildcat was the most important Allied naval fighter of the early war years, helping to thwart Japanese ambitions. When larger and better fighters came along, Wildcats continued to protect Allied shipping.

GRUMMAN F4F–4 WILDCAT

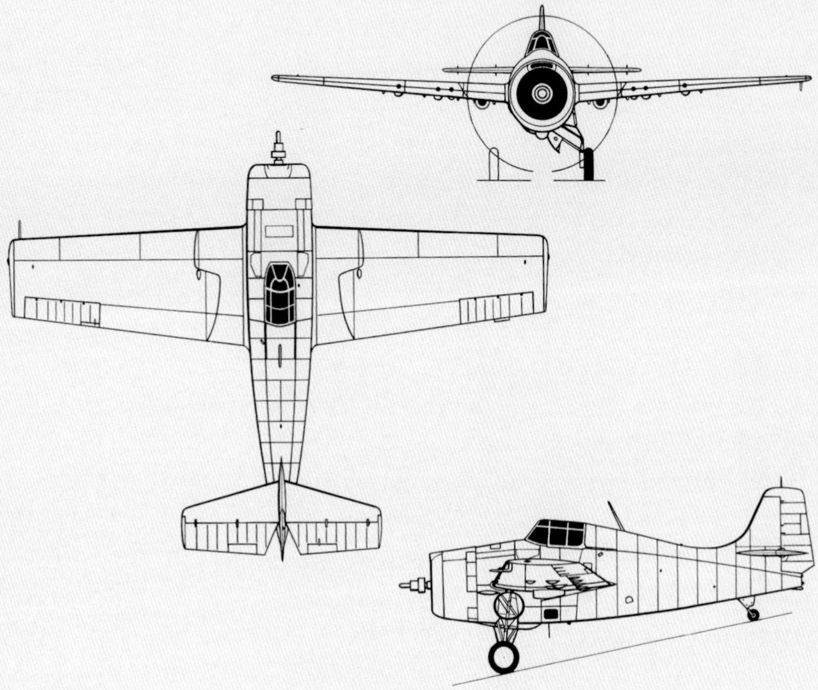

Crew: one

Powerplant: one 1,200-hp (895-kW) Pratt & Whitney R-1830-86 radial piston engine

Maximum speed: 318mph (512km/h)

Combat radius: 415 miles (672km)

Service ceiling: 34,900ft (10,640m)

Weight: 7,952lb (3,607kg)

Armament: six 0.50-cal. (12.7-mm) Browning machine guns in wings; FM-2 had four guns and provision for two 250-lb (113-kg) bombs or six 5-in (127-mm) rockets

Dimensions: span 38ft (11.58m); length 28ft 9in (8.76m); height 11ft 10in (3.6m)

Far right: *The Wildcat served aboard the many small escort carriers built for the US Navy. In the Atlantic they wore gray.*

The F4F Wildcat was the first of Grumman's famous "cat" series of naval fighters, which were all strongly built and at the cutting edge of technology when they appeared. Despite this, the Wildcat still had one paw in the biplane era when it appeared in 1939.

The Wildcat can trace its ancestry to the two-seat FF-1 (sometimes called "Fifi") biplane fighter of 1931. This was the first US Navy fighter to feature a retractable undercarriage. The first "F" came from the letter designation signifying Grumman and the second from its role as a fighter. The "1" meant that it was the first model of the type to enter production. The US Navy ordered a single-seat version as the F2F-1 in 1932, and this was followed by the larger F3F-1, -2, and -3 with Pratt & Whitney or Wright engines of between 650 hp (485 kW) and 950 hp (709 kW). The last of these portly biplanes, sometimes called "flying barrels," was still in service with the US Marine Corps in October 1941.

Meanwhile, in March 1936, Grumman, based on Long Island, New York, had been awarded a contract for a smaller biplane

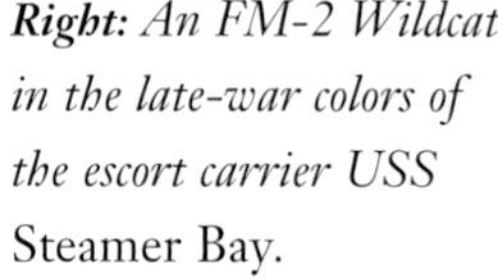

Right: *An FM-2 Wildcat in the late-war colors of the escort carrier USS* Steamer Bay.

4
2
5
8

Right: Royal Navy Wildcat Vs like this one were a British version of the FM built by General Motors, armed with only four guns.

prototype designated XF4F-1. Almost as soon as work began, it was realized that the biplane was becoming uncompetitive. The other fighters in the race for the navy contract were all-metal monoplanes, and Grumman scrapped the original XF4F-1 design and went ahead with a monoplane, designated XF4F-2 even though it owed little to its precursor.

The engine was the Pratt & Whitney R-1830-66 or Twin Wasp with a single-stage supercharger. With this fitted, it retained 90 percent of its sea level power of 1,060 hp (783 kW) at medium altitude. Armament was powerful by contemporary standards—two 0.30-cal. (7.62-mm) machine guns in the cowling and a pair of 0.50-cal. (12.7-mm) guns in the wings. The fuselage strongly resembled that of the F3F, although the biplane wings were replaced with mid-mounted round-tipped wings with no taper and no provision for folding. Automatic flotation bags were installed in wing bays. As with the biplane Grummans, the narrow-track undercarriage retracted into the fuselage behind the engine and was activated by cranking many times on a handle.

PILOTING THE GRUMMAN F4F WILDCAT

The Wildcat was the only US carrier fighter in the great battles of 1942 at the Coral Sea and Midway. Against unescorted bombers and dive-bombers, the F4F was quite effective, but no real match in combat with the A6M Zero, except in the hands of an expert pilot. The most successful Wildcat pilot was Joe Foss of VMF-121 based on Guadalcanal, who destroyed 29 Japanese aircraft, 19 of them Zeros, and was awarded the Congressional Medal of Honor. On October 23, 1942, VMF-121's commanding officer, Major Leonard Davis, and Captain Foss, his second-in-command, took two flights of F4F-3s to counter large numbers of fighters and bombers that were approaching Henderson Field. Both flights quickly engaged the enemy. Foss's first opportunity was a Zero, tearing after an F4F, firing with all guns. Foss closed in, clamped down on the trigger, and the Zero exploded. Next he closed on another, which attempted to evade in a loop. Foss had never been taught to shoot when inverted, but he followed and caught the Japanese pulling over the top.

Below: The F4F-3 without wing folding was the first production model. This photograph shows the basic markings used by Wildcats in the mid-war period.

Nosing down to regain airspeed, Foss spotted an exuberant Zero pilot performing a slow roll. It was a quick setup, but Foss put his gun sight on the fighter as its wings rolled through the vertical, and fired. He gazed in amazement at the spectacle of the enemy aviator blown out of his cockpit, minus his parachute. His Wildcat was badly damaged in a combat with another Zero, which he destroyed before limping back to Henderson Field, landing with his aircraft too badly damaged to fly again, the fourth time this had happened to the Marine ace.

The first flight of the XF4F-2 came on September 2, 1937, with Robert L. Hall at the controls. In April 1938, it was flown in comparative trials with the Brewster F2A and the Seversky NF-1, during which it was forced to land in a vegetable patch and turned over. While it was under repair, the US Navy announced that the XF4F-2 had lost out to Brewster's F2A, later to win infamy as the Buffalo, due to the latter's better handling. In actual combat, the Buffalo's limited advantages were to be nullified by the addition of armor plate and other operational equipment.

The failure to win this competition was a blessing in disguise for Grumman. Designers Dick Hutton and Bill Schwendler literally went back to the drawing board and had the XF4F-2 rebuilt as the XF4F-3. Out went the flotation bags; in came an uprated Twin Wasp with a two-stage supercharger that developed 1,200 hp (895 kW) at sea level and 1,000 hp (746 kW) at 19,000ft (5,790m). The curved tips to the flying surfaces were squared off, and most of the basic structure was revised. Flying again in February 1939, the XF4F-3 was still undergoing government tests when the first order for 53 F4F-3S came. By now, the company called the little fighter the Wildcat.

Only the first two production aircraft had the fuselage guns. Subsequent Wildcats had four guns in the wings and racks for a pair of light bombs. One F4F-3 was tested on floats in an effort to provide fighter cover on islands where friendly airfields had not yet been established. Designated F4F-3S, and sometimes known as the "Wildcatfish," the unique float-equipped F4F was intended to counter the "Rufe" floatplane version

Above: *The Wildcat was not quite a match for the Zero, but better formation tactics helped the US counter Japanese moves in 1942.*

Left: *Martlet IIs pack the deck of a Royal Navy carrier. This model was delivered directly to India to support British operations.*

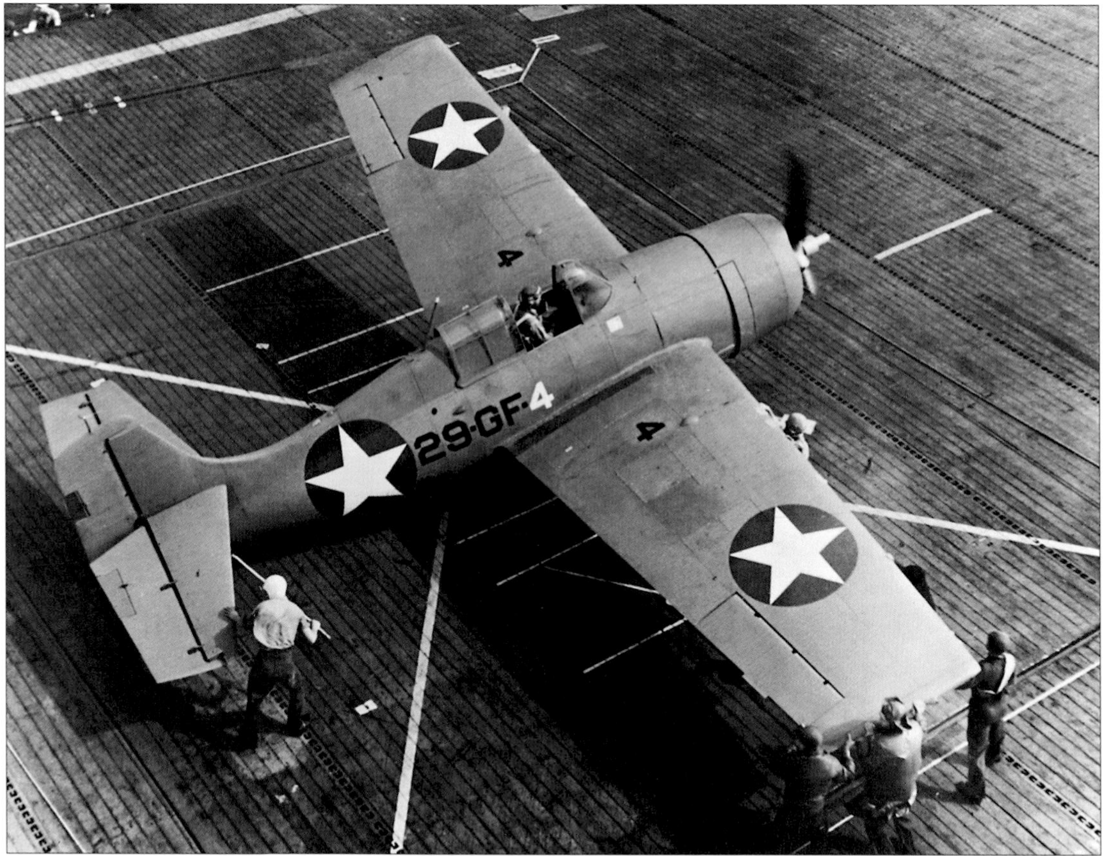

Right: *Deck crew help maneuver an F4F-4 onto the catapult of the USS* Santee, *an auxiliary aircraft-carrier, November 1942.*

of the A6M, which was often encountered away from known Japanese airfields. Like the Rufe, the Wildcat floatplane had a greatly degraded performance, and by the time it had been tested the rapid advance of US forces through the Pacific islands and the capture or construction of airfields had negated the need for it.

At the same time as production was gearing up for the US Navy, foreign nations started to order the F4F for their own naval air arms. Due to a lack of available R-1830s, France specified the Wright R-1820 Cyclone for its 81 aircraft, known by the company designation G-36A. Unfortunately, the first French aircraft only flew a few weeks before the fall of France. The aircraft were delivered to Britain's Fleet Air Arm (FAA) instead, and they entered service as the Martlet Mk I. Meanwhile the FAA had itself ordered 100 F4Fs, powered by Pratt & Whitney R-1830s. These became the Martlet Mk II, although the first 10 differed from the rest by having nonfolding wings.

Wing folding was introduced on the F4F-4 and

Right: *Early war markings on USN Wildcats provided camouflage and color. In May 1942 the rudder striping and red spot in the star were ordered removed.*

made a huge difference to carrier operations, allowing aircraft to be used on the small escort carriers then being produced for the US and British navies. The patented wing-folding system, also used on the TBF Avenger and later the F6F Hellcat, was developed with the help of bent paperclips and a pencil eraser, and allowed the wings to pivot and lie backward along the line of the fuselage. This saved overhead space in the hangar deck compared to the upward-folding wings of other naval types. Hydraulic wing folding was fitted to the first aircraft, but deleted to save weight. With the arrival of the F4F-4, most F4F-3s were transferred to land-based Marine squadrons. Armament on the F4F-4 was increased to six 0.50-cal. (12.7-mm) machine guns, self-sealing fuel tanks were installed and provision for drop-tanks was included.

The Martlet Is were mainly used in a land-based role in the Middle East, and the Marine F4F-3s saw action at such places as Wake Island and Guadalcanal. Marine fighter squadron VMF-211 was instrumental in driving off the initial Japanese invasion of Wake Island beginning on December 8, 1941, destroying numerous bombers and even sinking a destroyer with a lucky hit from a 100-lb (45-kg) bomb.

British Martlets first saw action against bombers attacking the Royal Navy's anchorage at Scapa Flow and in the Norwegian campaign. Their numbers were boosted in 1941 by 30 Martlet IIIs originally intended for Greece. Martlets were able to help close the mid-Atlantic gap in air cover for the vital convoys supplying the United Kingdom. Operating from tiny escort carriers such as HMS *Audacity*, they were able to thwart many of the deadly Focke-Wulf Condor patrol bombers.

Grumman was soon unable to meet the demand for its fighter, floatplane and torpedo products, and production of Wildcats was shifted to the Eastern Aircraft Division of General Motors. The first GM-built Wildcat was a four-gun version of the F4F-4 designated the FM. One-third of the 1060 FMs built became Martlet Mk Vs, but were renamed the Wildcat Mk IV in early 1944.

The FM-2 was a lightweight model designed for the escort carriers, powered by the Pratt & Whitney R-1820-56 with a single-stage supercharger, giving 1,350 hp (1,007 kW) at sea level. The new engine installation required a single, large exhaust just above and ahead of each wing root; this and an extended tailfin were the key recognition features for the FM-2, of which 4,777 were built, 340 of them as the Martlet Mk VI/Wildcat Mk VI.

A relatively small number of Wildcats were available for restoration as war birds by the 1970s and 1980s. Unlike more high-performance types, including Grumman's own F8F Bearcat, Wildcats were not modified for air racing. All the airworthy aircraft were FM-2s until the rebuild of some of the numerous aircraft that had been recovered from Lake Michigan allowed a couple of F4F-3s to join them during the 1990s. About 15 Wildcats fly today, with others under restoration.

Above: *The Wildcat was very important to the Royal Navy, who called it the Martlet and operated them from their smaller aircraft-carriers.*

Below: *These F4Fs wear the short-lived insignia with a red border. The border and bars were added in June 1943. The red was removed again in September.*

Yakovlev Yak-1 to Yak-9

The best known of the Soviet Union's wartime fighters were built by the Yakovlev Design Bureau. Although sometimes crudely manufactured, they were constantly developed and matched the best western fighters by the war's end.

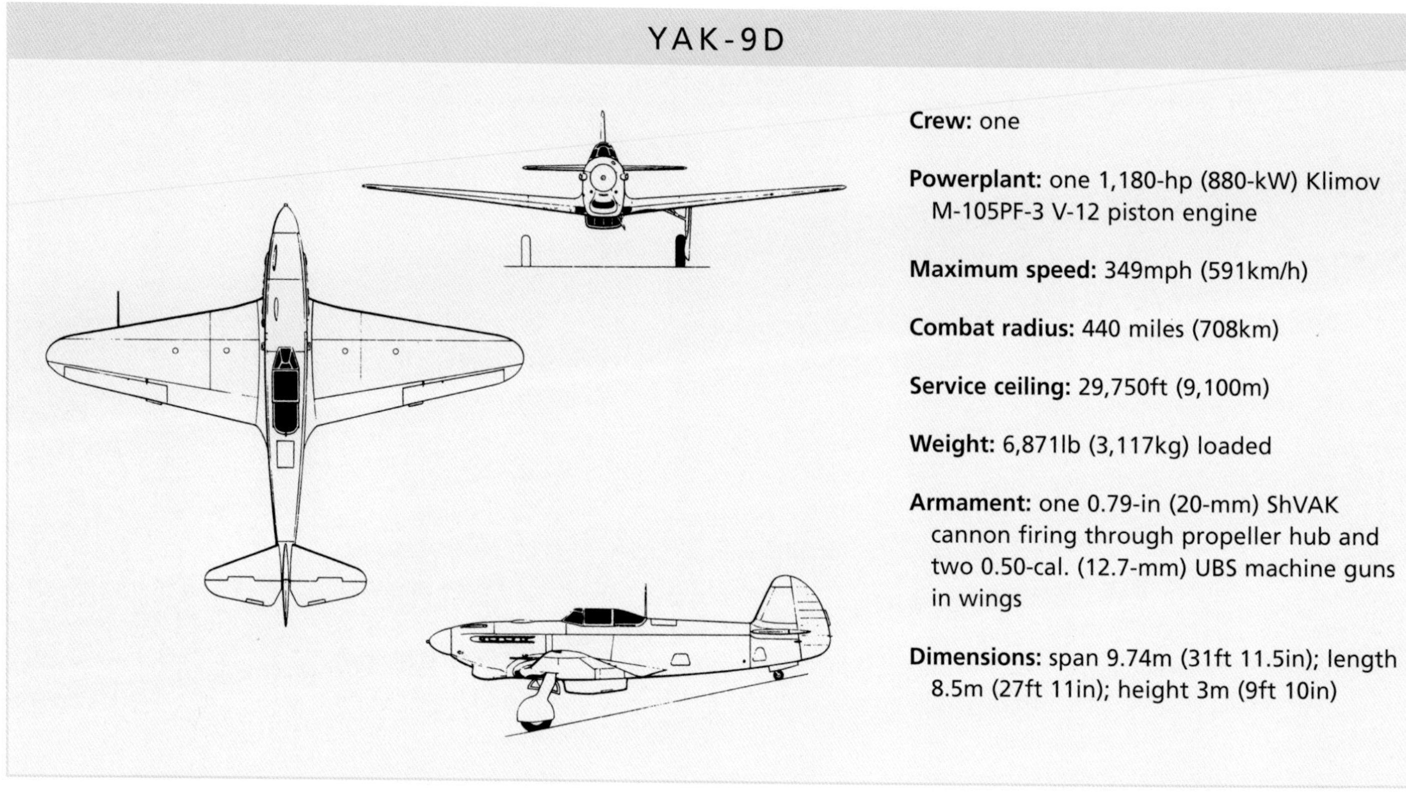

YAK-9D

Crew: one

Powerplant: one 1,180-hp (880-kW) Klimov M-105PF-3 V-12 piston engine

Maximum speed: 349mph (591km/h)

Combat radius: 440 miles (708km)

Service ceiling: 29,750ft (9,100m)

Weight: 6,871lb (3,117kg) loaded

Armament: one 0.79-in (20-mm) ShVAK cannon firing through propeller hub and two 0.50-cal. (12.7-mm) UBS machine guns in wings

Dimensions: span 9.74m (31ft 11.5in); length 8.5m (27ft 11in); height 3m (9ft 10in)

***Far right:** Yak-9s of the 18th (Guards) Fighter Aviation Regiment during the summer of 1943.*

The Yak fighters became the backbone of the Soviet Air Force in World War II and saw widespread postwar use by the communist countries. Although generally less sophisticated than western types, they were the first Soviet fighters to take on the German Me 109 and Fw 190 on equal terms and helped in wresting air superiority back from the *Luftwaffe* as the tide of war turned.

Alexsandr S. Yakovlev, a pupil of Andrei Tupolev, was one of the few designers Stalin regarded as trustworthy in the 1930s. His first fighter design was the Ya-26 of 1939, offered for a 1938 Soviet Air Force "frontal fighter" requirement. The Ya-26 flew on January 13, 1940, and an order for 64 as the Yak-1 was made before the end of the year, despite the crash of the first prototype in April.

The Yak-1 was of conventional low-wing monoplane configuration, with a main structure of steel tube, the forward fuselage skinned with duralumin and the aft with plywood. The wing was of wooden construction. The engine was an 1,100-hp (820-kW) Klimov M-105 liquid-cooled V-12. It was designed for simplicity of manufacture by semiskilled workers.

***Right:** A Yak-1M of the Polish-manned 1st "Warszawa" Fighter Regiment in late 1944.*

Малый театр
фронту
ЕАТР

Unfortunately, it also suffered from poor quality control, and when Germany launched Operation Barbarossa on June 22, 1941 more than half the aircraft of some units were not in an airworthy state. The threat from the advancing enemy saw most aircraft factories relocated east of the Ural Mountains, greatly hampering the flow of replacement aircraft. Nonetheless, production reached prewar levels again within two months.

When the Germans had had time to assess the aircraft opposing them in 1942, they rated the Yak-1 as the best Soviet fighter, possessing as it did a similar performance to the Bf 109. The MiG-3, which was a close contemporary of the Yak, was

PILOTING THE YAK-1

Above: Finest of the Yak-1s was the Yak-1M, which soon evolved into the Yak-3. Reduced weight helped give agility, although oil cooling was problematic.

Due to the desperate shortage of young men with the aptitude to be combat pilots, permission was given to famous aviatrix Marina Raskova to organize three regiments of women fliers. One of the first to be selected in October 1941 was 21-year-old Lydia Vladimirovna Litvak, usually known as Lilya ("Lily"). Lilya had learnt to fly as a teenager with prewar Soviet aero clubs, where she later became an instructor.

After military training, Lilya helped to form the 586th IAP women's fighting regiment, flying the Lavochkin La-5, and she saw her first air combats in September 1942 along the Volga River north of Stalingrad. She scored her first three victories on the La-5, before she was transferred as a flight leader to the 287th IAD, commanding female pilots within this otherwise male regiment. The male pilots apparently resented her presence and forced her transfer to the 296th IAP near Stalingrad in January 1943, where she converted to the Yak-1. Lilya Litvak became known as the "White Rose of Stalingrad," allegedly because of a flower painted on the side of her Yak-1, which may have been a lily or, more likely, a propaganda invention. During February and March 1943, Lilya shot down a further five German bombers and shared in the destruction of an Fw 190. Two more victories followed in May, one of them over an observation balloon. She was shot down twice in July and injured, but continued to fly despite doctor's orders and even returned to her squadron early from convalescence.

In the afternoon of August 1, 1943, she made her third (some sources say fourth) combat sortie of the day, a patrol along the front line looking for enemy bombers. Somehow she became separated from her unit and ran into a formation of eight German fighters. Ivan Borisenko, one of her fellow pilots, wrote: "Lilya just didn't see the Messerschmitt 109's flying cover for the German bombers. A pair of them dived on her and when she did see them she turned to meet them. Then they all disappeared behind a cloud." Through a gap in the clouds, Borisenko saw Lilya's Yak falling out of control, its pilot probably killed by a single wound to the head. The aircraft fell near the village of Dmitrievka, and villagers buried Lilya's body under the wing of her fighter. She was just 22.

Lilya Litvak was credited with 12 confirmed victories, two of them achieved on her last day, and three shared kills at the time of her death. The commander of her unit, by now renamed the 73rd Guards Fighter Aviation Regiment, nominated her for award of the Hero of the Soviet Union; however, as her body was not recovered, this was turned down. The final location of her body was not confirmed until 1986, and in May 1990 President Mikhail Gorbachev conferred the Hero of the Soviet Union award.

not highly rated. The Soviets came to the same conclusion and chose to abandon the MiG and develop the Yak series. Later Yak-1s had a cut-down rear fuselage and a semibubble canopy for better vision, and were powered by the VK-105PF engine. This version has received the retrospective designation Yak-1M (for *Modifikastsirovanny*, or "Modified").

Many of the features of the Yak-1M found their way into the Yak-3, which flew in early 1943 and had a new wing that was broader, but also 2ft 7in (79cm) shorter. The radiator was moved aft and a retracting tailwheel was fitted. The armament of two fuselage-mounted ShKAS 0.30-cal. (7.62-mm) machine guns and a ShVAK cannon firing between the engine cylinders was supplemented by a pair of 0.5-cal. (12.7-mm) UBS machine guns in the wings.

At an empty weight of only 5,862lb (2,661kg), the Yak-3 was the lightest non-Japanese fighter of the war. Its light weight and short wingspan gave the Yak-3 more agility than most of its contemporaries. The roll rate was particularly good, and the all-round performance at low levels (11,500ft/3,505m and below) where most of the Eastern Front air action took place was superior to the Bf 109G and FW 190A.

The Yak-3 prototypes completed their acceptance trials in October 1943, and the first production examples appeared in March 1944. It was first issued to the 91st IAP operating over Poland in June 1944. A month later, the Normandie-Niemen Regiment of French volunteers chose Yak-3s as its first equipment and began to amass an impressive score against the Germans. Soon a famous edict was issued to *Luftwaffe* fighter units to "avoid combat below 16,405ft (5,000m) with Yakovlev fighters lacking an oil cooler under the nose."

Yak piston-engined fighter development took two distinct paths from 1941, with the Yak-3

Below: **Below:** *The inscription on this Yak-3 is a dedication to pilot Sergey Luganskiy from the Young Communist League of Alma-Ata.*

Above: *The tricolor spinner and rudder identifies this Yak-3 as belonging to the French Normandie-Niémen volunteer regiment, pictured probably in France postwar.*

Left: *These new Yak-7s wear black and green camouflage. These colors were used as there was a surplus of them from tractor production in peacetime.*

representing the *legky*, or lightweight, models and the Yak-7 and Yak-9 the tyazhely, or heavy, fighters. The Yak-7 actually began as a two-seat conversion trainer dubbed the Yak-7UTI and developed from one of the preseries Yak-1 models in 1940. A second cockpit for an instructor or "priority passenger" replaced the radio compartment, and the radiator was moved forward to maintain center of gravity. Wingspan was increased with new pointed wingtips. These changes greatly improved the handling qualities over the Yak-1, and a single-seat variant was developed with an extra fuel tank in place of the rear cockpit. The Yak-7B had the higher powered 1,210-hp (902-kW) M-105PF engine and blunter wingtips. More metal was used in the wing structure, allowing more fuel and a load of air-to-ground rockets to be carried, otherwise the armament was two 0.50-cal. (12.7-mm) machine guns and an engine-mounted 0.79-in (20-mm) cannon.

The Yak-9 was the most versatile of the breed, being built in a number of specialized variants. It was derived from a version of the Yak-7, the Yak-7DI with a cut-down rear fuselage and a three-piece bubble canopy. After a batch of preseries Yak-7DIs was completed in the fall of 1942, a refined version entered full-scale production as the Yak-9, and the first of these saw operational service in November as the Soviets began counterattacks on the Stalingrad front. Powered by the M-105PF and armed with two machine guns and one cannon in standard Yak-9M form, it was lighter than the Yak-7 and had better performance. The rudder shape was altered and the radiator was deepened. Variants included the Yak-9 that could carry four 220-lb (100-kg) bombs in a bay behind the pilot, the reconnaissance Yak-9R, and the high-altitude Yak-9PD with a two-stage supercharger and only a single cannon as armament. The Yak-9DD had additional fuel, giving a range of 1,367 miles (2,200km) and was used to escort US 8th Air Force bombers on "shuttle" raids that flew across Germany and landed in the western Soviet Union.

The "second-generation" Yak-9U was intended to have the 1,650-hp (1,230-kW) VK-107A engine, but teething troubles saw the first batches delivered with the VK-105PF. Otherwise the airframe was aerodynamically refined, lacking the undernose oil cooler and having a shallow radiator bath situated aft. The Yak-9U saw service in the last months of the war, and afterward was supplied to many Soviet allies, as was the Yak-9P with three 0.79-in (20-mm) cannon. The Yak-9 was given the Allied postwar reporting name "Frank," although this was seldom used. North Korea received a number of Yak-9Ps from China, and these were the principal fighters in service before the MiG-15 arrived at the end of 1950. North Korean Yaks

***Below:** Yak-7s roll out of the State Aircraft Factory (GAZ) 292 in Saratov. Nearly 6,400 Yak-7s were built by three plants.*

***Right:** A captured North Korean Yak-9P. Evaluated at Wright-Patterson AFB by the US, they found it superior to the P-51D only in maneuverability.*

Left: *The Yak-9 evolved from the Yak-7 and represented a different line of development from the later lightweight Yak-3.*

fought a number of combats with US Air Force P-51s, with which they were roughly equal in performance, and jets, with which they were not. In general, they came off worst against US fighters.

Yak-9 production continued until 1947, by which time 16,769 had been built. To this can be added 6,399 Yak-7s, 4,848 Yak-3s, and 8,723 Yak-1s. This total of 36,739 piston-engined Yaks plus assorted experimental models makes them the most widely produced fighter series in history.

Production was actually revived in the 1990s, when western collectors commissioned small numbers of Yak-3s and Yak-9s from former Yak plants in the former Soviet Union. These have flown with Allison V-1710 engines, as have a number of Yak-3 conversions made from Yak-11 trainers, which were essentially the same as Yak-3s but for their second seat and radial engine.

Below: *Before the MiG-15 appeared in 1950, the North Korean Air Force was largely equipped with Yak-9Ps. This one was shot down by a US fighter.*

Mitsubishi A6M Zero-Sen

One of the most feared fighters of the war, the A6M Zero sacrificed protection and heavy firepower for agility and endurance. The US countered it with the Hellcat and Corsair, but by then the Zero had reached the end of its development.

MITSUBISHI A6M5-KO REI-SEN

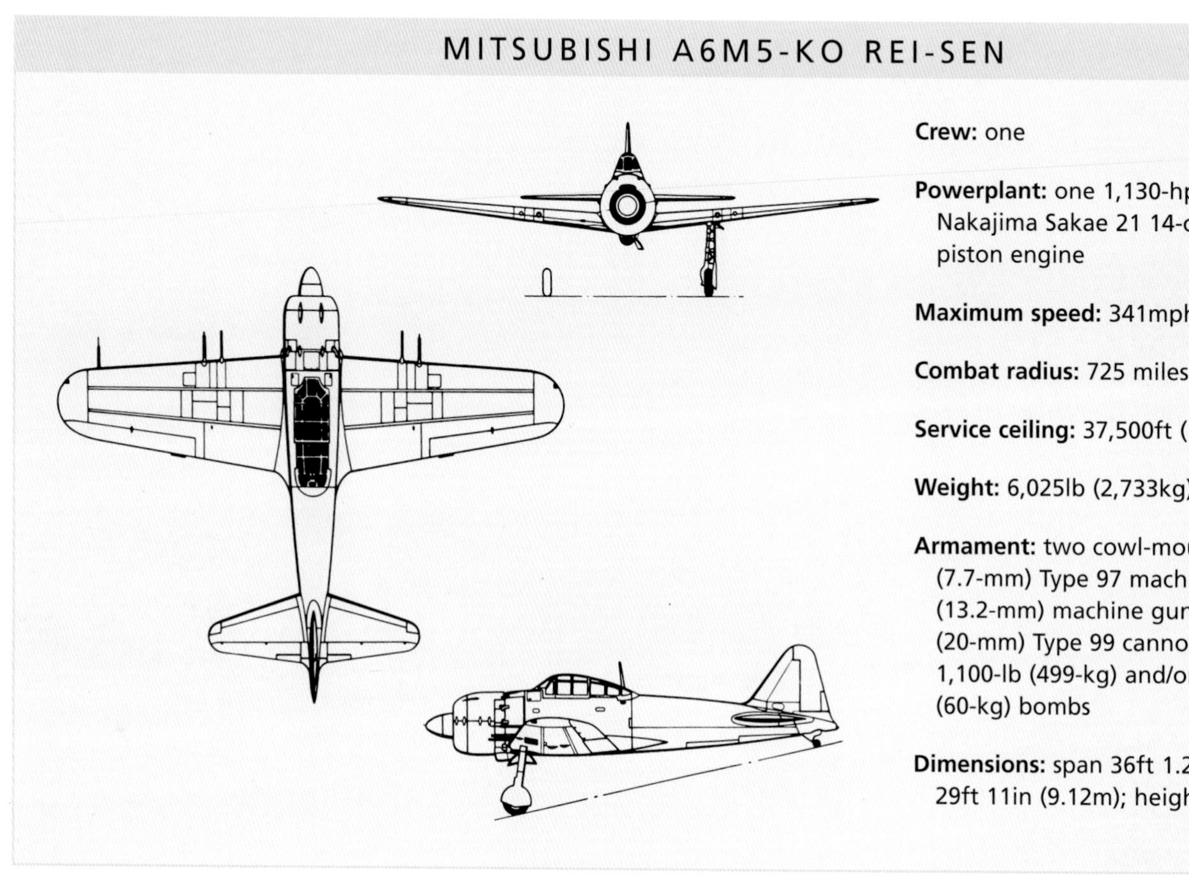

Crew: one

Powerplant: one 1,130-hp (842-kW) Nakajima Sakae 21 14-cylinder radial piston engine

Maximum speed: 341mph (565km/h)

Combat radius: 725 miles (1,166km)

Service ceiling: 37,500ft (11,500m)

Weight: 6,025lb (2,733kg) loaded

Armament: two cowl-mounted .303-cal. (7.7-mm) Type 97 machine guns, two 0.5-in (13.2-mm) machine guns, and two 0.79-in (20-mm) Type 99 cannon in wings, one 1,100-lb (499-kg) and/or two 132-lb (60-kg) bombs

Dimensions: span 36ft 1.25in (11m); length 29ft 11in (9.12m); height 11ft 6in (3.51m)

Far right: *This Zero (with a US Pratt & Whitney engine) has flown for many years with the Confederate (now Commemorative) Air Force (CAF) in Texas.*

Right: *An A6M2 based at Clark AFB in the Philippines in 1944. Zeroes built by Nakajima under license were delivered with dark green topsides.*

Mitsubishi's Type O Carrier Fighter, more commonly known by its Allied name "Zeke," or simply as the "Zero," was a big surprise to the Allies in 1941. After a period of seeming invincibility, however, it was surpassed by American and British designs. Despite increasing obsolescence, the Zero was in production until the end of World War II and remained deadly in the right hands.

In 1937, the Imperial Japanese Navy (IJN) issued a specification for a long-range carrier fighter to replace the Mitsubishi A5M ("Claude") then just entering service. The Claude, or Type 96 Carrier Fighter, was a monoplane, but had a fixed undercarriage and an open cockpit. It was the first major design of Jiro Horikoshi and was a great success over China, being highly maneuverable with an extremely long range.

The IJN's performance requirements were extremely stringent, including better armament, a retractable

EII-102

***Right:** The CAF A6M5 saw combat with the 5th Carrier Division in the Solomon Islands. It was restored from a wreck in Canada in the 1980s.*

***Right:** Gunners on the battleship* Missouri *duel with a Kamikaze, which glanced off the hull and caused little damage.*

landing gear, an enclosed cockpit, and full radio equipment, all while giving improved performance over the A5M, and Mitsubishi was the only manufacturer to bid for the contract. Jiro Horikoshi set to work on the new carrier fighter, using the most modern technology then available. Early in the process, a Mitsubishi Sues 14-cylinder, twin-row radial engine, rated at 875 hp (653 kW) was selected, and the size of this dictated the dimensions of the airframe.

Horikoshi designed a modern fighter optimized for range and maneuverability with a lightweight structure of a new aluminum alloy. The priority was to make it the best possible fighter first and worry about its carrier-landing equipment and characteristics later. As such, it was to be the first naval fighter to be superior to its land-based contemporaries. It was a low-winged, conventional all-metal fighter with a raised but heavily framed canopy. The wing was single piece, although the tips folded upward to fit on carrier elevators. The cockpit and center fuselage were attached to the wing, and the powerplant and rear fuselage were added to this strong core. Armament was particularly heavy for the time, with two 0.79-in (20-mm) Type 99 cannon and two .303-cal. (7.7-mm) Type 97 machine guns.

The prototype, known as the 12-Shi because its

***Below:** When the Allies evaluated captured examples of the Zero they were able to design new fighters to exploit its weaknesses and counter its strengths.*

PILOTING THE MITSUBISHI A6M ZERO-SEN

Above: *Cheered on by groundcrew, a bomb-toting Zero leaves on its final Kamikaze mission during the Philippines campaign, November 1944.*

At the Battle of Midway in June 1942, carrier-based Zeros defeated the first waves of attacking army and navy aircraft, but were refueling on deck when the SBD Dauntless dive-bombers struck, sinking four carriers with most of their air wings. More important than the ships and aircraft destroyed was the loss of many of the IJN's most experienced pilots.

On New Guinea, there was a lull in activity after the Midway operation, of which the land-based pilots had been unaware. Then in mid-June the Americans returned with a heavy attack on the Japanese airfield Lae, the base of ace Saburo Sakai, who wrote in his autobiography *Samurai*: "On the sixteenth the air war exploded with renewed fury. It was a field day for our fighters, when twenty-one Zeros caught three enemy fighter formations napping. We hit the first group of fighters in a massed formation dive, which shattered the enemy ranks. I shot down one plane, and five other pilots each scored a victory. The remaining enemy six enemy fighters escaped by diving.

"Back at high altitude, we dove from out of the sun at a second enemy formation of twelve planes. Again we struck without warning and our plunging pass knocked three fighters out of the air. I scored my second victory in this firing run.

"A third wave of enemy planes approached even as we pulled out from the second diving attack. Some two dozen fighters came at us as we split into two groups. Eleven Zeros dove to hit a climbing formation, and the others met us at the same height. The formations split into a tremendous free-for-all above the Moresby air base. The enemy planes were new P-39s, faster and more maneuverable than the older models; I jumped one fighter, which amazed me by flicking out of the way every time I fired a burst. We went around the sky in a wild dogfight, the Airacobra pilot running through spins, loops, Immelmanns dives, snap rolls, spirals, and other maneuvers. The pilot was superb, and with a better airplane he might well have emerged the victor. But I kept narrowing the distance between our two planes with snap rolls to the left. Two cannon bursts and the fighter exploded in flames.

"That was my third victory of the day. The fourth, which followed almost immediately after, was ridiculously simple. A P-39 flashed by in front of me, paying attention only to pursuing a Zero, which zoomed upward in a desperate climb, firing as he went. The Airacobra ran directly into my fire and I poured 200 rounds of machine-gun bullets directly into his nose. The fighter snapped into an evading roll. I was out of cannon shells, and fired a second [machine-gun] burst into the belly. Still it would not fall until a third burst caught the still-rolling plane in the cockpit. The glass erupted and I saw the pilot slam forward. The P-39 fell off in a spin, then dove at great speed to explode in the jungle below."

Below: *The light gray of most early Zeros gave way to various types of camouflage green later in the war. Engine cowlings remained black.*

Above: These Model 22 Zeros of 251 Kokutai were based at Rabaul in 1943 and wear a field-applied green camouflage over the original gray color scheme.

Below: Zeros share a Japanese airfield with examples of its predecessor, the fixed-gear, open-cockpit A5M "Claude."

specification was issued in the twelfth year of the current imperial era, was finished in mid-March 1939 and made its first flight on April 1 in the hands of Katsuzo Shima. The third prototype was fitted with the new Nakajima Sakae 12 engine of 950 hp (708 kW), which improved performance far beyond the original specifications. Reports of the performance of the new fighter reached the squadrons in China, and, despite some structural failure accidents during testing, the pilots clamored for a chance to fly the new fighters. A total of 18 preproduction and early series aircraft were sent to China in July 1940 and formed a new unit. Actual service acceptance in Japan occurred soon afterward, and the new fighter became the Type Zero Carrier Fighter, or *Rei Shiki Sento Ki*, usually abbreviated to *Rei-Sen*, or Zero-Sen. "Zero" referred to the year of acceptance—2,600 in the traditional Japanese calendar. To add to the many names and designations, the Allied reporting system allocated "Zeke" as the code name for the A6M.

The A6M's first great success occurred over Hankow in September 1940, when in one battle 27 enemy aircraft were claimed for no losses. In reality it seems that 13 Polikarpov biplanes and monoplanes were actually destroyed, with a further 11 damaged. The IJN immediately presented Mitsubishi with a citation praising its good work on the Zero.

Although American General Claire Chennault, who spent much of the late 1930s reorganizing the Chinese air force, had warned Washington about the capabilities of the new generation of Japanese fighters, little notice appears to have been taken. When the Zero appeared over Pearl Harbor in December 1941, albeit in a supporting role, few in either the US Army or Navy had any idea that such a modern fighter existed in the previously little-regarded Japanese air services.

By adjustments to the engine and use of the auxiliary fuel tank, the IJN was able to launch the assault on the Philippines from bases on Formosa (Taiwan), without the use of the precious carriers. The US bases were more than 496 miles (800km) distant, and the A6Ms arrived over Clark Field and Iba with enough fuel reserves for 30 minutes of combat. Despite the warning given by the Pearl Harbor attack a few hours previously, MacArthur's forces on Luzon were largely unprepared, and around 60 American P-36 and P-40s were destroyed for the loss of three Zeros. The medium bombers then completed the job by destroying most of the remainder on the ground.

Almost at once, Japan turned its attention to the Dutch and British forces in the Dutch East Indies, Malaya, and Singapore. The A6Ms and other fighters cut a swathe through the Brewster Buffaloes and Hawker Hurricanes stationed around Singapore. By early February 1942, the Japanese had won air superiority, and Singapore fell soon afterward.

At the same time as the Midway operation, a diversionary attack was made on the Aleutian Islands. One Zero made a forced landing in boggy ground and flipped over. When discovered by the

Americans and restored to flight for testing, it revealed many of its secrets and weaknesses. The Allies discovered that lightness and thus performance were achieved largely at the expense of armor protection for the pilot or self-sealing for the fuel tanks.

Although all models were superficially similar, the Rei-sen (Zero-sen) went through many changes in its five years of production. The prototypes were retrospectively designated A6M1 (first model of the sixth carrier fighter from Mitsubishi). The first series model was the A6M2-21 (Navy Model 21), with a Nakajima Sakae engine of 950 hp (708 kW) and armament consisting of two .303-cal. (7.7-mm) machine guns in the cowl and two 0.79-in (20-mm) cannon in the wings. Most of the A6M2s had manually folding wingtips for carrier stowage. The A6M3-32 of 1941 had shorter wings with fixed tips and the 1,130-hp (843-kW) Sakae 21. It was superseded by the similar A6M3-22 with folding tips again. The A6M5, introduced in March 1944, featured "jet" exhaust stacks, fixed wingtips, and thicker gauge skins to prevent wing failure in high *g* pullouts. The A6M5-ko had even heavier skins and revised cannon.

The A6M6 addressed some of the weaknesses of the type with its self-sealing fuel tanks and a water/methanol-boosted Sakae 31; however, by this time, production standards were falling and output was much reduced by US bombing. Although rival manufacturer Nakajima had declined to compete for the original requirement, its factories built thousands of Zeros under license. Nakajima even developed a floatplane version designated the A6M2-N (or "Rufe" to the Allies). Although useful for patrolling island areas without airfields and attacking larger patrol aircraft, it was no match for any Allied fighter opposition.

As the war progressed, higher fuel consumption, heavier armament, and thicker skins reduced the range and climb rate of the Zero-Sen by more than one-third, although the speed did increase. The Zero's weaknesses included the lack of armor protection for the pilot and fuel tanks in most versions and unreliable radios. By mid-1943, it was basically obsolescent, but remained in production until the end of the war, making a total of 10,449, built by Mitsubishi and Nakajima. More than 6,000 of these were A6M5s. Horikoshi said that the F6F Hellcat was the first Allied fighter that was better in all respects than the Zero. Others such as the P-38 and F4U had some superior characteristics, such as top speed and dive speed, but the Zero still had the edge in maneuverability.

With most of the carriers gone, the Zero became a largely land-based fighter. Its intended successor, the A7M Reppu, was beset with many design and performance problems, and failed to enter production. The Zero had to soldier on long after it was superseded by Allied fighters. The fate of many Zeros was to be expended in Kamikaze attacks after 1944. A few were saved in museums and two original examples were kept airworthy in America. These have been joined by others rebuilt from wrecks found in Russia's far east.

Above: *This restored A6M5 represents the most numerous version of the Zero, introduced in late 1943.*

Below: *The A6M7 was the two-seat conversion trainer version of the Zero. Like most Japanese trainers, the majority were painted in overall orange.*

Focke-Wulf Fw 190

Germany's best fighter produced in quantity during the war, the Focke-Wulf 190 struck fear in the hearts of Allied pilots and Russian ground troops. Many of the Luftwaffe's *aces, however, stayed loyal to the Bf 109 until the bitter end.*

FOCKE-WULF FW 190A-8

Crew: one

Powerplant: one 2,100-hp (1,567-kW) BMW 801D-2 14-cylinder radial piston engine

Maximum speed: 402mph (647km/h)

Combat radius: 249 miles (402km)

Service ceiling: 37,400ft (11,400m)

Weight: 9,646lb (4,380kg) loaded

Armament: two 0.5-in (13-mm) MG 131 machine guns in nose cowl, two 0.79-in (20-mm) MG 151/20 cannon in wing roots and two MG 151/20 or 0.79-in (20-mm) MK 108 cannon in outer wings. Up to 2,200lb (1,000kg) of bombs; two 8.3-in (210-mm) WGr.21 underwing rockets

Dimensions: span 34ft 5.5in (10.51m); length 29ft 1.5in (8.95m); height 13ft (3.95m)

Far right: *With its powerful engine in a streamlined cowl, the Fw 190 outshone its contemporaries when it appeared in September 1941.*

Right: *An Fw 190A-8 of JG 26, based at Lille in April 1944 and flown by Josef "Pips" Priller who scored 101 victories.*

Known as the "Butcher Bird," the Focke-Wulf Fw 190 was a great shock to the Allies when it first appeared over the Channel front in September 1941. It was the only second-generation piston-engined monoplane fighter developed in Germany and the only new *Luftwaffe* combat aircraft to enter large-scale service during World War II.

The *Luftwaffe* sought a new fighter to supplement the Messerschmitt Bf 109 even as the first examples of the Bf 109B entered service. At this time, the spring of 1938, the Spitfire and Hurricane were also beginning their Royal Air Force (RAF) careers. Kurt Tank, the technical director of the Focke Wulf company of Bremen, saw the Spitfire and Bf 109 as "racehorses," which sacrificed durability for speed and climb rate. In drawing up a design to meet the *Luftwaffe*'s requirement, Tank adopted a

SB

wide-track undercarriage as used on the Hurricane, which was more stable on the ground, and a radial engine, which was more resistant to battle damage. Senior engineer R. Blaser conducted the detail design, which included a sliding bubble canopy giving exceptional vision for the pilot.

Piloted by Hans Sander, the Fw 190V1 first flew on June 1, 1939 with a 1,550-hp (1,155-kW) BMW 139 air-cooled radial with a three-bladed propeller and large ducted spinner. The unusual spinner was soon abandoned, thus saving weight and complexity, but having little negative effect on performance. The BMW 139, although powerful, had a great propensity to overheat, despite the use of a novel cooling fan mounted between the propeller and engine. The 10-bladed fan rotated

PILOTING THE FOCKE-WULF FW 190

Above: A 1943 scene of Fw 190Gs of II./SG 2, "Immelmann," which was one of the main ground-attack units on the Eastern Front.

On the Eastern Front, the ground-attack units (*Schlachtgeschwadern*, literally "slaughter wings") equipped with the Fw 190 were mainly used against Soviet armor, vehicles, outposts, and troops, but often encountered Russian fighters. *Oberfeldwebel* Hermann Buchner recalls one mission by II./SG 2 from a base in the Crimea in April 1944 flown by a mixed formation of two Fw 190Fs and two Bf 109s.

"Shortly before 1100 hours we taxied out for takeoff. Unfortunately, my wingman did not spot a fresh bomb crater and his mission ended right there and then standing on his nose. I reached the takeoff point somewhat late myself, to find only a single Bf 109 waiting for me. Obviously his wingman had had some difficulties too!

"The Bf 109 pilot signaled that he would fly as leader. We took off westward, and I soon discovered that my Fw 190 could more than hold its own against the Bf 109.

"We were some 1,000 meters above the Black Sea when the first message came through from ground control: '*Indianer* in harbor area SEWA; *Hanni* 3-4.' ('Bandits over Sevastopol Harbor, height 3,000 to 4,000 meters.')

"My *Schwarmführer* [formation leader] continued to climb while I covered his tail and kept a careful watch for bandits. We were soon flying at 4,000 meters approaching Sevastopol from the west. Then we spotted them, somewhat lower: enemy fighters. The *Schwarmführer's* voice crackled over my headphones: '*Pauke, Pauke!*' ['Tally-ho!']

"He dived into the attack, scattering the enemy fighters. They were Yaks and we twisted and turned among them for about ten minutes without scoring a single kill. Then they broke away. Ground control quickly came back on air: 'Fly to Balaclava area, large formation of Il-2s and *Indianer*.'

"The Bf 109 reduced speed and its pilot indicated that I should take over the lead. Now I was in front with the Messerschmitt protecting my tail. We were soon approaching Balaclava and could see the smoke-bursts of our own flak. Another wild dogfight with Yak-9s began, and this time I was able to bring one down. It crashed to the ground in flames. The rest of the *Indianer* broke for the east. Far below us the Il-2s were attacking our ground positions north of Balaclava. Quickly losing height, we dived on the enemy *Sturmoviks* from astern. After a few bursts I managed to get an Il-2. His port wing erupted in flames. He tipped over and smashed into the ground."

Buchner had scored two more of an eventual 58 kills, 46 of them scored on the Eastern Front and the remainder against four-engined bombers while flying Me 262 jets over Germany. The most successful Fw 190 pilot of all was Otto Kittel, who scored 220 of his 267 victories in the type. Another four pilots scored more than 100 victories in Focke-Wulfs, and many hundreds became aces.

at three times the speed of the propeller, distributing airflow evenly to the cylinders and allowing a closer-fitting cowling and thus less frontal drag than on contemporary radial-engined fighters such as the P-47 and F4F.

The fifth prototype (Fw 190V5) was fitted with a 1,600-hp (1,192-kW) BMW 801 14-cylinder radial. The heavier engine required a longer nose, and the canopy was relocated aft to maintain the center of gravity. After initial testing, a new wing with 20 percent greater area and a larger tailplane was fitted to the V5. This restored the flying characteristics and was adopted for production aircraft.

The preproduction Fw 190A-0, some of which retained the small wing, underwent operational testing from March 1941. The first fully operational unit was II./JG 26, based at Moorseele in Belgium, which was fully equipped with Fw 190A-1s by September. This version was armed with four MG 17 0.3-in (7.9-mm) machine guns, two above the engine and two in the wings.

Although they suffered numerous losses over the following months to the new radial-engined German fighter—and claimed several victories against it—it was not until January 1942 that the RAF established conclusively what they were up against. The fast, maneuverable new fighter was superior to the Spitfire V by all measures except armament, and this was increased on later A models by replacing the wing guns with two, then four 0.79-in (20-mm) cannon. The most numerous model was the Fw 190A-8, with a variety of weapons options that included pods with paired 1.18-in (30-mm) MK 108 cannon, making those aircraft so equipped the most heavily armed single-seat fighters of the war. The A8 also added nitrous-oxide boost to the engine for better high-altitude performance.

Equipped with a rack to carry a 550-lb (250-kg) or 1,100-lb (500-kg) bomb under the fuselage, FW 190As began "tip and run" nuisance raids against the south coast of England in mid-1942. These required diversion of several squadrons of

***Above:** JG 54 Grünherz (green hearts), with their unique camouflage, earned fame on the Eastern Front. These are Fw 190A-4s of 1.JG 54 in 1943.*

***Below:** The Fw 190As of JG 26 often protected German shipping, including escorting the "Channel Dash" by the Tirpitz and other warships.*

RAF fighters to counter them. Success with the Fw 190 in the *Jagdbomber*, or "*Jabo*," role led to development of variants and subvariants as fighter-bombers.

The Fw 190F was a dedicated fighter-bomber with provision for a 1,100-lb (500-kg) bomb under the fuselage and two 550-lb (250-kg) bombs under the wings. The F-2 subtype introduced a new blown canopy. The Fw 190G was similar, but added an autopilot.

In the defense of Germany, the Focke-Wulfs mounted attacks on Allied bombers by day and night. The most effective day tactic against B-17s and B-24s was the head-on attack, which increased the impact of the cannon shells against the most vulnerable parts of the bomber, namely the crew compartment. Late in the war, armor-plated *Sturmbock* Fw 190A-8s made massed tail attacks at close range. At night, the so-called *Wilde Sau* ("Wild Boar") Fw 190s mounted defensive target patrols from the spring of 1943, using the light from the burning cities to silhouette RAF bombers.

The BMW 801 gave the Fw 190 excellent performance below 22,965ft (7,000m), but high-altitude performance was lacking. Installing a V-12 Junkers Jumo 213A of up to 2,240 hp (1,671 kW) produced the Fw 190D series of which the Fw 190D-9 was the main production version. An annular radiator kept drag down, and the "Dora-9" had a ceiling of 39,370ft (12,000m). Despite its potential as an interceptor, many 190Ds were lost flying fighter-bomber missions, notably in Operation *Bodenplatte* on January 1, 1945, when hundreds of *Luftwaffe* fighters were lost attacking Allied airfields in the Low Countries.

The Ta 152 ("Ta" standing for "Tank") was a

***Above:** A pair of diving Fw 190s was the last sight many British, US, and Soviet pilots ever saw.*

***Right:** FW 190As await delivery at a factory airfield. Nearly 20,000 were built during the war.*

***Left:** A rare color image depicts Fw 190A-6s of 5.JG 54 on an airfield in Russia in spring 1943. The near aircraft was flown by ace Oberleutnant Max Stoltz*

Jumo-powered high-altitude interceptor version. About 100 TA 152Cs were delivered, but they saw very limited combat. The ultimate version was the Ta 152H with a Jumo 213E/B and wings extended to 47ft 6.75in (14.5m). It was capable of more than 470mph (760km/h) at 41,010ft (12,500m). Only 10 were completed. In total, about 19,500 Fw 190s were built by Focke-Wulf and five contractors. At least 60 Fw190A-3s were supplied to Turkey in 1942. A squadron of captured Fw 190Ds served with the Soviet Union, just after the war. In France a production line built 64 A5s as the NC 500 in 1945–46, but *Armée de l'Air* service was brief.

No Fw 190s have flown since the 1940s, although several restoration efforts are under way. A German company has established a production line to build a limited number of accurate replicas.

***Left:** The Ta 152C was powered by the DB 603 and was planned in many versions, although none reached service before the war's end.*

Hawker Typhoon and Tempest

Designed as a fighter, the Typhoon proved more useful as a tankbuster, as did its successor the Tempest. Nevertheless, the pilots of both racked up impressive scores against Luftwaffe *aircraft and the V-1 flying bombs.*

HAWKER TEMPEST MK V

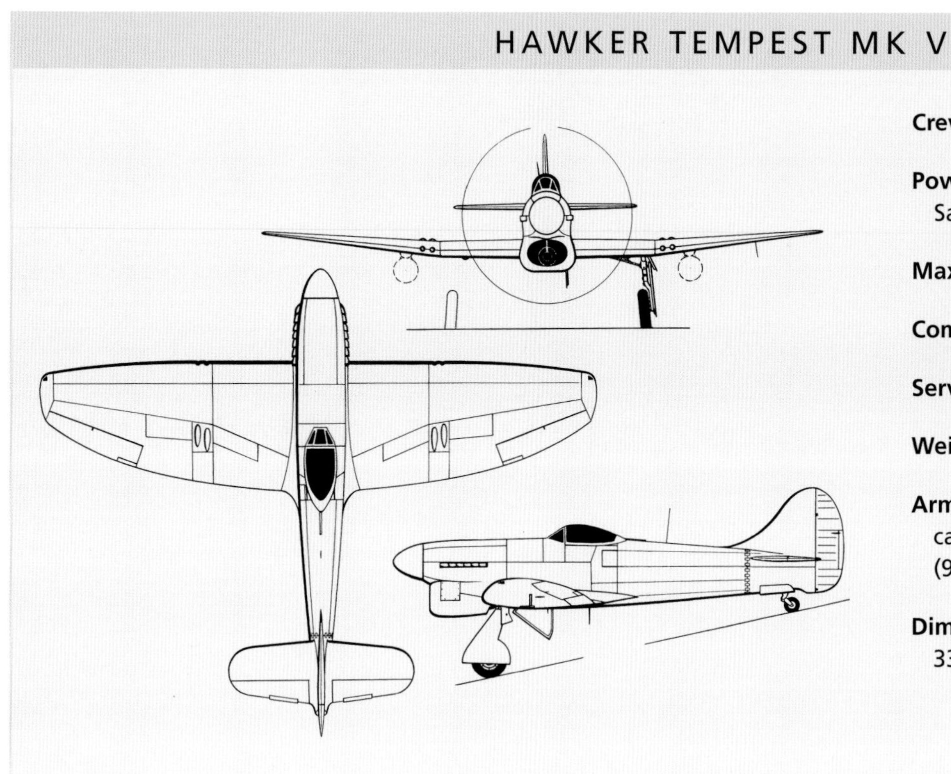

Crew: one

Powerplant: one 2,260-hp (1,686-kW) Napier Sabre VA H-24 piston engine

Maximum speed: 435mph (700km/h)

Combat radius: 300 miles (483km)

Service ceiling: 37,000ft (11,280m)

Weight: 13,640lb (6,187kg) loaded

Armament: four 0.79-in (20-mm) Hispano cannon, up to eight rockets and 2,000lb (907kg) of bombs

Dimensions: span 41ft (12.49m); length 33ft 8in (10.26m); height 16ft 1in (4.9m)

The Hawker Typhoon suffered a protracted development and proved more successful as a close-support aircraft than in its intended fighter-aircraft role. Its successor, the superficially similar but all-new Tempest, was one of the highest-performance piston-engined fighters ever built.

Even before the Spitfire and Hurricane had flown, the British Air Ministry issued a specification for their replacement, to be a single-engined four-cannon day-fighter. Hawker's Sydney Camm had already been thinking along these lines and replied with two similar designs, the Tornado with the 24-cylinder X-configuration Rolls-Royce Vulture engine of 1,760 hp (1,313 kW) and the Typhoon with the 24-cylinder, 2,200-hp (1,641-kW) flat-H Napier Sabre. The Tornado first flew on October 6, 1939 and the Typhoon on February 24, 1940. The Tornado was cleaner to the eye, but initially suffered from high drag caused by its radiator position. The Vulture engine was one of Rolls-Royce's few failures—it crippled the Manchester bomber, which was fortunately saved by fitting it with twice the number of Merlins and renaming it the Lancaster. Persistent con-rod failures led to the eventual abandonment of the Tornado.

Although the pressing war situation had seen 1,000 of each type ordered, the Tornado order was converted to more Typhoons. The Typhoon IA was armed with 12 0.303-cal. (7.7-mm) machine -guns and the Typhoon IB with four 0.79-in (20-mm) cannon. As Hawker was busy developing the Hurricane, Gloster was given the contract for the

Right: *To avoid confusion with the similar Fw 190, many Typhoons received black and white stripes in a pattern that differed from the later "D-Day" stripes.*

Right: *This is the first production Tempest, the pilot of which clearly enjoys the wind in his hair. Cannons were later mounted flush with the wing.*

Typhoon IA, while Hawker built the IB. Only 105 of the former were built, but Gloster was to produce the great bulk of the eventual total of 3,330 Typhoons delivered.

The Typhoon was a very large, all-metal fighter with a prominent chin radiator and noticeable dihedral on the outer wings. Early models had a framed canopy with a "car door" for entry and a three-bladed propeller. Later aircraft had a bubble canopy and a four-bladed prop. Service of the Typhoon IB began in September 1941 with No. 56 Squadron, but there were many teething problems such as exhaust gas in the cockpit and ammunition feed failures. Most worryingly, the tail had a tendency to break off when pulling out of a dive. More than 20 fatal accidents resulted from these structural failures. The immediate remedy for this was to reinforce the tail joint with a ring of fishplates, which resembled stitches, but did the job until a more permanent production-line fix could be devised. The cause was finally attributed to elevator flutter and cured by modification of the elevator balances.

Despite these problems, and a silhouette that frequently saw them mistaken for Focke-Wulf Fw 190s and attacked by their own side, the Typhoons proved to be extremely effective low-level fighters and ground attackers. Some squadrons specialized in the latter role, and their bomb-equipped aircraft were often unofficially called "Bombphoons." The fighter Typhoons were initially employed against *Luftwaffe* hit-and-run fighter-bomber attacks on the South Coast of England, and as escorts for low-altitude bombing raids in France and the Low Countries.

Below: *A No. 198 Squadron "Bombphoon" with the original canopy and "car door" for pilot entry.*

Above: *A Tempest V of No. 501 Squadron, showing the larger fin and longer nose compared to the Typhoon.*

The menace of the V-1 flying bombs was tackled by attacks on their known launching sites and by chasing them down as they approached the English coast and destroying them with cannon or

PILOTING THE HAWKER TYPHOON AND TEMPEST

Squadron Leader Des "Scottie" Scott, commanding officer of No. 486 (New Zealand) Squadron RAF flew a mock combat with a captured Fw 190 on the morning of June 24, 1943. This reinforced his view that combat with the radial-engined fighter best be avoided above 10,000ft (3,000m). That afternoon, Scott led nine 486 "Tiffies" on a Ramrod (bomber escort) for another squadron attacking Abbeville airfield in northern France. After the successful attack, the formation turned northwest, and Scott spotted a straggling "Bombphoon" low over the sea. Suddenly a group of Fw 190s appeared, and two dived on the straggler. Scott and Pilot Officer "Fitz" Fitzgibbon followed this pair. Latching onto the right-hand Fw, Scott broke to starboard after it.

"The Fw 190s foolishly dived under us towards the sea, and this gave us the immediate advantage. I took a quick look round while sprinting down after them. Fitz was hanging onto my tail, and I could see nothing else close to me except our own Typhoons. Within seconds I was firing directly down on a Fw 190. He turned to port close to the water. My deflection was astray—I could see cannon shells splashing in the sea just behind his tail. Suddenly we were at the same level and locked in a desperate battle to out turn each other.

Above: Pilots of No. 486 (NZ) Squadron with a Tempest at Brussels in 1945.

"I applied the pressure to get my sights ahead of him, but I kept losing my vision as the blood was forced away from my head; a little less pressure on the control column would bring my sight back into focus. I could see him looking back at me on the other side of our tight circle ... I was beginning to gain on him, but I was still well off the required deflection. With my heart pounding in my throat, I applied some top rudder to get above him. Just as I did so, his wings gave a wobble and he flicked over and hit the sea upside-down. I saw the great shower of spray his aircraft sent up, but not much else. I blacked out, went out of control myself, and recovered from my downward plunge just clear of the water. According to Fitz I had spun upwards. It could easily have been the other way, and both my *Luftwaffe* opponent and I would have finished up under water."

Below: A Typhoon Ib of No. 183 Squadron.

tipping them over using the airflow over the fighter's wingtip. Even though the pilotless bombs could not fire back, both of these methods could be hazardous to the attacking pilot. Several squadrons were held back from supporting the invasion forces in Normandy to mount patrols against these "Divers," as they were known.

Studies to improve the high-altitude performance of the Typhoon had begun within weeks of its first flight. The thick wing was the first to go, replaced by a new, more elliptical design that was nearly 5in (13cm) shallower at the roots. A new tank behind the engine in a slightly extended fuselage replaced the fuel tankage lost

***Above:** The Centaurus-engined Tempest II had much cleaner lines than the Napier-powered Mk V. Relocating the radiator greatly reduced drag.*

from the wings, and a much stronger undercarriage was fitted. The new wing was tested on a modified Typhoon, and the project was initially called the Typhoon II, two proper prototypes of which were ordered in November 1941. Later this was increased to six prototypes, by now renamed Tempest, each of which was to test a different engine—versions of the Sabre, Rolls-Royce Griffon, or Bristol Centaurus radial. The two that offered the most promise were the Centaurus IV-powered Tempest II, and the Tempest V with the Sabre II.

The Tempest V was selected for priority production and entered service with No. 3 Squadron in February 1944. Very similar in appearance to the Typhoon, particularly the late-model Mk IB, the Tempest could be distinguished by its much larger fin and lack of protruding cannon barrels. Underwing racks could carry bombs or eight rockets. The Tempest soon joined the Typhoon in anti-V-1 patrols, and the most successful pilot, Flight Lieutenant Joseph Berry, destroyed 60 of the flying bombs.

As the V-1 threat subsided, many of the

***Right:** Armed with rockets the Typhoon was particularly effective against trains and German motorized transportation.*

Typhoon and Tempest squadrons moved to bases on the continent. Now closer to the battlefront, the big Hawker fighters often flew "cab rank" patrols to provide close support for advancing ground troops. During fighting in the Falaise pocket in Normandy in August 1944, the fighter-bombers were instrumental in the huge German defeat, destroying much armor and many thousands of vehicles and troops.

The Tempest had much better high-altitude performance than the Typhoon, but the same squadrons usually used it at low and medium levels. This exposed them to heavy concentrations of light flak guns, which the Germans had in abundance, and many experienced pilots fell victim to ground fire in the last months of World War II. The Tempest was also successful in the air-combat role, destroying 20 Me 262 jets, as well as numerous other *Luftwaffe* aircraft.

Production amounted to 1,149 Napier-powered Tempests, including 142 Tempest VIs with the 2,340-hp (1,746-kW) Sabre VA. The Mk VI served in the postwar Royal Air Force (RAF) until 1949, latterly in the target-towing role. The Tempest II was another postwar version, powered by the 2,520-hp (1,880-kW) Bristol Centaurus. RAF Tempest IIs mainly served in the occupation of Germany and with squadrons in the Middle East after the war. Of the 452 Mk IIs built, India received 89 and Pakistan 24, the only export Tempests.

Relegated to decoy duties after retirement, a few of the Indian aircraft were recovered for long-term rebuild to fly. Otherwise, only two Tempest Vs and a single Typhoon have been preserved.

***Above:** A view of a bomb and the starboard 0.79-in (20-mm) Hispano cannons.*

***Below:** Tempest Vs under construction in a wartime factory.*

Chance Vought F4U Corsair

Despite initial rejection by the US Navy for its role as a carrier-borne fighter, the Corsair went on to be one of the most successful American fighters on land or sea. Several foreign users also contributed to the Corsair's great combat record.

Far right: *An impressive lineup of F4U-1D Corsairs on a Pacific airfield. This model introduced bomb racks under the center fuselage.*

Vought's F4U Corsair was in production longer than any other American fighter of World War II, and it was still rolling off the assembly line during the Korean conflict. When the final example was delivered in 1952, it was the last piston-engined fighter to be accepted by the American forces.

Entries for the US Navy's 1938 shipboard fighter requirement came from Bell, with the Model 5 Airabonita (derived from the P-39 Airacobra); Grumman, with a development of the F4F Wildcat; Curtiss with versions of the P-36 Mohawk; and Brewster, with two types of souped-up F2A Buffalo. Except for the Bell entry with its mid-mounted Allison V-1710, all of these were to be powered by radial engines. The only all-new designs were from the Vought-Sikorsky company of Stratford, Connecticut, usually known as Vought or Chance Vought.

The larger of Vought's two offerings was designed around the huge new Pratt & Whitney R-2800 Double Wasp 18-cylinder double-row radial engine, rated at 1,800 hp (1,343 kW) at sea level. Although this powerplant was later to see use in several important fighter,

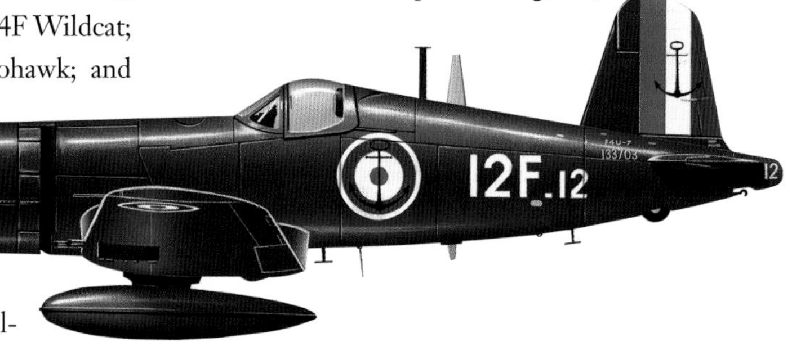

Right: *An F4U-7 of the Aéronavale's 12 Flotille in the early 1950s. French Corsairs saw action in North Africa and Indochina.*

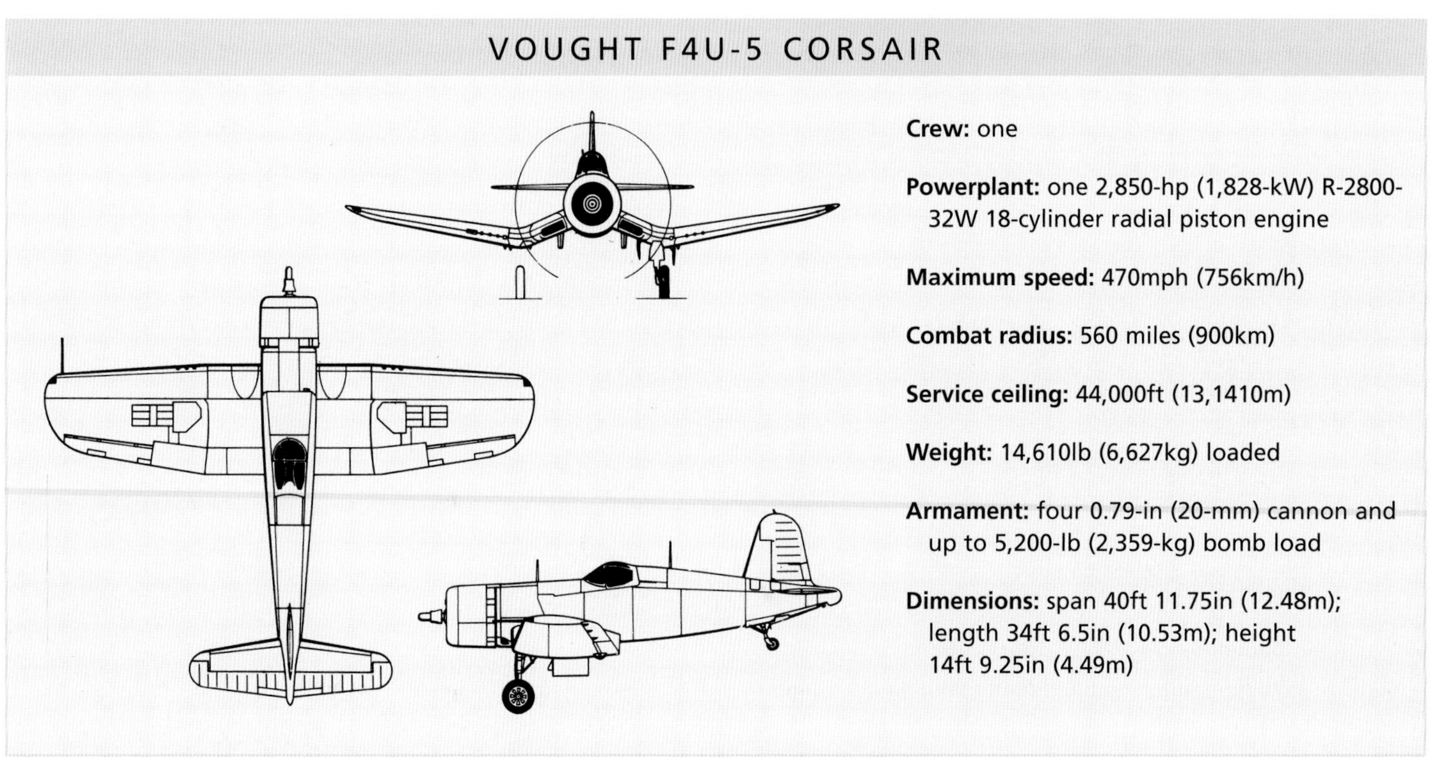

VOUGHT F4U-5 CORSAIR

Crew: one

Powerplant: one 2,850-hp (1,828-kW) R-2800-32W 18-cylinder radial piston engine

Maximum speed: 470mph (756km/h)

Combat radius: 560 miles (900km)

Service ceiling: 44,000ft (13,1410m)

Weight: 14,610lb (6,627kg) loaded

Armament: four 0.79-in (20-mm) cannon and up to 5,200-lb (2,359-kg) bomb load

Dimensions: span 40ft 11.75in (12.48m); length 34ft 6.5in (10.53m); height 14ft 9.25in (4.49m)

252
267

bomber, and transport aircraft, Vought's V-166B proposal was the first to use it. After evaluating the proposals, the US Navy ordered prototypes from Vought on June 11, 1938.

Rex Biesel and his Vought design team turned their proposal into metal over the next 18 months. The big engine required a large Hamilton Standard propeller, and in order to give ground clearance for this the wing was given a "gull" effect, where the inboard sections had significant anhedral and the outer, folding, sections had dihedral. The main gear legs were mounted at the bend, or lowest point, and retracted backward, rotating to lie flat within the wing. Large flaps covered much of the wing trailing edges. Armament was two 0.30-cal. (7.62-mm) machine

PILOTING THE CHANCE VOUGHT F4U CORSAIR

***Above:** Marine Corsairs flew from coral airstrips all through the southwest Pacific. This F4U-1D sports an impressive tally of bombing missions.*

Marine Captain Donald Balch was assigned to VMF-221 based in the Russell Islands in July 1943. On the 6th, his division of four "birdcage" F4U-1s was directed to make a patrol over New Georgia. "There we were jumped by several Zeros which we broke up like a covey of quail, each section going in a different direction. I got onto the tail of one Zero and shot him down. I then started looking for the other members of my division while simultaneously patting myself on the back for my splendid marksmanship. All of a sudden all Hell broke loose, with part of my hatch disintegrating along with some of the instruments in front of me. I immediately 'split essed' out to the left and down, pulling out at around 6,000 feet, never having seen anything. My wingman joined up with me and, because I couldn't hear anything on my radio, kept pointing at my tail. I put my gear and flaps down on final, but I lost complete control of the aircraft on flare out. I cut the power and slammed into the runway. We found later that my controls had been badly shot up, just holding together until the moment I flared out for my landing."

Left: An F4U-1 Corsair Mk I of the Royal Navy. This first production model was distinguished by its heavily framed "birdcage" canopy.

guns above the cowl and two 0.50-cal. (12.7-mm) guns in the outer wings.

Lyman A. Bullard flew the silver-painted XF4U-1 prototype from Bridgeport Municipal Airport on May 29, 1940. It was badly damaged in a forced landing on a golf course on its fifth test flight, but was repaired and rejoined the test program. The rebuilt prototype proved extremely promising in some respects, demonstrating a top speed of 405mph (653km/h), faster than any other fighter of 1940. Unfortunately, there were many changes needed before the new fighter, now named Corsair, could enter service. The Navy insisted that the armament be changed to six 0.50-cal. (12.7-mm) guns in the outer wings and that all fuel be concentrated in a large fuel tank behind the engine. This forced the cockpit even further back—the pilot now sat 14ft (4.27m) behind the propeller—and the forward view got even poorer than it already was. Armor and fuel-tank self-sealing were added, and the flaps were changed to a split NACA type arrangement.

So modified, the first batch of 584 F4U-1 Corsairs was ordered in June 1941, and deliveries began on July 31, 1942. More serious problems arose when the Corsair failed its carrier suitability trials in September. As well as the very poor view on the approach, when the pilot could barely see the deck, the stall characteristics were unacceptable, and on landing it had severe bouncing characteristics because of its stiff undercarriage.

Above: Among the last Corsair versions produced was the F4U-7, built for the French Navy. This one flew for many years on the British airshow circuit.

Pending fixes to these problems, Corsairs were issued to land-based Marine Corps squadrons. The first to take it into combat was VMF-124 on Guadalcanal in February 1943. Soon all the Marine fighter squadrons had traded their Wildcats for Corsairs and proved its superiority over the contemporary Japanese fighters. The Corsair's bomb-carrying ability was put to good use in close-support missions for the "mud Marines."

The first units to take the Corsair aboard ship were actually British. The Fleet Air Arm took a total of 2,012 Corsairs during the war, the first of them in mid-1943. Ninety-five Corsair Is (F4U-1s) and 510 Corsair IIs (F4U-1As and -Ds) were acquired, along with Goodyear-built Corsair IIIs and Brewster Corsair IVs. They were the best Fleet Air Arm fighters of the war and saw limited combat in Europe, notably in strikes on the

***Above:** The head-on view of the Corsair's gull wing was unmistakable. A tight cowling and radiators in the wing roots reduced drag and increased top speed.*

German battleship *Tirpitz* in Norway, before participating in the final assault on Japan and Japanese-controlled industries in Indonesia and other occupied territories.

US Corsairs were cleared for carrier use in April 1944. Changes included replacement of the "birdcage" canopy with a clear bubble, revision of the main and tail undercarriage legs, and addition of a wedge on the starboard leading edge, which cured the wing-drop tendency. VMF-124, the most experienced Corsair unit, became the first carrier-based squadron.

Corsair production was split among three manufacturers, including Goodyear, which produced 2,010 FG-1s, and Brewster, which turned out 735 F3A-1s. Goodyear later developed the F2G with the massive 3,000-hp (2,238-kW) R-4360 engine and a teardrop canopy, but only 18 were built. Several subvariants of the F4U-1 appeared, including the F4U-2 night-fighter with podded radar and four guns.

***Below:** With 0.79-in (20-mm) cannon, rocket rails, and bomb racks, the last ground-attack models were far more capable than the first Corsairs.*

The main late-war variant was the F4U-4, with an R-2800-18W of 1,828 kW (2,450 hp) driving a four-bladed propeller. An air scoop appeared on the cowl, which became more oval. The "dash four" had underwing rocket stubs, and the F4U-4B had four 0.79-in (20-mm) cannon. Unlike most other fighters, production continued after the war. The F4U-5 flew in April 1946 with intakes relocated to the cowl cheeks.

At the outbreak of the Korean War in 1950, the Corsair was still the main fighter in the US Sixth and Seventh Fleets and was still in widespread use with others. Its role switched mainly to ground attack, and new versions were ordered, namely the F4U-5N night-fighter and the F4U-5NL, which was optimized for winter conditions, having de-icing equipment on the flying surfaces, windshields, and propellers. The AU-1 was a special attack version for the Marines with armored undersides and the single-stage supercharged R-2800-83W. Together with Pacific-veteran F4U-4s and derivatives, the US Navy and Marine Corsairs excelled in the close-support missions that the US Air Force had largely neglected since 1945 in favor of fleets of big bombers. Marine night-fighters also had successes against North Korean Yaks and "bedcheck Charlie" night-harassment biplanes.

The Royal New Zealand Air Force (RNZAF) was the third-biggest user, receiving the first of 424 F4U-1A, -1D and FG-1D Corsairs in April 1944 to replace P-40 Kittyhawks. By the time they arrived, the Japanese air threat in the Southwest Pacific had been eliminated, and the Kiwi Corsairs were used entirely in the ground-attack role. The last were retired in 1947 after serving with the occupation forces in Japan.

France received the last Corsairs built—94 of the F4U-7 model based on a mix of AU-1 and F4U-4B features. The *Aéronavale* also received 66 AU-1s from US stocks, the first of them when the Indochina situation worsened. In Indochina, the ground-based Corsairs used their 13 weapons pylons to good effect in close air-support missions, but could not prevent the eventual French defeat. The French Corsairs flew from carriers in the Suez operation and from land bases in the Algerian civil war. The Corsairs' swansong was in Tunisia in July 1961, when their intervention prevented the overrunning of the large base at Bizerte by government troops.

The last Corsairs in service were in Latin America. Argentina flew their F4U-5 and F4U-5NLs from the carrier *Independencia* until December 1965. Earlier that year they saw action in a border conflict with Chile. The last air combats between piston-engined fighters took place between Honduras and El Salvador in the "Soccer War" of 1970. Honduran F4U-4s and -5Ns, and El Salvadoran FG-1Ds and F-51D Mustangs met several times during the brief war. Most combats were inconclusive, but Major Fernando Soto of the Fuerza Aerea Hondureña scored three kills in his F4U-5N, two of them against Salvadoran Corsairs.

A healthy population of approximately 30 Corsairs are still flying today, most of them in the United States, but others are in Canada, Brazil, France, Austria, and the United Kingdom.

Above: *Corsairs have flown in civilian hands since the late 1940s, initially as air racers and then as warbirds in a variety of more or less authentic color schemes.*

Left: *More than 30 F4U-1Ds share the deck of the USS* Bunker Hill *with TBM Avengers and SB2C Helldivers.*

Macchi MC.200, 202, and 205V

Although equipped with a variety of engines, the wartime Macchi fighters shared the same basic airframes. Like other Italian fighters they were usually underarmed and underpowered compared to their contemporaries.

The best-known Italian fighters of World War II, the Macchi MC.200, 202, and 205V series were highly maneuverable and strongly built. Like other *Regia Aeronautica* fighters, they were lightly armed and underpowered compared to their contemporaries. The best of them, the MC.205V, was produced too late and in too few numbers to have much effect.

The Aeronautica Macchi company, originally Nieuport-Macchi, built a series of fighters in the years 1917–30, all of them biplane flying boats. Their first monoplane fighter was the MC.200 *Saetta* ("lightning"), built to a requirement for a bomber interceptor which specified armament of one machine gun and endurance of only one hour. The MC.200 was designed by and took the "C" in its designation from the surname of Mario Castoldi, creator of a number of Schneider Cup racing seaplanes. Mussolini's government had encouraged the development of radial engines in the early 1930s. Castoldi would have preferred to use an inline powerplant as in his racing aircraft, but all that was available to him was the 870-hp (649-kW) Fiat A.74 14-cylinder radial.

The prototype airframe, which was first flown on Christmas Eve 1937 by chief test pilot Burei, was an all-metal tailwheel monoplane with an open cockpit. Built to the same requirement as the

***Right:** MC.202s of a unit engaged over Malta in 1942. The Folgores were mainly used to escort small formations of bombers.*

MACCHI MC.205V

Crew: one

Powerplant: one 1,475-hp (1,100-kW) Fiat RA.1050 RC.58 12-cylinder inverted V piston engine

Maximum speed: 399mph (642km/h)

Combat radius: 323 miles (520km)

Service ceiling: 37,090ft (16,370m)

Weight: 7,514lb (3,408kg) loaded

Armament: two .50-cal. (12.7-mm) machine guns in fuselage, two .303-cal. (7.7-mm) machine guns in wings or two MG 151 0.79-in (20-mm) cannon in wings

Dimensions: span 10.58 m (34 ft 8.5 in); length 8.58 m (29 ft 0.5 in); height 3.04 m (9 ft 11.5 in)

***Right:** First of the production Macchi monoplanes was the MC.200 Saetta. Unlike this early example, most had open-topped cockpits.*

Fiat G.50, the MC.200 was very similar in appearance, but had a less streamlined upper fuselage, no spinner, and distinctive blisters over the cylinder heads on the tighter-fitting engine cowl. Due mainly to a more refined wing design, which featured hydraulic flaps, the MC.200 had a higher top speed and generally better performance than the Fiat.

The MC.200 entered service in October 1939, and 150 were in service by the time Italy entered the war in June 1940. The Saetta saw much service in Malta and North Africa, mainly in its MC.200AS tropicalized form. It was also used in the disastrous Italian campaign in Russia, where it

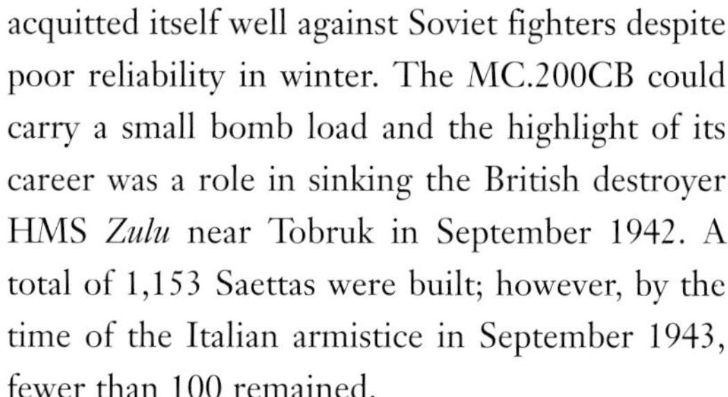

acquitted itself well against Soviet fighters despite poor reliability in winter. The MC.200CB could carry a small bomb load and the highlight of its career was a role in sinking the British destroyer HMS *Zulu* near Tobruk in September 1942. A total of 1,153 Saettas were built; however, by the time of the Italian armistice in September 1943, fewer than 100 remained.

Meanwhile, with Italian industry's failure to produce a useful inline engine, the Air Ministry instigated license production of the German Daimler-Benz DB.601, as used on the Messerschmitt Bf 109E. A handful of German-built engines were sent to Italy, and two were provided to Macchi. Castoldi took this engine and fitted it to an all new fuselage married to the wing and tail surfaces of the MC.200. Like some later MC.200s, the new MC.202 Folgore (Thunderbolt) had an enclosed, side-hinged canopy, but a more streamlined fuselage with a raised spine. A deep radiator was mounted below the fuselage. The armament was again concentrated in the fuselage, consisting of two .50-cal. (12.7-mm) Breda SAFAT machine guns mounted on top of the cowl. The MC.202 first flew on August 10, 1940 and was an immediate success, proving 60mph (100km/h) faster than any other *Regia Aeronautica* fighter, and having a service ceiling 8,500ft (2,600m) higher.

***Below:** One of the units sent to the Russian front was 21° Gruppo Caccia (fighter group), part of the modest Italian contribution to the campaign.*

Reports from test pilots were so favorable that the MC.202 was immediately ordered into production, the first aircraft entering service in July 1941. Unlike the prototype, the series aircraft had fixed tailwheels and a prominent radio mast behind the cockpit. After approximately 400 initial production models with German-built engines, production switched to engines license-built by Alfa Romeo as the RA.1000 RC.41 Monsone (Monsoon). Sand filters for the prominent supercharger intake on the port side appeared on later series aircraft.

The MC.202 made its combat debut over Malta in September 1941, proving superior on a one-to-one basis to the Hurricanes defending the island. Others were rushed to North Africa following the British offensive in November. After a period of retreat, they helped win air superiority over Tobruk and Bir Hakim by June 1942.

***Above:** An MC.200 of the 90a Squadriglia, 10° Gruppo, 4° Stormo based at Catania, Sicily in 1941.*

PILOTING THE MACCHI MC.202

Giorgio Solaroli di Briona of the 74th Squadriglia was based at Abu Haggag, Libya, when, on September 4, 1942, his flight of MC.202s encountered a formation of Royal Air Force (RAF) Boston medium bombers heavily escorted by P-40s. "My wingman, Sergente Maggiore Mantelli, and I swept down onto the left flank of the escort. I immediately began to fire at a P-40 which filled my gun sight. There was absolutely no reaction from the English pilot—so much that I got to within a few meters before I saw him turn on his back and crash into the ground. I vigorously pulled up, for I had to avoid other enemy fighters which were snapping at my heels. With the speed I had gained in the dive I soon found myself at a favorable altitude to attack another formation. This time I again managed to machine-gun a P-40 at close quarters. I hit the aircraft and observed that it caught fire."

***Left:** The well laid out cockpit of the MC.202. This is a late model with wing guns. The reflector gunsight is easily visible.*

But the fight was far from over, for Solaroli's fighter had been hit by numerous rounds fired by Sergeant N.D. Stebbings in his No. 260 Squadron Kittyhawk. Wounded in the head and leg, Solaroli crash-landed in friendly territory. Extricating himself from the wreck, the ace limped off in search of help.

"Finally, I saw three men waving their hands at me, telling me not to move as they carefully made their way toward me. They explained that I had landed in a minefield—it must have been pure luck that I had not blown the whole place up!" Solaroli recovered from his injuries and returned to his unit a month later. He ended the war with a total of 11 victories.

***Below:** An MC.202 in North Africa, sporting the "sand and spinach" camouflage widely used by the* Regia Aeronautica.

***Above:** The MC.205N Orione with a larger wing and new forward fuselage was intended to replace the MC.202, but the "interim" MC.205V was the last model.*

The arrival of Spitfires and the Axis defeat at the Battle of El Alamein saw the Folgore units retreat until only one remained in Tunisia by January 1943. They remained active over Malta, although now encountering increasing numbers of Spitfires.

Following the German invasion of the Soviet Union, Mussolini insisted on Italy taking part in the campaign in order to share the spoils. The *Regia Aeronautica* contribution included MC.200s, and later MC.202s. The open-cockpit Saettas had a hard time during the winter of 1942–43, but claimed 88 Soviet fighters for 15 losses. The MC.202s were sent as reinforcements in September 1942, but soon joined the general withdrawal on the Don River front.

Slow production of the Monsone engine and replacement of the DB 601 on German production lines by the 1,475-hp (1,100-kW) DB 605 saw many completed MC.202 airframes sitting at the factory awaiting engines. The logical mating of a C.202 airframe and a DB 605 first flew as the MC.202bis on April 19, 1942. Other changes included a retractable tailwheel, revised oil cooler arrangement, and a blunter spinner. The wings were unequal span to counter the powerful torque effect of the engine. Top speed increased by 29mph (47km/h) and range by 140 miles (235km). As on late MC.202s, the new version had a pair of .303-cal. (7.7-mm) machine guns in the wings. Production was quickly authorized as the MC.205V *Veltro* ("greyhound"), with the engine license-built as the RA 1050 RC.58 *Tifone* (Typhoon). Additionally, many MC.202s were converted to Veltros.

The MC.205V first saw action during the invasion of Sicily in July 1943, flying many strafing attacks against the Allied forces. It was never available in large numbers, however, partly due to Allied bombing of one of the two factories producing Veltros. When the Italian government surrendered in September, fewer than 100 were in *Regia Aeronautica* service. After the armistice, 43 MC.205Vs, 23 MC.202s, and some MC.200s remained in or went to the south to fight the Germans. Reorganized by the Allies as the Italian Co-Belligerent Air Force, these units were sent to the Balkans to avoid the prospect of Italian fighting Italian.

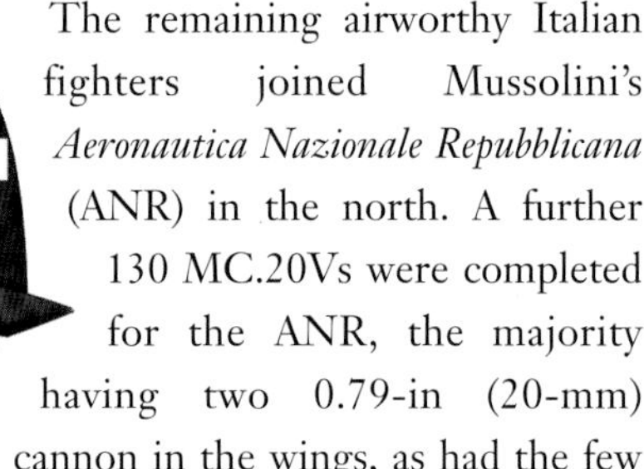

***Right:** An MC.205V of 70a Squadriglia, 23° Gruppo, 3° Stormo.*

The remaining airworthy Italian fighters joined Mussolini's *Aeronautica Nazionale Repubblicana* (ANR) in the north. A further 130 MC.20Vs were completed for the ANR, the majority having two 0.79-in (20-mm) cannon in the wings, as had the few

Left: *Mario Castoldi (in hat), designer of the wartime Macchi fighters supervises work on an early MC.205 outside the company's Turin factory.*

Serie III models completed before the armistice. Some other MC.205s were operated by the *Luftwaffe*'s JG 77 before transfer to the ANR. The Germans supplied a few C.202s to the Croatian air force. As the Germans withdrew, the Macchis became the sole air defense against 15th Air Force bombers based in Italy, but could do little against the escorting Thunderbolts and Mustangs.

Frontline Italian service continued until 1947, and some MC.205Vs were used as trainers into the 1950s. Production restarted after the war to satisfy an Egyptian order for 62 MC.205Vs. Of these, 41 were to be converted from MC.202s, but production halted after 42 deliveries when Jewish agents raided the production line.

The Egyptian Macchis claimed three kills over Israeli fighters during the War of Independence in 1948. Israeli Defense Force (IDF) Mustangs and Spitfires claimed 10 Veltros in return. Ten of the surviving aircraft were given to Syria in 1951.

Only two MC.202s and three MC.205s survive today, none of them airworthy, although Aermacchi restored and flew one for a number of years until it was damaged in an accident.

Below: *The last airworthy wartime Macchi was an ex-Egyptian MC.202 converted to MC.205 standard. Damaged in the 1980s, it has not flown since.*

Republic P-47 Thunderbolt

The P-47 Thunderbolt was known as the "Jug" or juggernaut due to its size. With its powerful engine and ability to withstand a beating, the P-47 was popular with pilots and with ground troops, who could rely on it for close support.

REPUBLIC P-47D-25 THUNDERBOLT

Crew: one

Powerplant: one 2,300-hp (1,716-kW) Pratt & Whitney R-2800-59 18-cylinder radial piston engine

Maximum speed: 428mph (689km/h)

Combat radius: 700 miles (1,126km)

Service ceiling: 42,000ft (12,800m)

Weight: 19,400lb (8,800kg) loaded

Armament: eight 0.50-cal. (12.7-mm) Browning machine guns in wings and up to two 1,000-lb (454-kg) bombs

Dimensions: span 40ft 10in (12.43m); length 36ft 2in (11.01m); height 14ft 2in (4.32m)

***Right:** A restored P-47D shows off the markings of the 78th Fighter Group and the "D-day stripes" introduced in June 1944 as a recognition marking.*

Republic's Thunderbolt was the largest single-engined US fighter of World War II. It was also the most numerous US fighter, not only of its era, but also, with a total of 15,638 produced, of all time.

Russian émigré Alexander Kartveli of the Seversky Aircraft Corporation designed the Seversky P-35, which the US Army had bought in small numbers in 1936, mainly to make up for delays in Curtiss Hawk production. Kartveli then improved on the design with a fully retracting undercarriage and other improvements under the designation XP-41. The company was renamed the Republic Aviation Corporation in 1938 and a revised XP-41 was offered for a new US Army competition and accepted as the P-43 Lancer with the 1,200-hp (894-kW) R-1830 radial. More than 200 were built, of which 51 were delivered to China. The P-43 was just about adequate for 1940, but reports from Europe suggested that far greater performance, armament, and armor protection would be needed for any new fighter if it were to confront the *Luftwaffe*.

Kartveli took the basic configuration of the P-43, but enlarged it to take advantage of the new Pratt & Whitney R-2800 engine as introduced by the US Navy's F4U Corsair. For high-altitude operation, this was equipped with a supercharger, which was mounted under the rear fuselage and fed with air from a duct in the bottom of the large oval cowling. To give ground clearance for the

MX

12-ft 2-in (3.71-m) four-bladed Curtiss electric propeller, the wide track undercarriage was very long. To save space in the wing for the retracted gear, a clever mechanism shortened the legs by 9in (23cm) as it went up, thus making room for the masses of ammunition needed by the four 0.50-cal. (12.7-mm) machine guns in each wing. The eight-gun armament was heavier than on any single-engined US Army fighter of the war years. The well-equipped cockpit was exceptionally large. The joke was that pilots avoided enemy fire by running around inside. The canopy had heavy framing and was hinged upward at the rear on the first aircraft, but later aircraft had a canopy that slid backward along the peak of the raised spine.

This new fighter was the XP-47B Thunderbolt (the XP-47A being an earlier, canceled product), and it flew on May 6, 1941 in the hands of Lowry Brabham. This was only eight months after the official go-ahead. The US Army very quickly ordered an unprecedented 773 of this huge fighter. Most of them were to be the P-47C, with slight changes, including a small forward fuselage extension. The P-47Bs were mainly used for home

PILOTING THE REPUBLIC P-47 THUNDERBOLT

Above: Thunderbolt pilots enjoy the view from a bombed-up P-47. It was effective in low-level attacks on airfields.

Polish pilot Mike Gladych had scored eight kills flying with the Royal Air Force (RAF) before he joined the 56th Fighter Group, who used the P-47 throughout the war, even after the other Eighth Air Force fighter squadrons had converted to the P-51. Gladych recalled one of his many hair-raising adventures: "We were over Germany escorting bombers when a fight developed fairly close to the ground. I suddenly found three Focke-Wulfs off at right angles to me and above, I tried to jump them but they kept away. I then went down on the deck among the trees. They followed me and that is exactly what I wanted. A rat race developed and they started shooting. Finally I got on the tail of one of them. He was one dead pigeon. To shoot him I had to straighten up, and one of the planes above me then put some holes in my wing. I started going home because my gas was running low, but the two remaining Focke-Wulfs started to fly in formation with me. They must have thought I was out of gas because they beckoned me to land. I motioned 'OK' and kept on flying just ahead of them until we reached a German airfield.

"I knew what I'd do. I gave the field a short burst and all the ground guns opened up with everything they had. The two Germans were flying less than 10 yards behind me and the antiaircraft fire landed right among them. I didn't stay to see what happened but headed for England." Gladych ran out of fuel as he crossed the English coast and he was forced to bail out of his P-47. After his landing, he took some time to convince a group of British army officers that he was not German, but Polish.

Right: Francis "Gabby" Gabreski was the top ace of the 56th Fighter Group and the top Thunderbolt ace in Europe.

defense and training, and the first Cs arrived in Europe for the Eighth Air Force at the end of 1942. Many teething troubles were encountered and the first squadrons, which had previously flown Spitfires, took time to get used to their heavy new fighters that climbed slowly, dove like bricks, and were often mistaken for Focke-Wulf 190s. The first actual combat with FW 190s in April 1943 was claimed as three-for-three by the Americans, but it seems in fact that the German side suffered no losses. Progressive improvements with successive production batches saw most of the bugs ironed out and, most importantly, provision for external drop tanks introduced. These allowed the Thunderbolts to escort US bombers much further into Germany than hitherto possible.

The extremely sturdy "Jug" (either a contraction of "juggernaut" or stemming from the rotund P-47's similarity to a milk jug) proved able to withstand heavy battle damage and return to base. Its good high-altitude performance and unsurpassed diving ability were used to good effect in "zoom" attacks on aircraft and in the ground-attack role.

Production mounted until three Republic factories were at full flow by mid-1943. The most numerous and significant model was the P–47D, of which 12,602 were produced. Curtiss-Wright

***Left:** This Thunderbolt was shot down over Germany and restored to flight to train* Luftwaffe *pilots in how to defeat P-47s.*

***Left:** The 358th Fighter Group of the 9th Air Force boasted this extremely colorful P-47D when based in Toul, in France, in 1944.*

***Below:** These colorful P-47Bs were used by the 56th Fighter Group for training and patrols in the state of New York before the unit moved to Europe.*

Above: ***Bomber pilots of the 8th Air Force called fighters "little friends," but the P-47 was hardly small, being the largest and heaviest single-engined fighter of the war.***

Below: ***One of the features of the P-47N was a long fillet at the base of the fin that increased lateral stability.***

built more than 350 as the P-47G. The D and G had an improved engine with water injection, more armor, and a better supercharger. Two wing pylons allowed carriage of either a pair of 1,000-lb (454-kg) bombs or two triple-shot bazooka rocket launchers. Alternatively, two more drop tanks could be carried. During P-47D production, the most visible change to the whole series was introduced—from the P-47D-25 block onward, a bubble canopy and a cut-down rear fuselage greatly improved pilot visibility. There was no change of designation, and units often flew both the "razorback" and "bubbletop" varieties side by side. Lateral stability was lessened by the reduced fuselage area, and a long strake was added forward of the fin on later aircraft.

There were several experimental versions with inline engines and bulky cooling systems, most of them spectacularly ugly. All production aircraft used the R-2800, in versions ranging from 2,000 hp (1,492 kW) to 2,800 hp (2,090 kW) at 32,500ft (9,913m) with water injection.

The P-47M was optimized for high speed, particularly to catch V-1 flying bombs, with an uprated supercharger and airbrakes. It was capable of 504mph (811km/h). The P-47N was a long-range model for the Pacific, with a longer, fuel-containing wing with squared tips.

After the initial shaky start, the Thunderbolt became well respected by the Allies and feared by the Axis. One Eighth Air Force group preferred to retain the Thunderbolt after the others had switched to Mustangs. The two leading American aces in Europe, Francis Gabreski (28 kills) and Robert S. Johnson (27), flew only P-47s in combat. Thunderbolts were also issued to the Ninth Air Force in England and Europe, and to the 15th in Italy, where they were wreaked havoc on Axis troops and armor. Attached to the 15th Air Force was an extremely successful group of the Brazilian Air Force with P-47Ds. Likewise a Mexican Thunderbolt unit operated with American forces in the Philippines.

The RAF received a large number of P-47s—120 "razorback" Ds as the Thunderbolt I, and 710 "bubbletops" as the Thunderbolt II. They were issued to 16 squadrons and served almost

Left: *This P-47N shows the clipped wingtips of this version and its heavy armament of machine guns, bombs, and rockets.*

exclusively on ground-attack duties in the China-Myanmar (Burma)-India (CBI) theater.

After the war, P-47s served with France, Italy, Yugoslavia, Turkey, and in Latin America with the air forces of Bolivia, Brazil, Chile, Colombia, Cuba, Venezuela, Peru, and Nicaragua. In the postwar US Air Force, the P-47 (F-47 from 1947) Thunderbolt carried on until 1954. Air National Guard units were the last American users. It would have made an effective ground-attack platform in Korea, but P-51 units were sent instead and suffered accordingly from losses to ground fire due to their vulnerable water-cooled engines.

About 13 Thunderbolts, most of them Ds, are currently airworthy, out of a total of 60 survivors. Many of these aircraft formerly served in Latin America or with Yugoslavia. During the wars in the former Yugoslavia in the early 1990s, a group of Croatian militia seriously considered returning the P-47D in the Zagreb Aeronautical Museum to flight to use against Serbian forces, but they lacked the technical skills and it was not to be.

Left: *The P-47B was the first production version of the Thunderbolt and equipped units based in the US for home defense and training purposes.*

Messerschmitt Me 262

The best of Germany's many jets and rocket-powered aircraft projects, the Me 262 could have seriously prolonged the war if it had been available in sufficient numbers. Fortunately for the Allies, the Me 262 was too little too late.

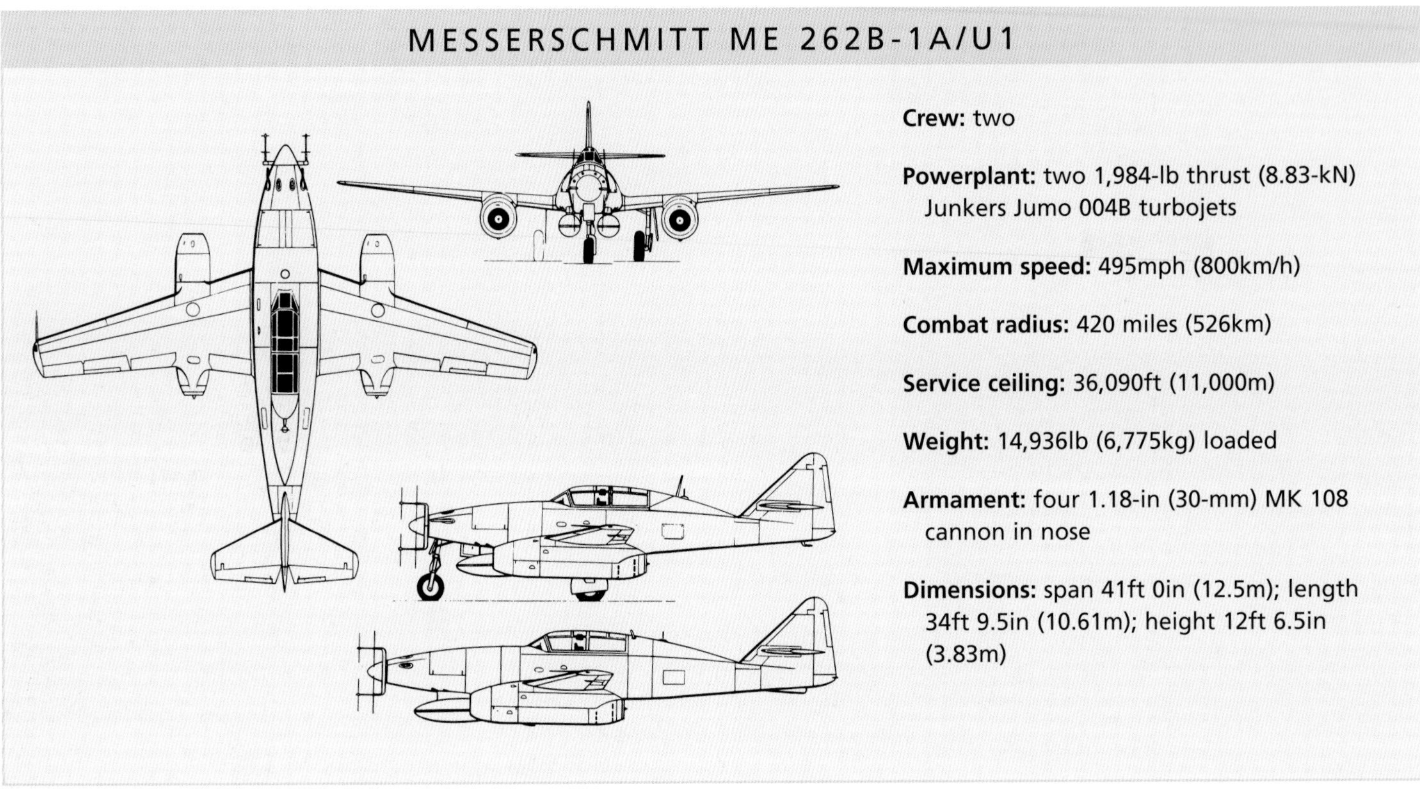

MESSERSCHMITT ME 262B-1A/U1

Crew: two

Powerplant: two 1,984-lb thrust (8.83-kN) Junkers Jumo 004B turbojets

Maximum speed: 495mph (800km/h)

Combat radius: 420 miles (526km)

Service ceiling: 36,090ft (11,000m)

Weight: 14,936lb (6,775kg) loaded

Armament: four 1.18-in (30-mm) MK 108 cannon in nose

Dimensions: span 41ft 0in (12.5m); length 34ft 9.5in (10.61m); height 12ft 6.5in (3.83m)

Far right: *This captured Me 262A was displayed in New York just after the war as an example of Nazi high technology.*

The first operational jet fighter was long delayed by technical problems with its engines, but more so by politics. The Nazis gave it low priority, believing the war was won, but, when the tide turned, found it was too late to produce, arm, and crew enough to make any difference to the outcome of World War II.

The Messerschmitt 262 began as a 1938 proposal by designer Waldemar Voigt for a turbine-engined research aircraft. Other German manufacturers had similar ideas and Heinkel's He 178 made the first flight by a jet aircraft on August 24, 1939, just before the outbreak of war. This single-engined experimental aircraft had little potential as a warplane, and Heinkel moved onto the twin-engined He 280, which flew in March 1941.

The Me 262, which had begun as the Projekt 65, had progressed slowly, partly due to delays with development of the proposed BMW 003 powerplant, which was giving half the hoped-for thrust by the end of 1940.

Lack of reliable thrust meant

Right: *An Me 262A-2a of fighter-bomber unit 1/KG51 at Achmer, in the spring of 1945.*

AIR POWER IS PEACE POWER
MESSERSCHMITT 262A
AIRCRAFT-TWIN
JET. GERMANY
EMPTY SHELLS

Right: This once-only version had a 2-in (50-mm) cannon that could destroy a bomber with a single shot. It was captured and tested by the US.

that the Me 262 V1 prototype made its first flight on April 18, 1941 with a Junkers Jumo 210G piston engine in the nose, as well as two 003s under the wings.

Fritz Wendel made the first flight under jet power alone in the Me 262 V3 on July 29, 1942. With its conventional tailwheel undercarriage, the V3 proved almost impossible to rotate into the takeoff position. A sharp application of the wheel brakes was needed during the takeoff roll to lift the tail. The design was soon revised with a nosewheel, which gave a level ground attitude, and testing continued, albeit at a slow pace. General Adolf Galland flew the fourth prototype in late May 1943 and immediately recommended maximum priority for the project. Unfortunately, his call fell on deaf ears—mainly Hitler's.

Nonetheless, in March 1943, the RLM had ordered further development of the Me 262, despite the Heinkel's higher speed and better climb rate. Its twin tail arrangement was regarded as unsound, and its range was less. More importantly, however, Ernst Heinkel was out of favor with the political hierarchy.

The production Messerschmitt Me 262 was a sleek aircraft with two engines slung under a moderately (18-degree) swept wing, a triangular section fuselage, and a blown canopy. In the nose was a quartet of 1.18-in (30-mm) MK 108 cannon, with a high rate of fire of 680 rounds per minute, but a low muzzle velocity and short effective range. Three hits were enough to destroy a heavy bomber. A battery of 24 R4M rockets mounted on two underwing racks could back up this punch.

Below: The Me 262 V3 had a tailwheel undercarriage, but proved reluctant to leave the ground. Fitting a nosewheel and moving the mainwheels back cured the problem.

Production aircraft used Junkers Jumo 004B axial-flow turbojets, giving about 1,984-lb thrust (8.83 kN) each. The materials needed for high-temperature resistant alloys were in extremely short supply. BMW made do by baking an aluminum coat over ordinary steel, which worked to a point, but gave a working life of less than 10 hours for early engines.

In the autumn of 1943, Hitler asked *Luftwaffe* chief Hermann Göring if the Me 262 would be able to carry bombs, and Göring in turn was assured by W illi Messerschmitt that it could, but, crucially, not that it *would*. Hitler put greater and greater store in the ability of a fleet of Me 262s to penetrate fighter cover and strike at any invasion force, delaying them until his Panzer divisions arrived. He failed, however, to impress this on his air force commanders or those in charge of aircraft production.

The first training unit was established in May

***Above:** An unpainted Me 262 shows the clean and futuristic lines of the first operational jet fighter.*

PILOTING THE MESSERSCHMITT ME 262

Galland was fired as general in charge of fighters in January 1945, but was permitted to return to the cockpit in command of a new Me 262 unit, designated *Jadgdverband* ("fighter unit") 44, or JV 44. Galland was able to choose the best pilots, and JV 44 became known as something of a club for which you needed the Knight's Cross to join. JV 44 flew its last sorties on April 26, 1945, scrambling a dozen rocket-armed Me 262s, led by Galland himself, to intercept a formation of US and Free French B-26 Marauder twin-engined bombers attacking targets north of Munich. In the engagement that followed, four of the B-26s were brought down. Two fell to the cannon of Adolf Galland, who, distracted by accurate return fire from the tail gunners of the closely formated bombers, had tripped only one of the two safety switches necessary to release his rockets. A third Marauder was claimed by his wingman, Unteroffizier Schallmoser, who had collided with a B-26 a few weeks earlier and been forced to bail out. On this occasion, unlike Galland, Schallmoser had correctly armed his rockets, which destroyed the bomber.

***Above:** Adolf Galland was the youngest wartime* Luftwaffe *general and one of the most successful jet pilots.*

Galland's machine had, in fact, suffered damage during his attack on the bombers. He was then caught again by one of the P-47 escorts, which "split-essed" down on him unseen. A two-second burst from the Thunderbolt's eight machine guns scored hits in the Me 262's starboard wing root area before Galland managed to break left and disappear into the clouds. With his right engine cowling flapping loose in the wind, his instrument panel shattered and shrapnel embedded in his right knee, Galland nursed the jet back to base, where he made a deadstick landing—trailing smoke and with a punctured nosewheel—in the middle of a low-level fighter-bomber raid.

Above: *The Me 262 was adapted to the fighter-bomber role with 550-lb (250-kg) bombs. None were ready in time to confront the Normandy landings.*

1944, only weeks before the invasion. Experienced twin-engined fighter pilots soon realized that the throttle response was much slower than with piston engines, making a go-around in the final stages of landing almost impossible. It was no aircraft to issue to newly graduated flight students.

In late May, Hitler asked how many of the available aircraft could carry bombs—when told the answer was none, at least not without extensive design changes—he flew into a rage and ordered that every new Me 262 be delivered as a fighter-bomber. The necessary changes were indeed ordered to allow a pair of bombs to be carried rather awkwardly on the forward fuselage. This has often been said to have greatly delayed the introduction of the Me 262 fighter until it was too late to make a difference to the defense of Germany, but the order was in fact rescinded after the Allies had driven the Germans from France. The test and training unit, now named *Kommando Nowotny* after its leader, the 283-victory ace Walter Nowotny, was declared operational in late September and moved to airfields in northwest Germany. The concrete runways needed by the jets were easy to spot, however, and were repeatedly pounded by Allied bombers. P-51 Mustangs were on the lookout for the jets making their relatively slow takeoffs and landings, and shot many down when they were at their most vulnerable. Nowotny himself was killed in an encounter with Mustangs in November. General Galland, the chief of fighter forces, ordered the unit to southern Germany to retrain and regroup.

Although more reliable engines were by now available, serviceability was poor. The first fighter-bomber unit was only able to mount sporadic (and inaccurate) attacks on Allied forces. The first full jet wing, JG 7, was never able to put up more than about 30 Me 262s at any one time, the peak of their operations and successes coming in March 1945. A typical mission saw 22 jets destroy nine B-17s for the loss of four of their own. A total of 27 pilots scored five or more victories on Me 262s. Seven of these added to scores greater than 100 scored on conventional fighters. For the less experienced, flying or fighting in the Me 262 was a highly dangerous business, and many died on or before their first operational jet mission.

Although widespread use of a two-seat trainer would have greatly eased pilot conversion and saved lives, only about 15 were built, and half of

Right: *The heavy cannon of the Me 262 could be backed up with batteries of R4M rockets under each wing. These were effectively used against USAAF bombers.*

Left: *Only a few Me 262B-1a night-fighters were built, but they had some success. The fuselage racks proved useful for carrying additional fuel tanks.*

these were lost in accidents. Another half-dozen were delivered as night-fighters with Lichtenstein radar in the nose. The Me 262B-1a night-fighters had limited success against the much slower Royal Air Force (RAF) bombers, but shot down a number of Mosquito bombers and night-fighters in the first months of 1945.

At the end of the war, the chaotic supply and transportation system reduced Me 262 sorties to a trickle. The fuel that the jets used was less of a problem than that for the tow tractors that moved the fighters in and out of their hiding places in the woods. At times, oxen were used to move the world's most advanced aircraft to their takeoff positions. Even Adolf Galland admitted that availability of Me 262s in large numbers might have delayed the advance of the Western Allies, but would have only allowed more German territory to fall into Soviet hands. He was thankful that Hitler's failings prevented this from happening.

Of the 1443 Me 262s built, only about 300 actually saw combat. The Me 262 had a brief postwar life in Czechoslovakia, where the production facilities has been captured by the Soviets. A further 17 were completed as the Avia S.92 and two as the two-seat CS.92, and these served until 1950. Only a few genuine Me 262s survived to be displayed in museums, but an ambitious project in the United States has seen the completion of a quartet of accurate airworthy replicas powered by modern and reliable J85 engines.

Below: *Pilot of the first Me 262, Fritz Wendel waits for more work to be done on one of its BMW 003 turbojets. The engines of the Me 262 had short working lives.*

North American P-51 Mustang

Sometimes called "the fighter that won the war," the P-51 Mustang allowed the B-17s to reach Berlin and the B-29s to reach Tokyo. A blend of American and British technology, it was superior to most of its adversaries in many ways.

NORTH AMERICAN P-51D MUSTANG

Crew: one

Powerplant: one 1,450-hp (1,080-kW) Rolls-Royce V-1650-3 Merlin V-12 piston engine

Maximum speed: 437mph (703km/h)

Combat radius: 800 miles (1,287km)

Service ceiling: 41,900ft (12,771m)

Weight: 12,100lb (5,493kg) loaded

Armament: six .50-cal. (12.7-mm) Browning machine guns, up to 2,000lb (908kg) of bombs

Dimensions: span 37ft (11.28m); length 32ft 3in (9.83m); height 13ft 8in (4.16m)

Right: *Loaded with drop tanks, P-51Ds of the 21st Fighter Group set off from the island of Saipan to escort B-29s over Japan.*

Widely regarded as the greatest fighter of World War II, the North American P-51 Mustang arose from a British requirement. It failed to sparkle until given a Rolls-Royce powerplant. The Royal Air Force (RAF) introduced it to combat and also gave it its name, but it was in the hands of the US Army Air Forces that the P-51 achieved lasting fame.

As war broke out in Europe, a British Purchasing Commission was established in New York to liaise between the UK government and American arms manufacturers to acquire new equipment for British forces, and additional sources of supply for previous purchases. The head of the Commission visited North American Aviation (NAA) at Inglewood, California, in December 1939, to see if it could provide an extra production line for the Curtiss P-40, of which the RAF had already ordered nearly 2,000.

The answer from NAA's head "Dutch" Kindelberger was that his company could build P-40s if it had to, but it could design and build a much better fighter itself. This was a bold claim from a company that had no fighter experience whatsoever. The British insisted that NAA work with Curtiss and have access to data on future Curtiss projects. Designers Raymond Rice and Edgar Schmued, together with aerodynamicist Ed Horkey, set to work and drew up plans for a highly advanced fighter. A deadline of 120 days was set for completion of a prototype, which was rolled out on September 9, 1940—although the engine took a bit longer to arrive, delaying the first flight,

87
55

Right: *A P-51A flown by the commander of the 1st Air Commando Group India in 1944. By this time there were few operational P-51As left elsewhere.*

which Vance Breese made on October 26. This NA-73X was a very clean monoplane with a wide-track undercarriage and a distinctive intake scoop under the center fuselage. This housed the radiator for the 1,150-hp (862-kW) Allison V-1710-F3R engine, similar to that used in the early models of P-40. The better aerodynamics gave the NA-73X superior performance to the Curtiss fighter, but this was barely tested before the prototype was severely damaged in an accident on only its fifth flight.

This setback helped to delay flight of the first production aircraft for the RAF until May 1941, the RAF having ordered 340 as the Mustang I a year earlier. The first examples tested in Britain

PILOTING THE P-51 MUSTANG

Right: *The trigger fingers of Mustang pilots destroyed more than 5,000 German, Italian, and Japanese aircraft in air combat during World War II.*

On January 11, 1945, Captain William Shomo of the 81st Tactical Reconnaissance Squadron was on an armed reconnaissance mission to two airfields on the island of Luzon. Nearing their first objective, Shomo, flying his regular F-6D "Snooks 5th," and his wingman Lieutenant Paul Lipscomb spotted a G4M "Betty" bomber escorted by a dozen fighters. The Mustangs jumped the formation and quickly brought down four Ki-61 "Tony" fighters, then engaged another group, as Shomo's report stated:

"The second element of two 'Tonys' on the right side of the formation turned to the left and started after my wingman. As this element crossed over, they passed directly in front of me and I fired a burst into the [Japanese] wingman and he exploded in flames. Lt. Lipscomb then fired at the wingman of the first element and this burst into flames ... [he] made a pass on the bomber, but apparently did no damage. I then started to make a pass on the bomber, and as I closed on its tail from the right quarter, a rear gunner started to fire at me so I dropped my wing tanks to be less vulnerable. I dropped below the bomber and raked the underside of the fuselage with a long burst. The right wing root caught fire and black smoke started streaming from the bomber as I passed under and beyond it."

Shomo subsequently saw it crash in flames. The F-6Ds attacked two further fighters, Lipscomb destroying another "Tony," before Shomo chased two more at low level and brought them both down. For this mission, Lipscomb was credited with three kills and Shomo seven. Shomo was only credited with one other victory, but was awarded the Medal of Honor for this epic battle.

Below: *A happy P-51D pilot of the 47th FS, 15th FG, which was based on Iwo Jima at the war's end in August 1945.*

proved that the new fighter was faster and longer ranged than the Spitfire V, although the Spitfire climbed faster and performed better at higher altitudes. The RAF used the Mustang I mainly as a ground-attack and reconnaissance aircraft, so these were not important deficiencies. Mustang Is had six .303-cal. (7.7-mm) machine guns in the wings and two .50-cal. (12.7-mm) in the lower nose. The Mustang IA had four 0.79-in (20-mm) cannon in the wings, but no nose guns.

The US Army Air Forces (USAAF) eventually took notice of the Mustang, having retained the XP-51 prototypes for its own testing. It ordered 150 cannon-armed P-51s (no suffix) and 310 P-51As armed with four .50-cal. (12.7-mm) machine guns. Other P-51s were aircraft originally intended for the RAF, but held back by the United States after the attack on Pearl Harbor. Many of these had two K-24 cameras installed and were used as tactical reconnaissance aircraft as the F-6A. In April 1942, the United States ordered 500 of a ground-attack model designated A-36 and also known as the Apache or the Invader. This model had either four or six .50-caliber guns, and dive brakes in the upper and lower surfaces of each wing, making it an effective dive-bomber. The A-36 was mainly used in Sicily and Italy.

The secret to the Mustang's speed was its laminar flow wing. This had its maximum thickness at 50 percent of the chord, and significant camber on the underside. Airflow stayed close to the wing and did not break up and cause drag. Maintaining the laminar flow required as smooth a surface as possible, so the P-51 was very precisely built using flush rivets and fasteners. The fuel was stored in tanks in the inner wings, including the central section under the pilot's seat, and behind the cockpit. Armor plate was provided behind the pilot's back and head, and at the front of the engine. The windscreen was made of armored glass.

The development that was to transform the Mustang from a low-altitude attacker and reconnaissance aircraft to a long-range, high-altitude escort ship was that of the Rolls-Royce

__Below:__ This Mustang was flown by Lt. Urban Drew of the 361st Fighter Group. He destroyed two Me 262s in another P-51D named "Detroit Miss."

__Left:__ P-51D "Ferocious Frankie" of the 374th FS, 361 FG, was the personal aircraft of Wallace Hopkins, who scored six kills over Europe.

Right: *A Mustang pilot of the 4th Fighter Group strikes a heroic pose for the press camera. USAAF fighter pilots were rarely more than 25 years old.*

Below: *This P-51B "razorback" Mustang was one of those fitted with the British-designed Malcolm hood bubble canopy for improved visibility.*

Merlin 60 engine with its two-stage supercharger, and its installation (by the British) to create the Mustang X in April 1942. By November, a cleaner installation of the Packard-built version of this powerplant by NAA led to the first flight of the XP-51B in November that year. Deliveries of the production P-51B with a 1,520-hp (1,134-kW) Merlin V-1650-3 began in late 1943; by March 1944, the first Mustangs appeared over Berlin escorting B-17 heavy bombers. The B was soon joined by the identical P-51C, built at NAA's new Dallas factory.

The ultimate wartime model was the P-51D, which had six wing guns, greater external load capacity, and a cut-down rear fuselage with a full bubble canopy. The new K-14 lead-computing gyro gun sight was the world's most advanced at the time the P-51D made its combat debut just after D-Day in June 1944. Mustangs scored more than half of the 8th Air Force's "kills." These included several Me 262 jets, mainly caught at low speed near their bases. In all, P-51 pilots were credited with more than 5,000 aerial victories in all theaters.

The P-51D was also widely used in the Pacific War, escorting B-29s to Japan and active in the China-Myanmar (Burma)-India theater. The battles to recapture the Philippines saw many dogfights between Japanese aircraft and P-51Ds, including the reconnaissance version, the F-6D.

The P-51H (F-51H after 1947) was a lightweight version, which had only a superficial resemblance to the P-51D. It had a new structure, a deeper fuselage and a larger fin and tailplane, among other changes. The engine was a Merlin V-1650-9 capable of 2,220 hp (1,685 kW) with emergency boost. Most Hs were stored at the war's end and only issued to Air National Guard squadrons in the early 1950s.

P-51s served with a number of nations other than the United States and United Kingdom during the war years. South Africa, Canada, Australia, Nationalist China, Sweden, and the Netherlands East Indies were among them. Australia's Commonwealth Aircraft Corporation (CAC) built 200 Mustangs between 1945 and 1951. After the war, Mustangs (almost all P-51Ds) were supplied to or otherwise obtained by more than 20 countries.

The Korean War saw widespread use of the Mustang, mainly in the ground-attack role with bombs, rockets, and guns, although some aerial victories were scored. USAF, SAAF, and RAAF squadrons were all active with F-51Ds, as was South Korea's Republic of Korea Air Force (ROKAF). Although possessing long endurance and heavy firepower, the Mustang was not entirely suitable for low-level missions, its water-cooled engine being very vulnerable to damage from even small-caliber ground fire.

Mustangs soldiered on in many Latin American air forces long after the last F-51H had left US Air National Guard service in 1959. Some were modernized by the Cavalier company in Florida for countries such as Bolivia. The very last military Mustangs were retired by the Dominican Republic in 1984.

The Mustang is the most popular warbird fighter. Approximately 120 are still flown, most of them in the United States. The Reno air races have seen many Mustangs, some highly modified, compete in the "Unlimited" class over the years.

Above: *The P-51D arrived in England before D-Day in 1944, but the earlier (and faster), "razorback" Mustangs stayed in service for some time afterward.*

Left: *Flying from bases in England, the 4th Fighter Group destroyed more than 1,000 enemy aircraft during the war in the air and on the ground.*

Northrop P-61 Black Widow

One of the few aircraft designed and built especially for the night-fighting role, the complex P-61 Black Widow suffered its share of teething troubles. However, it served in Europe and the Far East with considerable success.

NORTHROP P-61B BLACK WIDOW

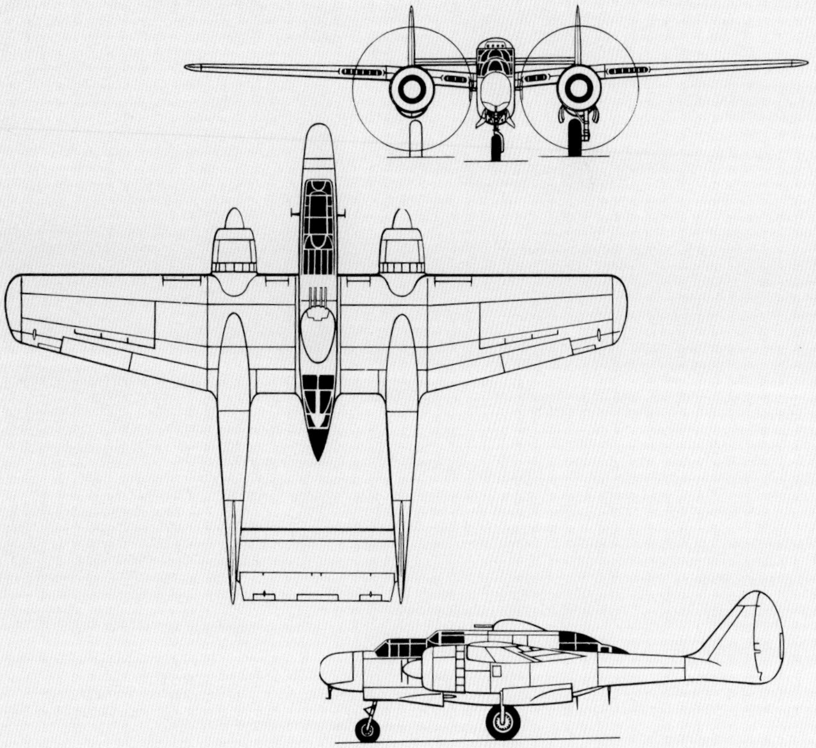

Crew: three

Powerplant: two 2,000-hp (1,492-kW) Pratt & Whitney R-2800-65 18-cylinder radial piston engines

Maximum speed: 366mph (589km/h)

Combat radius: 950 miles (1,529km)

Service ceiling: 33,100ft (10,090m)

Weight: 38,000lb (17,240kg) loaded

Armament: four 0.79-in (20-mm) cannon under nose, four 0.50-cal. (12.7-mm) Browning machine guns in remotely-controlled dorsal turret, and four 1,600-lb (726-kg) bombs

Dimensions: span 66ft (20.12m); length 49ft 7in (15.11m); height 14ft 8in (4.46m)

The P-61 Black Widow night-fighter was one of the most specialized aircraft ever built, and, although it did all that was asked of it, development delays saw it reach the battlefront after the threat it had been designed to counter was largely gone.

The invention of radar for detecting aircraft dated to 1936, and initially required giant sets of aerial towers with a wavelength measured in meters. As war loomed, progress in miniaturizing radar was rapid, and by 1940 the British were fielding reasonably effective if somewhat temperamental centimetric airborne intercept (AI) radars in various aircraft such as the Bristol Beaufighter and the Douglas Havoc. Even before the United States entered the war, American liaison officers in London were briefed on developments in airborne radar. As the night Blitz on the British capital and other cities got under way in the last months of 1940, they reported to their superiors and advised the development of radar-equipped night-fighters for the US Army Air Forces (USAAF). At the same time, the British were also searching for a specialized night-fighter to replace the various converted day-fighters and bombers then in use.

Without being told any of the specifics of radar, the Northrop Aircraft design team became aware

Right: *The crew of "Lady in the Dark" of the 548th Night Fighter Squadron based on Iwo Jima was credited with the last combat victory of World War II.*

Lady in the Dark

PILOTING THE NORTHROP P-61 BLACK WIDOW

Above: *The pilot and radar operator of this P-61A are clearly seen through the cockpit "greenhouse."*

The teamwork needed for a successful night interception is shown in this account of a mission flown by Captain John Wilfong and his radar operator Lieutenant Glenn Ashley of the 426th Night Fighter Squadron (NFS) at Chengtu, China, in November 1944. Their P-61A was named "I'll Get By."

"After taking off, we came under GCI [ground control intercept] control, who promptly vectored us onto any enemy aircraft which was flying at 6,000 feet. Due to our fast closure speed, we overshot and lost him. Minutes later we were again directed onto another aircraft at the same altitude. The heading was 270 degrees. GCI brought me to within four miles, at which time Lt Ashley picked the 'bogey' up on his radar screen. While closing in, the enemy aircraft started taking evasive action, initiating a rapid climb up to 14,000 feet. We continued to close the gap, and with the bright moonlight, we were able to get a positive ID at 600 feet. It was a Japanese [Mitsubishi Ki-46] 'Dinah' [a twin-engined reconnaissance aircraft]. From a position of five degrees above and five degrees starboard, I gave it a quick burst with my 20 mms. No sooner than I had quit firing, the Dinah exploded in front of us. It was a textbook intercept!"

of the requirement for a well-armed night-fighter with a long flight endurance, and they began preliminary design work, submitting a detailed proposal before the end of 1940. Northrop was well ahead of any other manufacturer, and, although the crew layout and armament went through several revisions, the design was frozen in December and an order for two XP-61 prototypes was issued in March 1941.

Radar development was equally rapid, and an American-developed set called the SCR-520 (AI.10 in UK parlance) was chosen to equip the new Northrop design. When the XP-61 (soon named "Black Widow" after an in-house competition) emerged, it was unlike any previously designed British or American fighter. With a tricycle landing gear and a twin-boomed tail configuration, it superficially resembled the P-38 Lightning, but had a much greater wingspan and wing area, and was shorter overall. The central nacelle housed a crew of three—a pilot and gunner in stepped cockpits, and a second gunner/radar operator in a glazed enclosure at the rear of the pod. The nose cone, which was frosted Plexiglas on early models, housed the radar scanner, so other

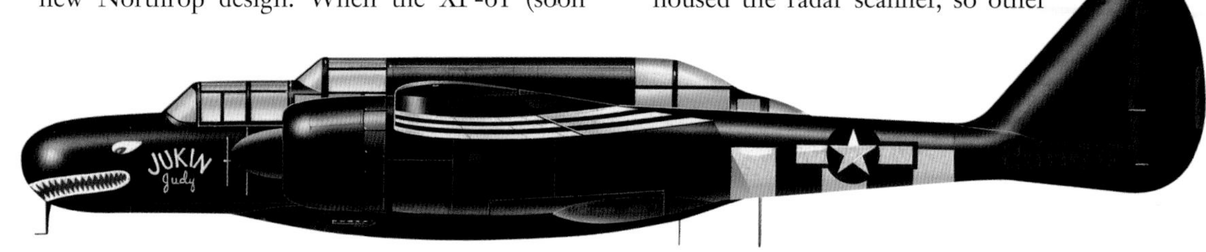

Right: *"Jukin' Judy" was a P-61A based at Etain, France, in late 1944. Like most European-based Black Widows, it lacked a top turret.*

locations were found for the main armament. A battery of four cannon was mounted under the fuselage, and on top was a remotely-operated barbette with four 0.50-cal. (12.7-mm) Browning machine guns. The two large R-2800 radial engines drove four-bladed propellers. Powerful spoilers supplemented conventional ailerons.

The XP-61 was flown at Hawthorne in greater Los Angeles on May 26, 1942 by Vance Breese, and was followed by 13 YP-61 service test aircraft. The first aircraft was unpainted, and some of the YPs were matt black, but the initial production deliveries were largely olive drab with gray undersides. The first 100 P-61As were ordered before the YP-61 had flown, and hundreds more were soon added. At this point, problems began to arise—tail cones imploded, nose cones sagged in hot weather, and there were endless troubles with airflow buffeting around the top turret. These became so bad that the rotating turret was eliminated during P-61A production, sometimes replaced in the field with a fixed unit or with an extra fuel tank in the turret well. The problem was fixed with a new teardrop turret design on the main production variant, the P-61B.

After extensive stateside training, the first Black Widows were dispatched to the front lines in May 1944. In that month, both the 422nd Night Fighter Squadron (NFS) in England and the 6th NFS in Hawaii received their Widows. The 422nd became operational soon after D-Day and, soon joined by the 415th NFS, was active against V-1 flying bombs, destroying nine before moving to the continent with the invasion forces. The European-based P-61As had a busy time, encountering all types of enemy aircraft by night, from Me 262 jets to Ju 52 transports. Two pilots and three radar operators in the European Theater of Operations (ETO) were credited with five kills. The P-61As were usually flown with only two crewmen as there was no need for a top turret gunner. P-61s arrived in Italy after most of the night action had passed, and only one squadron scored any kills in the Mediterranean Theater of Operations (MTO). When there were no enemy aircraft to hunt, the Black Widow had a useful secondary ground-attack capability and saw some action in the night-intruder role with bombs and rockets.

The Pacific Theater P-61 squadrons were largely equipped with turreted P-61As and, later, P-61Bs. They were often posted in small

Below: *Early Black Widows were delivered in olive drab finish. Only the first 38 P-61As were fitted with the top turret, which suffered from buffeting in flight.*

Above: John Myers was Northrop's main test pilot on the Black Widow, but he did not make the first flight.

Below: The F-15A Reporter was a photoreconnaissance development of the P-61. It was later used by NASA.

detachments at various outlying bases to provide local air defense. As such, some crews experienced intense action over short periods, whereas others saw none. The night-fighter squadrons ranged far and wide, from Guadalcanal in the Solomon Islands to New Guinea, the Netherlands East Indies, and finally the Japanese home islands.

P-61s also saw service in the China-Myanmar (Burma)-India (CBI) theater. Like the MTO, enemy air activity was scarce by the time the Widow squadrons arrived, but the aircraft were well employed on night and day interdiction missions against enemy road, rail, and river transportation. Some were fitted with triple "bazooka" rocket installations.

The sinister-looking P-61s adopted a wide range of names and colorful examples of nose art, many of them with a nocturnal theme, such as "Midnight Madonna," "Lady in the Dark," and "Sleepytime Gal." A series of trials had proved that gloss black was the least visible color when caught in searchlight beams, and from early 1944 all P-61s were delivered from the factory in overall jet black.

After the European armistice, P-61 squadrons stayed on as part of the occupation forces in Germany and performed a similar role in Okinawa after VJ Day. Most squadrons converted to the F-82G Twin Mustang, and a number of them soon transitioned again to the F-89 Scorpion, Northrop's twin-jet night-fighter.

Black Widow development continued with the P-61C, notable for its supercharged engines and paddle-bladed propellers. More than 500 were ordered, but only 41 had been completed when the Pacific War ended, and none saw combat service. A more radical development was the XP-61E, designed as a long-range escort fighter for the B-29 raids on Japan. This did away with the three-crew nacelle for a narrow tandem two-seat unit with a long bubble canopy. As well as the belly guns, the P-61E would have had four fixed

machine guns in the nose. One of the two prototypes was written off in an accident, and the USAAF chose the P-82 Twin Mustang for the long-range day-fighter role instead. The remaining XP-61E was converted to the first F-15 Reporter ("F" standing for "Photographic" in the nomenclature of the day). The 36 production F-15A Reporters (later redesignated RF-61C) were the last of the line, which amounted to 742 airframes of the Black Widow series. The F-15As were delivered in natural metal finish and served only in the Far East. One of their last tasks before retirement in 1949 was to conduct a photo survey of the Korean peninsula, work which proved invaluable when hostilities broke out there the following year.

A few P-61s and F-15s were used for various trials after the war, including missile trials, weather research, and the first US ejector-seat tests. A handful of Widows and Reporters entered the US civil register as fire bombers and survey aircraft. Just four P-61s survive today, only one of them restored to display condition. One example recovered from a mountainside in New Guinea in the late 1980s is the subject of a long-term effort to restore it to flying condition.

Above: *The P-61C was the last production model Black Widow. However, the war ended before the P-61C entered service.*

Below: *A lineup of olive drab P-61As showing the frosted Perspex radomes covering their SCR-720 radar sets.*

Grumman F6F Hellcat

The most successful of all US Navy fighters, the F6F Hellcat was powerful, tough, and well armed. The Hellcat's ability to survive battle damage and return to the carrier contributed to Grumman's reputation as the "Iron Works."

***Far right:** An F6F-5N night-fighter leads a trio of F6F-5s over San Francisco Bay. All were assigned to a postwar Naval Reserve unit.*

While bearing a superficial resemblance to the earlier F4F Wildcat, the F6F was an all-new aircraft. Its genesis, however, was in the XF4F-2, which was the precursor of the production F4F-3. Grumman had intended to re-engine the XF4F-2 with a 2,000-hp (1,491-kW) Wright R-2600 14-cylinder radial in 1938, but it was realized that doubling the power would require more than a simple strengthening of the airframe, and the project was shelved at that time. In 1940, these plans were dusted off when the US Navy was looking for a fighter to complement the Chance-Vought F4U Corsair.

Taking account of aircrew experiences from the Pacific and Europe, Leroy Grumman and Bill Schwendler completely redesigned the airframe to accommodate the R-2600 and the larger propeller it required. Grumman and Schwendler looked at Japanese construction techniques and the concepts behind the A6M Zero. They did not have a complete example to study, but were able to

***Right:** A land-based F6F-5 of Uruguay's Naval Air Arm in the 1950s.*

GRUMMAN F6F-5 HELLCAT

Crew: one

Powerplant: one 2,000-hp (1,492-kW) Pratt & Whitney R-2800-10W 18-cylinder radial piston engine

Maximum speed: 380mph (612km/h)

Combat radius: 945 miles (1,520km)

Service ceiling: 37,300ft (11,370m)

Weight: 15,413lb (6,991kg) loaded

Armament: six 0.50-cal. (12.7-mm) Browning machine guns in wings and up to two 1,000-lb (454-kg) bombs

Dimensions: span 42ft 10in (13.05m); length 33ft 7in (10.23m); height 13ft 1in (3.99m)

F
30
26 F
F
26
23 F
F
23
94439
3 F
F
3
79270

develop a good appreciation of the Mitsubishi fighter's strengths and weaknesses. It is true to say that the Hellcat was influenced by the Zero, but only in the sense that Grumman studied and rejected all of its design philosophies, creating a fighter that emphasized engine power, firepower, and pilot protection.

Following government inspection of Grumman's mock-up, two prototype XF6F-1s were ordered in June 1941. The XF6F-1 flew on June 26, 1942, three weeks after the Battle of Midway. It was piloted by Grumman test pilot Seldon Converse. It was a very large fighter for its day, having a low-set wing that had the greatest area of any on a US wartime single-seat fighter. The wing had a slight "gull" effect and was mounted at minimum angle of incidence to reduce drag. As on the Wildcat and Avenger, the wings folded back parallel with the fuselage for stowage aboard carriers. Unlike the Zero, the F6F, soon named Hellcat, was well protected, having self-sealing fuel tanks beneath the pilot and steel armor plate ahead of the oil

PILOTING THE GRUMMAN F6F HELLCAT

Above: Pilots of fighter squadron VF-16 walk out to their F6F-3s aboard the USS Lexington, *November 1943.*

Lieutenant L.G. Barnard of VF-2 aboard USS *Hornet* submitted his combat report on June 15, 1944 after fierce fighting over Iwo Jima, during a US attack designed to prevent Japanese air reinforcements from reaching Guam. "I would estimate that there were 30-40 'Zekes' [A6M Zeros] in the air when we arrived over the target. We were at 15,000 [feet] when I saw several Zekes making runs on some F6Fs below us at 1,000 feet. We pushed over after them and, as we did so, we saw eight to ten coming in below us. I made ahead-on run on one from above. I turned as I passed to see him blow up. Wings and debris went everywhere.

"I pulled up and missed one and a Zero pulled in front of me at 9,000 feet. I fired on him from six o'clock at the same level. He blew up and I went right through his fire.

"After that one, I turned around and there was a Zero on an F6F's tail. I fired a full deflection shot from nine o'clock below, and he blew up. By this time they were blowing up all over the place.

"From there I pulled around until I saw one on the water at about 200 feet altitude. I got it, level at eight o'clock, and it rolled over into the water.

"I climbed back up for altitude to 5,000 feet and saw a Zero above me. It was at 8,000 feet and making an overhead run on an F6F at 6,000. I followed it down to the water. It went into its run and pulled through faster than I did, so I went into a wing-over and shot it down from eight o'clock above, 100 feet above the water."

In this short action, Barnard became an ace. He was to score an eventual total of eight victories in the Pacific campaign.

tanks, behind the pilot's back and head, and protecting the intake under the nose. Thicker alloy skins protected the engine from fire coming from below. The armor plate added about 200 lb (98 kg) to the overall weight.

Between the flight of the first and second Hellcats, Grumman officials conferred with pilots just returned from the Midway operation; as a result, one radical and several minor changes were made to the design. Most significantly, the Wright R-2600 was replaced by the Pratt & Whitney R-2800 Double Wasp, which gave almost 25 percent more power and was the same engine as used in the F4U Corsair. This simplified the logistics trail from the factory to the front line. The conversion to the new engine was very rapid, and the second aircraft, now designated XF6F-3, flew on July 30, 1942. The propeller spinner and landing gear fairings of the "dash one" had gone, and a new cowling gave a slimmer look to the airframe. The first production F4F-3 aircraft flew in October 1942, a feat all the more remarkable when one considers that the production-line buildings were constructed at the same time. Hellcats were on the production line before the buildings themselves were actually completed.

The Hellcat was found to have much better deck landing characteristics than the narrow-tracked Wildcat or the Corsair, with its bouncy landing gear and long, vision-obstructing nose. Apart from some early problems with arrester hooks pulling off, the Hellcat passed its carrier qualification trials quickly and was soon cleared for unrestricted carrier service.

The first unit to receive the F6F was VF-9 of the *Essex* air group in January 1943, and the first squadrons to see action were those participating in the Marcus Island raid of August 31 that year. These included units aboard the carriers *Yorktown*, *Essex*, and *Independence*, but it was a pair of pilots on a detachment aboard the light carrier *Princeton*

Above: *As this Hellcat pilot is called forward after landing, deck crew swarm forward to change a damaged arresting cable.*

Below: *Engines roaring, a line of Hellcats head a group of Avengers and Dauntlesses preparing to take off for a strike on a Japanese base.*

Right: *Hellcats wearing the late-war markings of the USS* Randolph *air group take off on a strike on Japan propelled by hydraulic catapults.*

who scored the first victory for the Hellcat, shooting down a Kawanishi H8K2 "Emily" flying boat. The first major battles between Hellcats and Zeros took place over the Solomon Islands in September; however, despite huge claims on both sides, the results were fairly even, with a likely true figure of three Zeroes destroyed and two Hellcats damaged beyond repair in A6M versus F6F combats.

Hellcats avenged the loss of Wake Island and its small force of F4Fs in 1941 by winning air superiority over the island in October 1943. The island itself was not retaken, being bypassed with its garrison left to wither while the US Navy turned its attention to the "stepping stones" that led to the Japanese home islands. The Hellcat's finest hour was in the so-called "Marianas Turkey Shoot" of June 1944. US Navy Task Force 58 neutralized the remnants of Japanese carrier-based air power in one of the greatest aerial combats in history, paving the way for the occupation of the vital islands of Guam, Saipan, and Tinian.

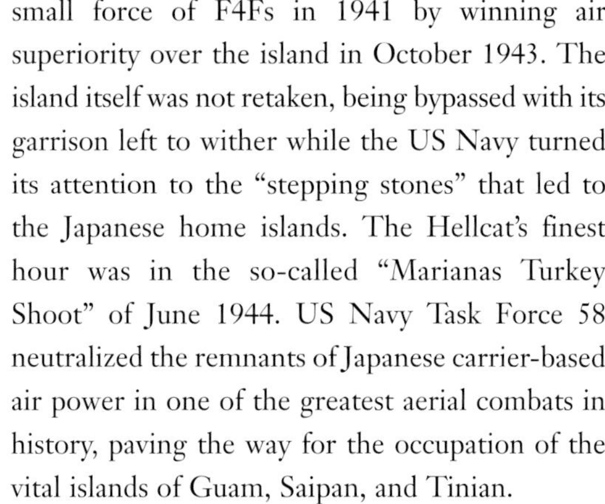

Variants of the Hellcat were relatively few. The F6F-3N was a night-fighter with APS-6 search radar in a wingtip pod, and the F6F-3E had the APS-4. The F6F-5 appeared from 1944 with relatively few changes from the F6F-3. The canopy glazing was altered and provision for bombs and rockets was added. This was the main production version, with 6,681 of the 12,275 Hellcats being F6F-5s. Added to this number were 1,189 F6F-5N night-fighters.

The Royal Navy took 252 F6F-3s as the Hellcat I and 930 F6F-5s as the Hellcat II. Some of these were converted to photoreconnaissance duties as the Hellcat PR I and PR II. The Fleet Air Arm (FAA) Hellcats were particularly active in the Indian Ocean and Far East.

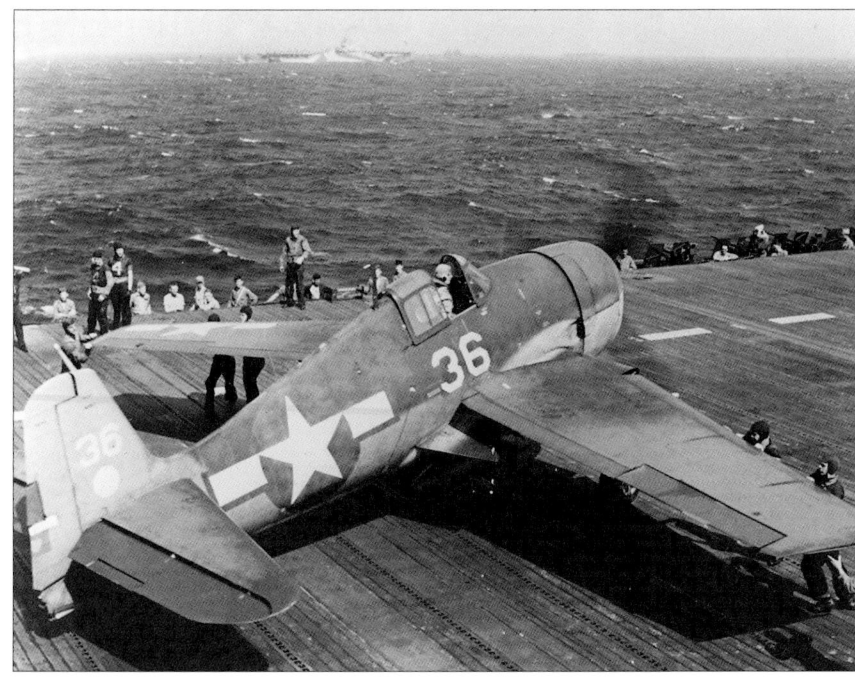

Below: *Following a raid on the Marianas Islands in mid 1944, deck crew help fold the wings of an F6F aboard the USS* Hornet.

Hellcats destroyed more than half the enemy aircraft credited to US Navy and Marine pilots during the war—just under 5,200. A total of 307 F6F pilots became aces by destroying five or more enemy aircraft. This was the greatest total for any US-built fighter. Air combat losses amounted to 270 Hellcats, for a kill–loss ratio of 19 to one.

In 1946, the Hellcat became the first aircraft to be used by the "Blue Angels" flight exhibition team. Four F6F-5s were used, alongside an SNJ trainer, which was painted yellow with Japanese markings and "shot down" during each show. Many surplus Hellcats were converted to remotely piloted drones and used in postwar missile tests, notably those of the early AIM-9 Sidewinder air-to-air missile (AAM) at China Lake, California. The F6F-3K and F6F-5K drones were complemented by the F6F-5D drone director, used as a relay aircraft for the ground control signal. A number of the F6F-3Ks were used as guided bombs in the Korean War.

As well as the United States and the United Kingdom, the Hellcat served with three foreign air arms. The French *Aéronavale* received 124 F6F-5s and 15 F6F-5Ns in 1950. They were deployed aboard the carrier Arromanches, used in action in the ground-attack role in Indochina up to 1954. A detachment of the night-fighters served in Algeria up to 1960. Argentina used 10 Hellcats from 1947, later passing some to Paraguay where they served until 1961.

Eight F6Fs have been rebuilt to fly on today's air-show circuits, some of them former drones that escaped destruction during the 1950s and 1960s.

Above: *A Hellcat, with "paperclip" folding wings, is hoisted from the pier aboard a US Navy carrier.*

Below: *Crewman Walter Chewning risked his life to rescue ace, Byron Johnson, from his burning F6F-3.*

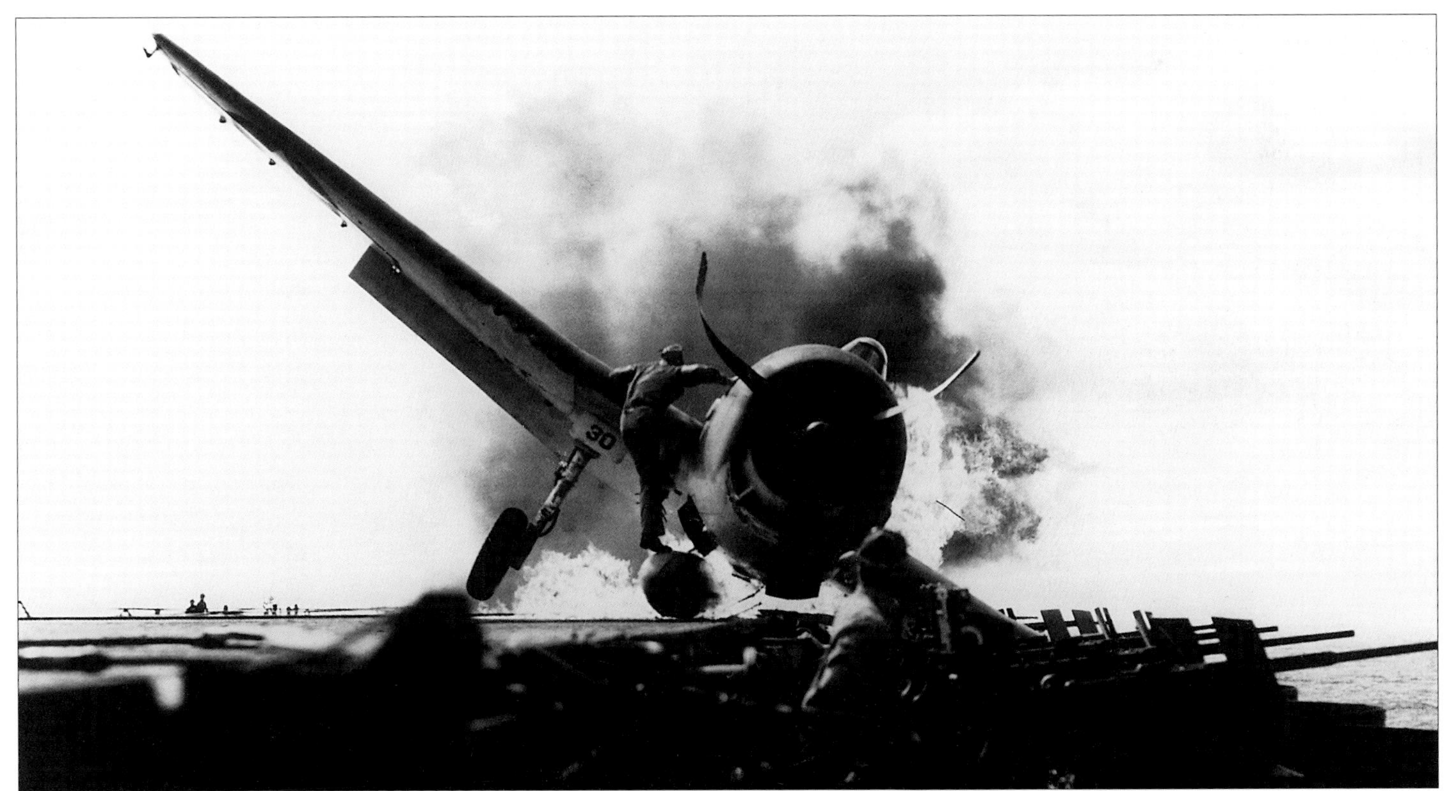

Gloster Meteor

One of the most successful early jets, the Meteor saw action in World War II, Korea, and the Middle East. Thousands were built for the RAF and friendly nations in versions for night-fighting, ground attack, and jet-conversion training.

GLOSTER METEOR F.8

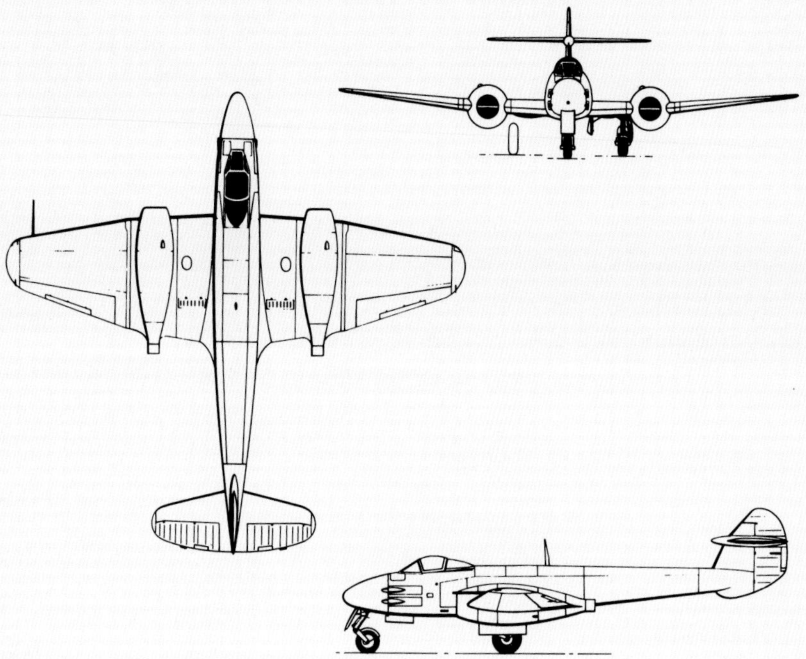

Crew: one

Powerplant: two 3,600-lb thrust (16-kN) Rolls-Royce Derwent 8 turbojets

Maximum speed: 598mph (962km/h)

Service ceiling: 43,000ft (13,100m)

Weight: 15,700lb (7,122kg) loaded

Armament: four 0.79-in (20-mm) Hispano cannon, up to two 1,000-lb (450-kg) bombs and eight HVAR rockets

Dimensions: span 37ft 2in (11.32m); length 44ft 7in (13.59m); height 13ft (3.96m)

Right: *A group of Meteor T.7s of the Central Flying School practice aerobatics. Two-seat Meteors served with the RAF after fighter versions were retired.*

Brilliant engineer Frank Whittle spent many frustrating years in the 1930s developing his gas-turbine engine and trying to encourage official interest in his work. Whittle's friendship with George Carter, the chief designer of Gloster Aircraft, was instrumental in the first jet fighter being a Gloster product. The Air Ministry contracted Gloster to build an airframe for the centrifugal-flow W.2 engine designed by Whittle's Power Jets company. The Meteor was preceded by a tubby single-engined test aircraft, the E.28/39, which was also, if seldom, called the Gloster Pioneer and more often, if less accurately, the Whittle. Flight trials which began in May 1941 proved the soundness of the W.2B engine, but also demonstrated that any operation jet fighter would need two of them. Air Ministry specification F.9/40 was written around Gloster's ideas, which bore fruit in mid-1942 with completion of the first F.9/40 prototype.

The honor of the first flight was to fall to the fifth prototype, powered by de Havilland Halford H.1s of 2,300 lb thrust (10.23 kN). Michael Daunt made the first flight at Cranfield on March 5, 1943. Problems with low thrust developed by the available W.2B engines—it was estimated that a takeoff run of nearly 45,934ft (14,000m) would be necessary!—nearly caused the cancellation of the project. The troubles were resolved and the Meteor F.Mk I became the first jet fighter to enter service

WH172
WH187
WH178

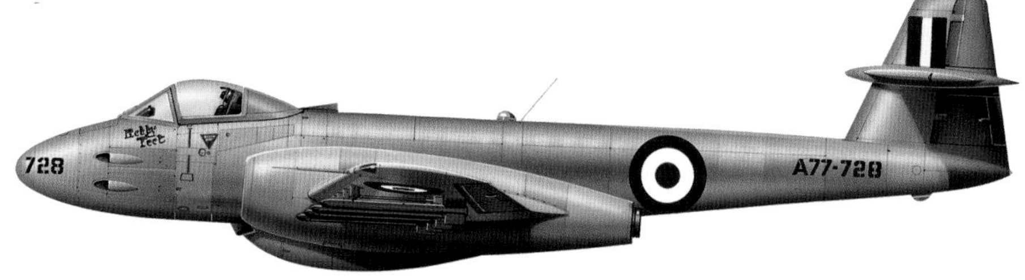

***Right:** A Meteor F.8 of No. 77 Squadron RAAF as used in the Korean War. This aircraft was credited with two MiG-15s destroyed.*

***Right:** The Meteor NF.11 night-fighter was developed and built by Armstrong Whitworth under license. It was sold in the Middle East.*

***Below:** The Meteor F.8 was the main production version, and used Derwent 8 turbojets. Unlike its predecessors, it was built with an ejection seat.*

in July 1944, with No. 616 Squadron at Manston, powered by the W.2B/23C or Welland engine.

No. 616's pilots soon became acquainted with the Meteor, conversion to which was a simple if often abbreviated process. Manston was in the heart of "flying-bomb alley" and, on August 4, 1944, Flying Officers Dean and Roger became the first Allied jet pilots to score kills when they brought down a pair of V-1s over Kent.

In total, the squadron destroyed 13 flying-bombs before Allied invasion forces overran their launch sites. The squadron re-equipped with the F.Mk III version, powered by the 2,000-lb thrust (8.9-kN) Rolls-Royce Derwent engine in December 1944 and was sent to Belgium and Holland on January 20, 1945. Orders prohibiting flying over enemy territory lest a shot-down aircraft give away the secrets of British jet technology prevented any combat being joined. When this policy was rescinded, the Meteors set about amassing a tally of enemy aircraft and other equipment destroyed on the ground and proved able to operate from rough airstrips and to absorb considerable battle damage. At low level, range was very short, and the squadron moved to Luneberg in Germany for the last weeks of the war. Despite a couple of inconclusive dogfights with *Luftwaffe* piston-engined fighters, no aerial kills were scored, let alone against any of the German jets. No losses were incurred to enemy action either.

After the war, development continued. Among the Meteor's many firsts was the adaptation of a Mk.1 to Rolls-Royce Trent turboprop power, becoming the first aircraft powered only by turboprops to fly. Early ejection-seat tests and aircraft-carrier landing trials were undertaken. In November 1945, a specially modified F.Mk IV with Derwent 5 engines successfully broke the world airspeed record when Group Captain H.J. Wilson flew at 606mph (975km/h) over the course

PILOTING THE GLOSTER METEOR

On December 1, 1951, a group of 12 Meteors flew north from Kimpo into MiG country. The official report tells the story. "ANZAC Able, Baker, and Charlie flights were flying at a heading of 070 degrees at 19,000 feet. About 40 MiGs were overhead. Two attacked Charlie 3 and 4 from six o'clock while two more came in from the rear at Baker flight. Able 1 held his break, then broke after a pair of MiGs and fired with no obvious result.

Above: *A pair of No. 77 Squadron's Meteor F.8s sit in a protected revetment at Kimpo airfield near Seoul.*

"Able 3 [Flying Officer Bruce Gogerly] ... observed one Meteor from Charlie flight in a hard starboard turn, streaming fuel. Able 3 slackened the break, still in a starboard turn, and the two MiGs which had attacked Charlie flight loomed up ahead.

"Able 3 left Able 1 and followed the MiGs in a port turn at 800 yards range, firing a two-second burst with no obvious result. The MiGs steepened the turn, but Able 3 pulled inside, closed to 500 yards and fired for five seconds, observing strikes on the rear fuselage and starboard wing root. The MiG pulled up to the left streaming fuel.'

The air battle turned into a wild melee, with the larger force of MiGs making numerous attacks on the Meteors, and the Meteors scoring hits on MiGs in return. When the Australians returned to Kimpo, they were three aircraft short. One pilot had been killed and two taken prisoner. In return, 77 Squadron was credited with two kills, one attributed to Bruce Gogerly and the other shared among the squadron as a whole.

of a series of runs off the Kent coast.

The "Meatbox" was a conventional and rather conservative design, more or less a piston-engined aircraft that happened to have jet power. It had a tricycle undercarriage, the designers not making the mistake of the Me 262 by starting with a tailwheel configuration. The next version, the F.4, had long-chord nacelles and a strengthened airframe, and this model was widely exported—to Argentina, the Netherlands, Belgium, Egypt, and Denmark.

Until 1949, all Meteor pilots had learned their trade without the benefit of a dual-seat version. The T.7 trainer had a heavily framed tandem cockpit, and 640 were built for the Royal Air Force (RAF) and many for export. The T.7 allowed more efficient conversion training, but its lengthened airframe masked some unsavory flying characteristics. Chief among these was a type of control loss called the "phantom dive." The asymmetric flight characteristics were poor, and more pilots were killed practicing simulated engine failures with one engine throttled back than in accidents due to actual malfunctions.

Above: *This Meteor F.3 of No. 616 Squadron was one of the first to be deployed to continental Europe in the last months of the war.*

Right: Refueling from a converted Lancaster, this Meteor set a jet endurance record of 12 hours in August 1949 over the south coast of England.

The principal fighter version was the F.8 with 3,600-lb-thrust (16-kN) Derwent 8 engines, a longer fuselage, ejection seats, and a new, taller tail. It was also widely exported. In the Korean War, the Meteor F.8 was the only non-US or Soviet jet used in the conflict, by No. 77 Squadron of the Royal Australian Air Force (RAAF). The RAAF's F.8s were outperformed by the MiG-15, but still scored a number of kills against the more maneuverable MiGs. The refrain of 77 Squadron's pilots was: "All we want for Christmas is our wings swept back."

After the end of 1951, the Australian Meteors were mainly used for ground attack with rockets and bombs, although later in 1952 they encountered more MiGs, which began to make sorties further south to counter the UN close air-support aircraft. By the war's end, about a dozen MiGs had been claimed by Meteors, which themselves suffered 32 losses to ground fire and MiGs.

Back in the United Kingdom, one F.8 was converted to the extraordinary prone-pilot Meteor with an extra cockpit mounted in a long nose extension. The idea was that a pilot lying down would have increased *g* tolerance and thus better combat effectiveness, which proved to be

Right: Some of the first Meteors based in Belgium in late 1944 were painted in overall white to distinguish them as Allied.

true: however, other factors such as fatigue and the difficulty of escape were to kill the concept.

The FR.9 was a photoreconnaissance model with a camera nose, but also retaining cannon armament. Only one camera was carried, but it could be mounted to shoot out of any of three windows. The PR.10 had the tail and outer wings of the F.3 and extra camera mounts in the rear fuselage.

Armstrong Whitworth had built numbers of single-seat Meteors under subcontract and was contracted to design and build a new radar-equipped night-fighter version in 1948. The first Meteor NF.11 flew in October 1949 and featured a Mk 7 fuselage with a Mk 8 tail and a lengthened nose with a bulbous radome containing AI Mk 10 radar, a version of the US SCR-720 set. The cannon were moved to the outer wings. One hundred NF.12s and 40 NF.13s with AI Mk 21 radar and a taller fin followed the 338 NF.11s. The NF.13 was a tropicalized version for the Far East. The definitive night-fighter was the NF.14, with a new canopy and Derwent 9 engines. The gun bays in the outer wings reduced the torsional stiffness, causing aileron reversal at high speed and thus limiting the maximum speed to below 550mph (885km/h). This was not a great problem for the night-fighter variants, but was to frustrate the development of a ground-attack variant sometimes called the Reaper.

The Meteor was one of the great British export successes, being sold or supplied to Argentina, Australia, Belgium, Denmark, Ecuador, Egypt, France, Israel, the Netherlands, and Syria. In order to be even-handed, Britain supplied equal numbers of night-fighters to Egypt, Syria, and Israel. Israel also purchased T.7s, F.8s (including some from Belgium) and FR.9s. The Israeli Meteors scored the first jet kills in the Middle East by downing two Egyptian Vampires in September 1955. An NF.13 later shot down an Il-14 transport believed to be carrying the Egyptian defense minister. In 1956, the Israeli Meteors were largely used for ground attack and reconnaissance. Although Israel retired the Meteor from the front line in 1962, it was retained as a trainer until the last examples were retired in 1970.

Apart from some trials of weapons such as Fireflash and Blue Boar, the Meteor was never equipped with air-to-air missiles and relied on its cannons for aerial combat, with rockets and bombs for ground attack. With its thick, straight wings, it was no match for swept-wing fighters.

The Meteor was Gloster's first fighter since the Gladiator, and with 3,875 built it was the most numerous British jet aircraft ever produced. A handful of Meteors still fly on in private hands. Two still fly with Martin Baker on ejection-seat test work.

Above: *When its active life was over, this Meteor F.4 was used as an instructional airframe to train apprentices.*

Left: *The Meteor, Israel's first jet, destroyed a few Egyptian Vampires in the 1950s but it was mainly used for ground attack.*

De Havilland Vampire and Venom

De Havilland's twin-boomed Vampire and Venom were stalwarts of the early postwar RAF and many other air arms. The simple original design evolved into a series of effective radar-equipped two-seat all-weather and night-fighters.

DE HAVILLAND VAMPIRE FB.5

Crew: one

Powerplant: one 4,400-lb thrust (19.57-kN) Goblin 2/2 turbojet

Maximum speed: 530mph (853km/h)

Range: 1,145 miles (1,842km)

Service ceiling: 41,000ft (12,500m)

Weight: 12,360lb (5,606kg) loaded

Armament: four 0.79-in (20-mm) Hispano cannon, eight 60-lb (27-kg) rockets, and two 500-lb (227-kg) bombs or two 1,000-lb (454-kg) bombs

Dimensions: span 38ft (11.58m); length 30ft 9in (9.37m); height 6ft 3in (1.91m)

***Right:** The Sea Venom was the ultimate development of the Vampire and Venom family, having two seats, radar, and folding wings for carrier stowage.*

The de Havilland Vampire was the second British jet fighter to fly, six months after the Meteor. It saw no service in World War II, but was used in many postwar actions, as was its evolutionary successor, the Venom. It was the 100th aircraft designed by or under the supervision of Geoffrey de Havilland and also the company's first jet.

R.E. Bishop, who also designed the DH.98 Mosquito, was the chief designer on the DH.100 project. Priority for axial flow engines was given to the Meteor, and Bishop turned to the centrifugal flow Halford H1 engine (which entered production as the de Havilland Goblin) of 2,700lb thrust (12kN) mounted in a central nacelle with wingroot intakes. The exhaust exited from a jet pipe protruding from the trailing edge between long tailbooms, which were joined by a straight tailplane. On September 20, 1943, the prototype flew from Hatfield on its maiden flight with Geoffrey de Havilland Jr. at the controls. At this time it was known as the "Spider Crab." Thankfully, however, the Air Ministry chose Vampire as the official name.

Development was delayed because the engine intended for the second prototype was actually supplied to the United States and was used to power the first Lockheed P-80 Shooting Star, America's second jet aircraft type. The Vampire F.1 entered service with No. 247 Squadron in June 1946. The improved F.3 soon followed, being a

ROYAL NAVY
WM569
WM5 69

longer-range version able to carry drop tanks. In July 1949, six F.3s of No. 54 Squadron became the first jet aircraft to cross the Atlantic.

The Vampire shared many components and construction techniques with the propeller-driven Mosquito. The fuselage pod was the same type of wood sandwich construction with armor-plate bulkheads, but the wing, tail, and booms were made of light alloy. The Vampire's nose wheel was the same as a "Mossie" tail wheel (it was recycled

PILOTING THE DE HAVILLAND VAMPIRE

Above: *Vampire night-fighters served with the RAF, Italy, and the Indian Air Force's No. 10 Squadron, as related here.*

As "Chandu" Gole, adjutant of No. 10 from mid-1955, recalled, flying jet night-fighters gave a unique perspective on India, but also had its dangers. "The exclusive night flying was quite an education and experience. To be flying alone, high up when the world below was asleep, where the moon and stars looked so exquisite and clear that you could even see the shadow of your hand on your knees on dark nights—sheer exhilaration! To keep track of your position purely by mental DR [dead reckoning] and with some help from the ground air defence radar (very primitive in those days), one had to learn to recognise towns and villages by street-light patterns—which invariably were switched off by midnight. Takeoffs and landings were along a single line of goose-neck flares to simulate operational conditions. One learned to discern and identify roads, railway lines, rivers, and canals even in no-moon conditions; it is amazing how much starlight can help. In fact we got so used to the dark night conditions that we preferred these to moonlight which, picturesque as it was, affected one's depth perception.

"The training of new navigator-radio operators [nav-rads] was always an exciting, if risky, business. In one such case, having ordered a closing speed of 30 kt in the final stage, my young nav-rad got tongue-tied as he saw the fast-approaching target on his scope and forgot to warn me. I had, perhaps, allowed things to go too far in trying to teach him a lesson. I pulled up just in time to avoid ramming the target. I felt my aircraft heave as I grazed past the target. The young navigator was so shaken up that he decided to quit night-fighters then and there. It took great persuasion to get him to change his mind. Finally he did make the grade and went on to retire as a very senior officer.

"If it became necessary to abandon the aircraft in an emergency, the pilot had to invert it (climbing out in the airstream was considered impossible), release the canopy top, push it, warn the nav-rad to disconnect his oxygen and radio plugs, tap on his knee as a signal to release his straps and 'bunt' the aircraft to help him drop out of the cockpit, wait for three seconds, then repeat the procedure for himself. [In IAF service] there was only one instance (fire in the aircraft) when the crew had to abandon aircraft. Neither of them survived, as expected."

again for the Devon/Dove transport). Fixed armament was a battery of four 0.79-in (20-mm) cannon under the nose, essentially the same installation as the Mosquito. The pilot sat on a conventional bucket seat.

The Vampire became the first jet aircraft to land aboard an aircraft carrier, when Captain Eric "Winkle" Brown brought the third prototype aboard HMS *Ocean* on December 3, 1945. The same day it made the first jet carrier takeoff. The Vampire was not adopted for shipboard use, mainly because of the slow acceleration of its engine. The Royal Air Force's (RAF's) Sea Vampires were mainly used for jet familiarization training. Nevertheless, the Vampire was used in a series of tests of a flexible-rubber carrier deck in 1947, the idea being that, by eliminating the undercarriage, weight and complexity would be reduced. Although, as with similar trials in the United States with F9F Panthers it was broadly successful, the impracticalities of the scheme outweighed any advantages.

Single-seat Vampires were exported to 16 nations, including Australia, Canada, Egypt, France, India, Iraq, Italy, Lebanon, New Zealand, Norway, South Africa, Southern Rhodesia, Sweden, Switzerland, and Venezuela. De Havilland in Australia built 80 Nene-powered Mks 30-32, the latter with ejection seats. Switzerland's F&W built 103 FB 6s, while 247 FB.52s were built by Hindustan Aeronautics in India and 80 FB.5s by Fiat and Macchi in Italy.

Left: *Swiss Venoms were used largely as target tugs in their latter years. This brightly-marked example was in service in 1987.*

France bought 157 FB.5s and the Sud-Est company built a further 251 under license as the SE.530 Mistral. The Mistral was powered by the 5,005-lb thrust (22-kN) Rolls-Royce Nene and also had an ejection seat of French design. Both versions saw action against Algerian rebels.

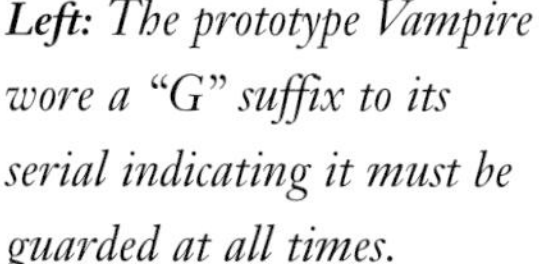

Left: *The prototype Vampire wore a "G" suffix to its serial indicating it must be guarded at all times.*

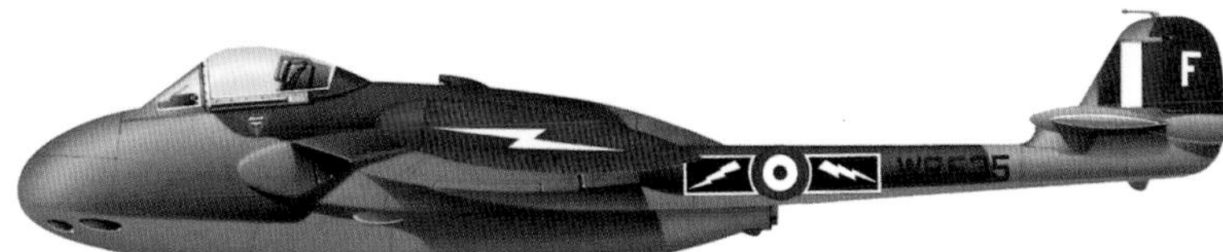

Above: *A Venom FB.4 of No. 60 Squadron was used for ground-attack missions during the Malayan Emergency.*

Indian single-seat Vampires flew ground-attack sorties at the beginning of the 1965 war, but were effectively withdrawn after the loss of several aircraft to Pakistani ground fire and Sabres. Egyptian Vampire FB.52s flew ground-attack sorties over the Sinai in 1956, losing several to Israeli Mystères.

Left: *RAF Vampires such as these FB.9s were used by squadrons based in the Middle East until replaced by Venoms and Hunters.*

***Right:** A damaged Sea Venom FAW.21 is cleared from the deck of HMS* Eagle *to make way for landing aircraft.*

A series of Vampire night-fighters began with the privately funded DH.113, which first flew in August 1949. This was the cockpit and AI.10 radar of the Mosquito NF.36 grafted onto a Vampire nacelle. Egypt quickly ordered 12, but these were embargoed. The RAF then ordered 78 as the Vampire NF.10 while it awaited delivery of the Meteor NF.11. A number were supplied to Italy, and India received 18 in 1954 as the Vampire NF.54. These equipped No. 10 Squadron for nearly a decade.

The two-seat night-fighter led to the DH.115 trainer, ordered by the RAF as the T.11. Despite its larger nose, the internal cockpit width was only six inches (15cm) greater than that of the single-seat versions, making it a tight squeeze for the pilot and instructor. More than 500 were supplied to the RAF. Most of the export customers bought two-seaters and so did Austria, Burma, Chile, Indonesia, Ireland, Japan, and Jordan. Two-seaters varied in having heavily framed Mosquito-type canopies or clear canopies and ejection seats. Some were fitted with underwing hardpoints for use as weapons trainers. Total Vampire production reached 3,268.

Originally known as the Vampire FB.8, the DH 112 Venom was ordered as an interim ground-attack fighter pending the entry into service of the Supermarine Swift and ground-attack versions of the Hunter. In the end, the Swift never quite succeeded and the ground attack version of the Hunter was some years away.

The Venom had the same basic layout as the Vampire, but had some important changes. The engine was a de Havilland Ghost 103 rated at 4,850-lb thrust (22kN). The new thinner wing had leading edges tapered at just over 17 degrees and usually featured removable but non-

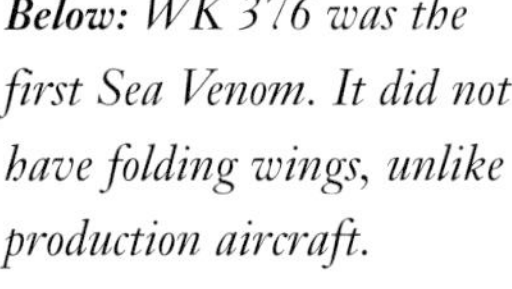

***Below:** WK 376 was the first Sea Venom. It did not have folding wings, unlike production aircraft.*

jettisoning wingtip tanks. The tailplane span was greater, with extensions outboard of the booms. Later aircraft had ejection seats.

The Venom FB.1 entered RAF service in 1952. The main Venom variant was the FB.4, which had reshaped fins, the 5,150-lb thrust (23-kN) Ghost 105 engine and powered ailerons. Many of the RAF's FB.4s equipped RAF squadrons in Germany and the Middle East.

The Venom had less export success than the Vampire. Switzerland's EFW group built 250 FB.1s and FB.4s, but only small numbers went to Venezuela, Iraq, and Italy. The Royal New Zealand Air Force (RNZAF) leased FB.1s that were never used in New Zealand, but flew attack missions alongside RAF Venoms using rockets and bombs against communist insurgents during the Malayan Emergency.

A two-seat Venom night-fighter evolved along the same lines as the NF Vampires. De Havilland flew a private-venture prototype with a new longer and widened nose in August 1950 with the 4,850-lb thrust (21-kN) Ghost 104 engine. The RAF took 90 as the Venom NF.2 and later modified many with revised tails and clear-view canopies as the NF.2A. More were built as the NF.3 with AI.23 radar, Ghost 105, and further tail changes. Sweden bought more than 60 as the J33 and fitted them with license-built RM 2A Ghosts.

Although the Vampire had never served as an operational carrier-based fighter, the Royal Navy developed the two-seat Venom into its first all-weather jet as the Sea Venom FAW.20 (fighter all weather). It had folding wings and revised tip tanks, and could carry bombs and rockets for ground attack. Poor performance and a lack of ejection seats were dealt with by the FAW.21 with the Ghost 104 and the FAW.22 with the Ghost 105. The latter model could be armed with two Firestreak air-to-air missiles. Royal Navy Sea Venoms attacked airfields and sank patrol boats during the Suez operation of November 1956.

France adopted the Sea Venom for its own first carrier-borne jet as the Sud-Est SE.20 and SE.202 Aquilon. Some single-seat SE.203s had US APQ-65 radar. The Aquilons made ground-attack sorties in Algeria and Tunisia in 1956–67. Australia's FAW.53s operated from the carrier HMAS *Melbourne* and later as target tugs, finally being retired in 1969.

Left: *The Vampire had a significant ground-attack capability with bombs and 6-in (152-mm) training rockets, as being fired here by this two-seat model.*

Production of Venoms amounted to 816 single-seat Venoms, 283 night-fighters, and 393 Sea Venoms. The final Venoms were retired by Switzerland in August 1983, but some Swiss Vampires lasted until 1990. Most of the Venoms and Vampires flying today in several countries are ex-Swiss.

Below: *Swiss Vampires are seen at Sitten Airfield in the mid-1960s. Switzerland built over 100 Vampires and kept some in service into the late 1980s.*

North American F-86 Sabre

Although well matched in performance to its main rival the MiG-15, the Sabre ensured US air superiority over Korea. It became widely exported with new engines, new weapons, and new technology constantly appearing.

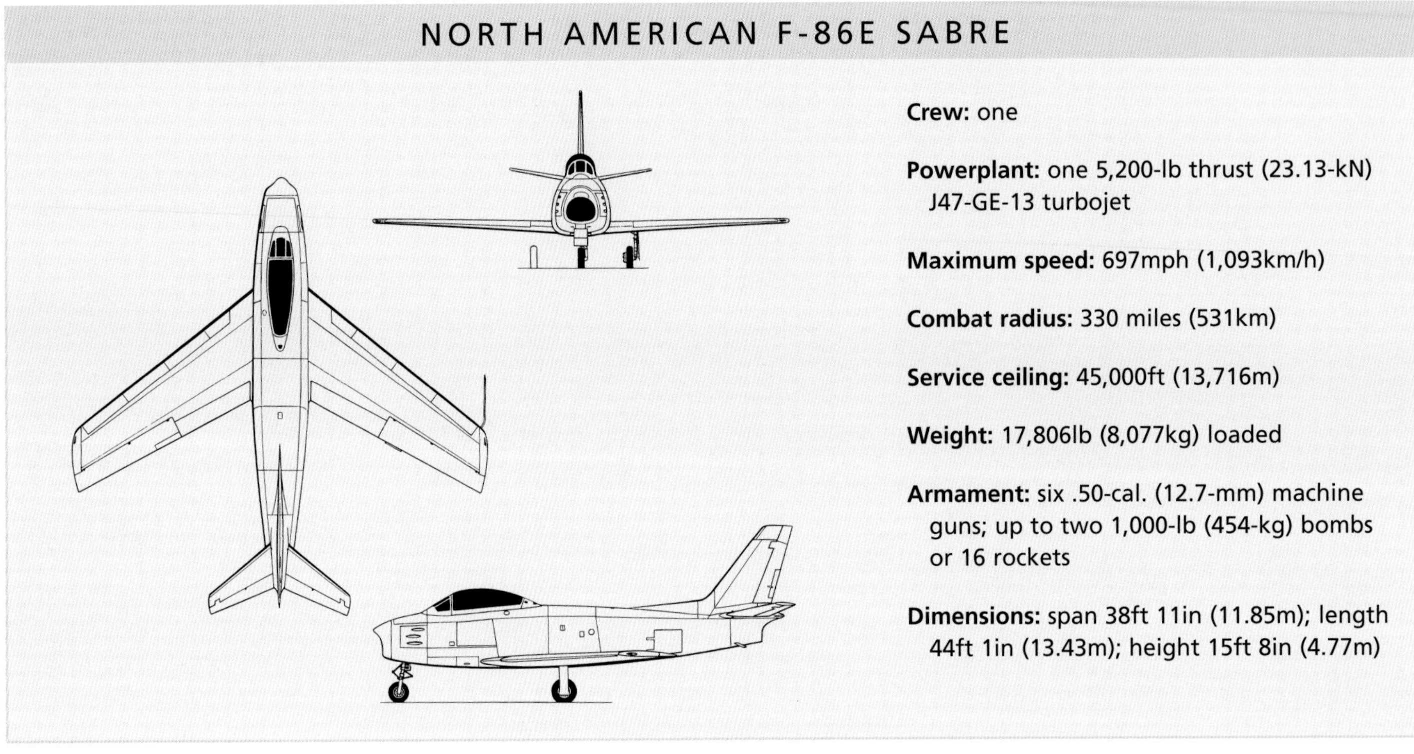

NORTH AMERICAN F-86E SABRE

Crew: one

Powerplant: one 5,200-lb thrust (23.13-kN) J47-GE-13 turbojet

Maximum speed: 697mph (1,093km/h)

Combat radius: 330 miles (531km)

Service ceiling: 45,000ft (13,716m)

Weight: 17,806lb (8,077kg) loaded

Armament: six .50-cal. (12.7-mm) machine guns; up to two 1,000-lb (454-kg) bombs or 16 rockets

Dimensions: span 38ft 11in (11.85m); length 44ft 1in (13.43m); height 15ft 8in (4.77m)

Benefiting greatly from wartime German research, the Sabre was the first swept-wing US fighter to enter service. In the Korean War, it participated in the last major dogfights before the missile era, and later saw service with dozens of nations, becoming one of the true classic jet fighters.

Work began on what was to become the F-86 Sabre in late 1944. North American Aviation's (NAA's) factories in California and Texas were at that time at the peak of production of P-51 Mustangs, B-25 Mitchells, and T-6 trainers, but the company could see that the future lay in jets and began work on a proposal designated RD 1265 that November. This led to the NA-134, which became the XFJ-1 Fury, for the US Navy, and the NA-140, three of which were ordered by the US Army Air Forces (USAAF) in May 1945 as the XP-86.

As originally designed, the XP-86 was to have had a straight wing lifted pretty much directly from the P-51, although with wingtip tanks and no guns. An intake in the nose led straight through to a J35 axial-flow turbojet. The J35 was a version of the de Havilland Goblin built under licence by General Electric and offered 4,000lb (17.79kN) of static thrust. A bubble canopy sat on top, and generally the appearance was not unlike the later Republic F-84 Thunderjet.

The straight-wing XP-86 reached the mock-up stage before NAA paused to digest the findings of teams of technical experts studying the masses of data captured from German industry at the end of the European war. Most promising was the work done by Messerschmitt into swept wings to delay compressibility and allow a higher Mach number.

Right: *F-86As of the 4th Fighter Interceptor Wing lined up on a Korean runway in July 1951. The leading-edge slats on this model can be clearly seen.*

FU-236
8261
FU-261
U.S. AIR FORCE
91251
FU-251
U.S. AIR FORCE
91276
FU-276

Right: *This RAF No. 92 Squadron Sabre was one of 428 Canadair-built aircraft supplied to the RAF. Others were assigned to RAF Germany.*

As faster aircraft had been developed during the war, more and more pilots discovered that drag built up at high speeds, and the shock wave of compressed air was putting great stresses on the airframe. Numerous aircraft were destroyed or badly damaged when diving from high altitudes and nearing the speed of sound, or Mach 1. Sweeping back the wing could be shown in theory to raise the point where serious buffeting due to compressibility (the critical Mach number) occurred, delaying the onset of shock waves.

One problem was stability at low speeds, particularly when landing, when a swept wing is close to stalling. Totally revising the XP-86 to have swept wings, NAA adapted Messerschmitt's solution of leading-edge slats that deployed at low speed. The improved design used more sweep than the Me 262—35 degrees on both the wing and tailplane. The tailplane had powered movement to trim the aircraft for high or low speed flight. All but the first aircraft built had airbrakes in the lower aft fuselage.

On October 1, 1947, George "Wheaties" Welch flew the XP-86 at Muroc Dry Lake, California. Even though the prototype was only powered by the interim J35 (production aircraft were to have the 5,000-lb thrust/22.24-kN J47), it seems that Welch exceeded Mach 1.0 during a shallow dive on an early test flight. The official story is that Charles E. "Chuck" Yeager was the first man to break the "sound barrier," in the Bell XS-1 on October 14, but Welch's earlier flight was not measured accurately at the time. In the spring of 1948, the XP-86, by this time named Sabre and soon to be redesignated F-86 in the F for Fighter series, made its first officially acknowledged supersonic flights.

The new swept-wing jet entered US Air Force (USAF) service in March 1949 as the F-86A. An improved version with wing pylons and a new windscreen was briefly called the F-86B, before reverting to F-86A-5. Armament on production aircraft was the same as the basic fit of the P-51 Mustang: six .50-cal. (12.7-mm) machine guns, installed in the nose. A radar-assisted gun sight greatly simplified the calculation of range at high speeds.

When war broke out in Korea in July 1950, the United States initially got by with older aircraft types; however, when Soviet-designed MiG-15s appeared over the battlefield in November 1950, Sabres were sent to the war zone with all haste.

Generally speaking, the Sabre and MiG were evenly matched, although the MiG had a better climb rate, superior high-altitude performance,

Below: *South Africa also operated Sabres in Korea. F-86F fighter bomber "B" of No. 2 Squadron SAAF was seen in the last months of the war.*

Right: *The F-86D "Dog Sabre" had a new nose with an air-intercept radar, which required a new intake design. The "Mighty Mouse" rocket tray can just be seen.*

PILOTING THE F-86 SABRE

The first Sabre victory was scored against a MiG-15 on December 17, 1950. Bad weather had finally cleared and the 4th Fighter Interceptor Wing (FIW) was able to make its first offensive patrol over the Yalu River, into what would be come to be known as "MiG Alley." Lieutenant Colonel Bruce Hinton led four F-86As of "Baker" Flight on a fighter sweep, acting as bait to get the MiGs, based in forbidden territory across the Chinese border, to come up and fight.

Above: A Sabre of the 4th FIW touches down after a mission. The black and white bands identified this wing in the early part of the Korean War.

The ploy was soon effective, and four MiGs appeared, probably flown by Russian pilots who mistook the Sabres for slower F-80 Shooting Stars. The MiGs crossed Baker Flight's path about a mile ahead and Hinton ordered drop tanks to be jettisoned, only to find that his radio was malfunctioning. Confusion followed as Hinton dropped his tanks and accelerated ahead of his flight. He quickly turned behind an element of two MiGs, the pilots of which apparently thought they could simply outrun the fighter behind them. Hinton dived after the MiG flight leader and was able to get on his six o'clock position. He fired a short burst and saw what looked like debris falling away from the MiG—the jet was also streaming fluid, possibly fuel.

Hinton then took on the number two MiG and found himself bucking in its jet wash. He adjusted his position and fired a long burst, which hit the MiG's engine. Hinton stayed in a left turn behind his opponent and had a spectacular view of the Russian fighter. He closed in and fired again, keeping the trigger depressed. Flames consumed the rear section of the MiG, and the jet rolled on its back and went plummeting to earth. It crashed 10 miles (16km) south of the Yalu and there was no parachute.

Left: One of the many aerobatic teams to use the Sabre was the "Blue Impulse" of the Japan Air Self-Defense Force. They used the F-86F from 1960-81.

and heavier armament. The Sabre was a more stable gun platform and better at low altitudes. More importantly, the American pilots were better trained than their Chinese or Korean counterparts, although were more closely matched with the Soviet pilots sometimes encountered flying North Korean MiGs.

The improved F-86E arrived from July 1951, followed by the F-86F a year later. Many of the latter had a revised "hard" wing without slats, which conferred better combat maneuverability. The F was also an extremely effective fighter-bomber. By the war's end in July 1953, Sabres had been credited with 792 victories versus 78 losses in

Right: *Australia's Sabres were built locally with a deeper fuselage containing an Avon engine, and were armed with two 1.18-in (30-mm) cannon.*

Above: *Sabres were rarely seen with underwing rockets. The F-86A only had two pylons and needed them for drop tanks, or occasionally bombs.*

aerial combat. The top-scoring pilot, Joseph McConnell, was credited with 16 victories, and there were 38 other Sabre aces.

Operational trials with a pair of 0.79-in (20-mm) cannon were not completely successful at the time, although cannon appeared on later models. Various tests of camera-equipped Sabres in Korea led to important postwar RF-86 reconnaissance models.

An all-weather or night-fighter version of the Sabre followed fairly closely behind the day-fighters, flying as the F-86D in December 1949. The "Dog Sabre," or "Sabre Dog," had a bulbous radome above the intake containing the radar components of the Hughes E-3 fire control system. The F-86D was powered by a J47-GE-17 with afterburner, giving a maximum 7,500 lb of thrust (33.4 kN). With a top speed of just under 700mph (1,135km/h), it was the fastest USAF interceptor of its day, and it was issued to the majority of Air Defense Command (ADC) squadrons. This was the first single-seat all-weather interceptor in US service, its contemporaries—the F-89 Scorpion and the F-94C Starfire—having a radar operator as well as the pilot.

On the F-86D, gun armament was replaced by a battery of 24 "Mighty Mouse" rockets in a retractable tray under the nose. The fire control system directed the pilot to a point where the target, namely a Soviet bomber, would pass into the lethal zone of the rockets. The F-86D had an all-flying tail, rather than having separate elevators as on earlier models.

The F-86K was the export version of the D with two 0.79-in (20-mm) cannon instead of rockets and was used by several Nato air forces. The F-86L was a similar version for Air National Guard (ANG) squadrons. The "lightweight" F-86H (sometimes called the "Hog Sabre") with a deeper fuselage was optimized for the nuclear strike role and carried the Mk 12 weapon. The fixed armament was a pair of T-160 0.79-in (20-mm) cannon and the engine was an afterburning J73-GE-3 giving 9,200 lb of thrust (40.94 kN). The F-86H was mainly issued to ANG squadrons and was not exported.

Left: This F-86E shows the all-round visibility due to the bubble canopy, a feature that largely disappeared on the next generation of American fighters.

The US Navy's FJ-2 Fury was essentially a navalized F-86E with four 0.70-in (20-mm) cannon, but the series diverged from then on, the FJ-3 and FJ-4 having J65 engines and few components in common with the Sabre.

Both Canada and Australia built their own versions. Many of the 1,800 Canadair-built aircraft were Sabre Mk 5s and Mk 6s with the 6,000-lb thrust (26.68-kN) Avro Orenda engine, and large numbers were supplied to Nato countries. Australia's Commonwealth Aircraft Corporation (CAC) built 112 CA-27 Sabres with the Rolls-Royce Avon 26 of 7,500 lb of thrust (33.38 kN) and two 1.18-in (30-mm) Aden cannons. Some of these were passed to Malaysia and Indonesia.

In all, at least 41 countries operated the Sabre, mainly the F-86F. They served on every continent except Antarctica, and took part in many of the wars of the 1960s and 1970s, seeing combat using early Sidewinder missiles in fighting between Taiwan and China, and India and Pakistan.

Argentine and Honduran Sabres lasted into the 1980s, while the last Bolivian F-86Fs were retired in the early 1990s. Many Sabres are preserved in museums, and about half a dozen, mostly Canadair-built examples, fly regularly.

Left: Mitsubishi built 300 of Japan's Sabres under license. All were F-86Fs, with some converted to reconnaissance configuration.

Mikoyan-Gurevich MiG-15 and MiG-17

The simple and sturdy MiG-15 shocked the US Air Force when it appeared in Korean skies in 1950. Evenly matched with the F-86 Sabre, the MiG-15 was developed into the MiG-17, which was later to trouble US pilots over Vietnam.

***Right:** The Shenyang FT-7 was the Chinese-built two-seat version of the MiG-17. Pakistan was one of the biggest users, retiring its last examples in 2002.*

Based, like the F-86 Sabre, on the results of German swept-wing research and British engine technology, the Mikoyan-Gurevich MiG-15 was the Soviet Union's first really successful jet fighter and led the way to the famous family of MiG interceptors. For 40 years, every Russian fighter was a "MiG," at least to western pilots.

A requirement for a high-altitude interceptor was issued to the Soviet fighter design bureaus in 1946. One of these was that founded by Artem I. Mikoyan and Mikhail Y. Gurevich, which had produced a number of piston-engined fighters during World War II. While built in large numbers, they were not among the Soviet Union's best. With a swept wing, a T-tail, and straight-through intake, MiG's initial design was similar in layout to the Focke-Wulf Ta 183, the prototype of which had not flown by the end of the war. This design was stalled due to lack of a suitable engine until Britain supplied the Soviet Union with 25 Rolls-Royce Nene centrifugal flow turbojets in May 1946, which the Klimov bureau immediately copied as the RD-45. The first prototype, designated the S-01 ("S" standing for *Strelowidnostji*, or "swept") flew with a Nene installed on December 30, 1947, piloted by Viktor Yuganov.

Although it met the stipulated speed and altitude requirements, and also the ability to

SS-1201
201
2215

***Above:** A MiG-15 seen in North Korean markings. In many ways it was a superior aircraft to the F-86.*

operate from unsurfaced airfields, the prototype demonstrated a number of unsatisfactory flight characteristics, including a tendency to fall into a spin during tight turns. Firing the nose-mounted guns also caused gas ingestion into the engine and compressor stalls, a problem cured by simple modifications. In all only a few, mainly cosmetic, changes were made before the fighter was ordered into service as the MiG-15 in late 1948. The first production aircraft flew one year to the day after the prototype, and deliveries of aircraft to the VVS (Soviet Air Force) began in 1949 and, when duly noted by western observers overflying that year's May Day parade, were given the NATO reporting name "Fagot-A."

The MiG-15 armament was three cannon in the nose, one 1.45-in (37-mm) N-37 and two 0.90-in (23-mm) NS-23, aimed with the help of a gyro gun sight. The pressurized pilot's cockpit had an ejection seat and a bubble canopy. The wing had 35 degrees of sweepback, the same as on the F-86 Sabre; however, this and the other similarities in

PILOTING THE MIG-17

***Above:** During the Vietnam War, the North fielded some radar-equipped MiG-17PFs. The radar scope is seen on the right of the cockpit.*

The MiG-17 saw air combat with most of Israel's Arab neighbors in the 1960s and, notably, in Vietnam, where this simple but reliable and maneuverable fighter often bested US warplanes when it came to a dogfight at close quarters. One such encounter took place November 19, 1967. Four Vietnamese People's Air Force (VPAF) MiG-17Fs took off from the forward airfield at Kien An to attack a 20-strong "Alpha Strike" force of US Navy A-4 Skyhawks and F-4 Phantom IIs from the USS *Coral Sea* that was headed for Haiphong. Two F-4Bs of VF-151 "Screaming Eagles" picked up a flight of MiGs that had taken off from the main base at Gia Lam. They failed, however, to spot two others, probably those flown by Nguyen Dinh Phuc and Nguyen Phi Hung of the 923rd Fighter Regiment, as they turned southwest to protect the striking Skyhawks. Suddenly, the pilot of the leading Phantom, Lieutenant Commander Claude Clower, reported MiGs off his right wing. He engaged afterburners and turned hard, but the Phantom was struck by cannon fire and exploded. Clower managed to eject and was taken prisoner, but his back-seater, Lieutenant (junior grade) Walter Estes was killed. Moments later, the second F-4B went down, either hit by a MiG's cannon or having been struck by debris from the first aircraft. In this case, the pilot, Lieutenant (jg) James Teague was killed, and his RIO Lieutenant (jg) Theodore Stier was made a prisoner of war. Events that day are not totally clear—the Vietnamese claimed four Phantoms destroyed—but the engagement illustrates how the cheap, small, and difficult-to-see MiG could surprise and defeat the much more powerful, missile-armed Phantom, which cost several times more and was a generation ahead in technology. The top "Fresco" ace of the Vietnam War was Nguyen Van Bay with seven kills. In April 1972, Van Bay led one of the few offensive actions by the North Vietnamese air force, an attack on two US destroyers, causing serious damage to the USS *Higbee*.

appearance were more coincidence than the result of copying or espionage, as the two design teams worked without knowledge of each other. The MiG's ailerons were hydraulically powered, and long flaps were provided to allow shorter landing distances. Early Soviet-produced MiG-15s varied greatly in quality from aircraft to aircraft and suffered buffeting at high speeds due in part to poor construction.

Left: *Hungary was one of many European MiG-15 users. This MiG-15bis was based in the Pécs district in the early 1960s.*

Above: *An Egyptian MiG-17F, it shows some of the differences to the MiG-15, including armament, wing pylons, and tailfin shapes.*

The major single-seat variant was the MiG-15bis, the suffix being a French term indicating a second major series of a design. The RD-45 was improved to give 5,950lb of thrust (26.5kN), up from the original 5,000lb of thrust (22.2kN), and was redesignated the VK-1. Fuel capacity was increased, and there were many detail differences.

Many MiG-15s were built in Poland, Czechoslovakia, and Hungary under various designations. These license-built aircraft were widely exported to Soviet-friendly nations and "client states" in Asia, Africa, and the Middle East. Well over 3,000 single-seaters were built in the Soviet Union and Eastern Europe, to which can be added an unknown large number supplied to China. It was long believed that China's Fagots were locally built as the Shenyang J-2, but in fact all were supplied from Soviet production.

North Korean MiGs and US Air Force Sabres met in many dogfights over Korea after the former's appearance over the battlefield in November 1950. Russian pilots flew many of the MiGs, with Yevgeny G. Pepelyaev the highest scoring of more than 50 Soviet aces in Korea, with a total of 23 victories. This total made him the top ace of either side, beating Joseph McConnell's tally of 16. A further six Chinese and two North Korean aces have been acknowledged.

The MiG-15 was faster climbing and had a higher ceiling and better acceleration than the Sabre, allowing it to make effective zoom attacks from above; however, the better training of the F-86 pilots and its faster-firing armament were instrumental in the high kill ratio in fighter versus fighter combat. Nevertheless, the MiGs destroyed

Left: *Just after the Korean armistice in 1953, a Korean MiG-15 was subjected to extensive testing by the USAF to discover its secrets.*

Above: *The heavy armament of a MiG-15—one 1.45-in (37-mm) and two 0.90-in (23-mm) cannon—can be seen here on this Arab example.*

many B-29s and other aircraft, as well as more than 70 Sabres. The improved MiG-15bis also saw combat in Korea, spurring the development of better versions of the Sabre.

The most important version numerically was the MiG-15 UTI "Midget" two-seat conversion trainer, which had an elongated canopy and a second seat for an instructor. More than 5,000 were built and were often retained to train pilots for the MiG-17 long after single-seat Fagots were retired. It is thought that many more than 13,000 MiG-15s were built in total, a record for any jet aircraft. Some of the last known single-seaters in service were a dozen used by the Albanian air force up to about 1999, but MiG-15UTIs may still fly with the air arms of China, Cuba, and Yemen. Since the collapse of the Soviet Union, significant numbers of surplus MiGs have appeared on the civil registers of the United States, the United Kingdom, Australia, New Zealand, and elsewhere.

Seeking to cure some of the less satisfactory aspects of the MiG-15, and improve its performance, the Mikoyan-Gurevich OKB (design bureau) mated a new 45-degree wing to a lengthened MiG-15 fuselage containing a VK-1A, giving 5,952lb of thrust (26.5kN). Armament was the same as the MiG-15, namely two 0.90-in (23-mm) and one 1.18-in (30-mm) cannon. The first flight of this aircraft, the SI-1, was made by test pilot I.T. Ivaschchenko, on January 14, 1950. He was killed unfortunately when the SI-1 crashed mysteriously on March 17. Development progressed, but production was delayed because priority was given to the MiG-15, which was desperately needed in Korea. Deliveries of the new fighter, dubbed MiG-17 in the Soviet Union and "Fresco" by NATO, did not begin until late 1951.

The developed MiG-17F version had a VK-1F turbojet with afterburner that gave 5,73 lb of thrust (25.5kN) dry and 7,451lb of thrust (33.1kN) with augmentation, and first flew in September 1951. The rear fuselage and airbrakes were redesigned, and 7.5-in (190-mm) or 8.3-in (210-mm) rockets could supplement the cannon. The airbrake shape and the presence of wing fences were the easiest ways to tell a MiG-17F from a MiG-15 when seen

Right: *Morocco was one of the many African nations to receive Mig-17s. This one was given to a US museum.*

side on. The radar-equipped MiG-17PF appeared in 1952. Its Izmrud radar was in two parts, a search radar in the upper intake lip, and a fire control set in a cone within the intake. The 1.18-in (30-mm) cannon was replaced with a third 0.90-in (23-mm) weapon. A variant was the MiG-17PFU, which was one of the first missile-armed interceptors in service anywhere.

Like the MiG-15, the MiG-17 was widely exported and built under license, mainly in Poland (as the Lim-5 and Lim-6) and China (as the Shenyang J-5 or F-5). The only two-seaters were built in China as FT-5s. In their later years, most MIG-17s were used as fighter-bombers or trainers. Like the MiG-15, a number of MiG-17s have found their way into private hands, mainly in the United States. A few may still serve in China and with nations such as Cuba, Algeria, and Mali.

Above: *MiG-17s were built in their thousands for Soviet allies including Poland and "client states" in the Third World. Poland only retired the type in the early 1990s.*

Left: *A formation of Polish MiG-17s, built locally as the Lim-5 and Lim-6. The Polish-built aircraft were supplied to most of the Warsaw Pact nations.*

Hawker Hunter

Seen by pilots as a true "sports car" of a fighter and sometimes called the "jet Spitfire," the Hawker Hunter was the last of the RAF's guns-only day fighters. As well as having a long British career, the Hunter served with 20 nations.

***Far right:** The RAF's last Hunter unit was No. 208 Squadron, which used T.8Bs with modified cockpits to train pilots for the single-control Buccaneer until 1994.*

***Right:** The Hunter T.12 was a once-only model that served with the Royal Aircraft Establishment (RAE) at Farnborough from 1963.*

Although a pioneer of jet fighters, Britain somewhat lost the lead in fighter development in the late 1940s to the United States and the Soviet Union with their swept-wing F-86 and MiG-15, respectively. Even Sweden flew the first of its swept-wing J-29 Tunnan fighters in 1948. The Royal Air Force's (RAF's) straight-winged Meteor and Vampire were limited in speed and no longer state of the art during the Korean War of 1950–53. Well before this, Hawker's Sir Sydney Camm took the basic design of his P.1040, which had been rejected by the RAF, but later formed the basis of the Sea Hawk naval fighter, and modified it to create the swept-wing P.1052, which first flew in November 1948. In March that year, the Air Ministry issued specification F3/48 calling for a single-seat landplane capable of 629mph (547knots) at 45,000ft (13,716m) and Mach 1.2 in a dive.

The two P.1052s gave Hawker valuable information about the characteristics of swept-wing aircraft, and the design was considered briefly in 1948 for adoption as the next RAF fighter, but work was already advanced on a new design based around the Rolls-Royce AJ.65 engine, later known as the Avon. This was a larger aircraft with wings and tail swept at 40 degrees and a main armament of four 1.18-in (30-mm) Aden cannon in a

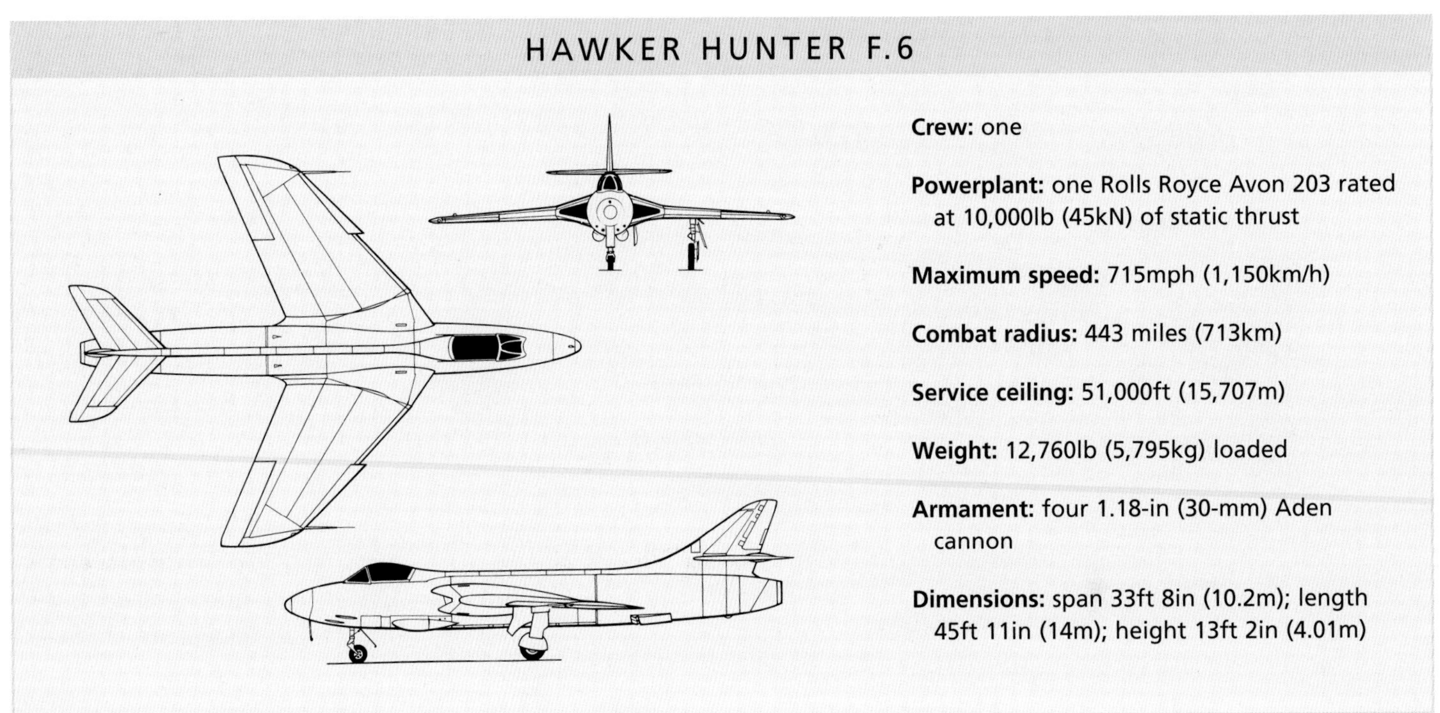

HAWKER HUNTER F.6

Crew: one

Powerplant: one Rolls Royce Avon 203 rated at 10,000lb (45kN) of static thrust

Maximum speed: 715mph (1,150km/h)

Combat radius: 443 miles (713km)

Service ceiling: 51,000ft (15,707m)

Weight: 12,760lb (5,795kg) loaded

Armament: four 1.18-in (30-mm) Aden cannon

Dimensions: span 33ft 8in (10.2m); length 45ft 11in (14m); height 13ft 2in (4.01m)

XF995

Right: No. 92 Squadron formed the "Blue Diamonds" aerobatic team in 1961/62 with up to 16 Hunter F.6s.

Below: The Hunter was one of the few nonindigenous jet-fighter types to enter service with the Swedish Air Force or Flygvapnet.

Below: The first of many two-seat Hunters was XJ 615. The shapely fairing behind the cockpit prevented instability at high speed.

ventral tray that could be lowered beneath the aircraft when empty for replacement with a full pack. Neville Duke first flew the P.1067, dubbed Hunter before completion, at Boscombe Down on July 20, 1951. Further flights expanded the envelope until Mach 1 was exceeded in April 1952. Duke took the world absolute speed record on September 7, 1953 with a run of 727.6mph (1,171km/h) off the south coast of England in the sole Hunter F.3, modified from the P.1067.

Hedging its bets, the RAF ordered equal numbers of Hunters powered by the 5,700-lb thrust (33-kN) Avon as the F Mk 1 and the 8,000-lb thrust (35-kN) Armstrong-Siddeley Sapphire as the F Mk 2. No. 43 Squadron introduced the F.1 into service in July 1954, and No. 257 inaugurated the F.2 in September. Neither version was long-lived, having to operate with many restrictions due to engine surging, which was often caused by gun gas ingestion. With only around 330 Imperial gallons (1,502 liters) total fuel capacity, the F.1 and F.2 had inadequate endurance. The solution was found in the F.4, which had 414 gallons (1,884 liters) internal fuel and could carry two 1,000-gallon (455-liter) drop tanks. Most also had a pair of prominent ammunition link collectors with underfuselage bulges. These were known as "Sabrinas" after a pinup girl of the day. The Avon-powered F.4 was partnered by the F.5 with the Sapphire. The latter model saw action during the Suez Crisis in 1956. F.4s were the first model issued to RAF Germany (RAFG), as well as to home defense squadrons. RAFG Hunters replaced Sabres and Venoms. Later some surplus F.4s went to the Royal Navy as the Hunter GA.11 for use as tactical weapons trainers.

The Hunter's airframe, particularly on the early models, was very aerodynamically clean, and the Hunter is regarded by many as one of the most

PILOTING THE HAWKER HUNTER

The Hunter saw a great deal of action in the hands of its export operators. India was the first to use a swept-wing British jet in air combat, in 1965 during the first war with Pakistan. Results of the dogfights of this conflict are still argued over, but generally the Hunter came off second best against Pakistan's F-86F Sabres, some of them using AIM-9B Sidewinders. The Hunters, armed only with cannon, did score against Sabres. This pattern was largely repeated in 1971.

Narenda Gupta later became an air commodore, but in 1971 was a Hunter pilot flying ground-attack sorties against advancing Pakistani tanks. One sortie was particularly memorable, as he describes: "An IP [initial point] was not necessary. The columns of black smoke from the Pakistani tanks hit by the previous strikes that morning was homing enough.

"'Alfa pulling up.'

"'Alfa, your tail clear.'

"As I eased up, I glanced to the right. My No. 2, Dan Singh in the other Hunter, was in broad front and also 30 degrees to the horizon. The shoulder straps unlocked, I swiveled my head as far as I could to the right and looked. Only the blue winter sky.

"'Bravo, your tail clear.'

'With the altimeter at about 2,500 feet I wing-overed to the left. The other tanks couldn't be too far from the ones that were burning.

"'Two tanks, 11 o'clock, 500 yards from the nearer smoke. Going in for the farther one.'

"'In contact; I'll take the other one.'

Above: The Hunter F.56A stayed in service with the Indian Air Force as late as 1999. This one served with the Target Tug Flight in West Bengal.

"As I rolled in I glanced at the switches. The R/P [rocket projectile] master was on and the R/P selector was on 4. The Hunter was loaded with eight French T-10 rockets, two inboard 100-gallon drop tanks, and the four cannon with 150 rounds each.

"I rolled out, nursing the 'pipper' of the gyro sight onto the track of the tank. Uncage. Closed in to about 1,100 yards, fired, and pulled out of the dive. Four rockets had snaked out from below the wings, heading ahead and below. At the same time I could see yellow sparks on the ground around me. Those were the tank machine guns firing back. There was a cluster of them 10 o'clock to the tank I had gone in for. My next target would be there.

"'You've got one,' called out Dan. I turned hard left in the climb to get out of the range of the guns. Dan was in the dive. Tail clear. His clutch of rockets fired—a flash followed by gray-black smoke. That made it one tank each. In the next attack I fired out of range. The rockets undershot. No rockets left, but I wanted one more tank. I made another pass, the four 30-mm cannons reverberating in a long burst, flying through the antiaircraft sparks all around. I pulled out low and could see the rounds thumping into the tank. The smell of cordite in the cockpit was exhilarating. The tank was on fire. One did not know if the thin armor of the top portion of the tank had punctured or the extra barrel of fuel that each tank carried had ignited. That low pull-out must have caused my Hunter to pick up holes from the ground fire, as I discovered in the post-sortie walk around the aircraft; two holes in the starboard aileron, one in the wing tip, and a nick on the right side of the rear fuselage. No problems, the riggers would patch them."

attractive military jets ever produced. For its time it was also better armed than its contemporaries, with four 1.18-in (30-mm) cannon. Later export models could carry a pair of air-to-air missiles, usually Sidewinders, but British Hunters never received air-to-air missiles other than for use in trials. Those models with the "Mod-228" wing had four weapons pylons and the ability to carry a wide range of bombs and rockets. The pilot sat on a Martin-Baker Mk. 2H ejection seat and had good vision out of the large canopy, although not as good as the Sabre, for instance. The cockpit was also considerably more cramped than that of the F-86.

Below: *WT555 was the first production Hunter F.1 and made its first flight in May 1953. It never saw service in the RAF.*

The definitive RAF Hunter was the F.6, powered by the Avon 203 engine rated at 10,000lb of thrust (44.48kN). The so-called "big-bore" Hunter equipped 18 RAF Squadrons and was the only pure fighter version in use after 1963. The FGA.9 (Fighter Ground Attack) was built mainly for Far East use, with better air conditioning and other "tropical" features. FGA.9s could carry larger fuel tanks and bombs or rockets, and saw action with the RAF in Borneo, Malaya, and Aden.

More peacefully, Hunters equipped the Blue Diamonds aerobatic team formed by No. 92 Squadron and the Black Arrows of No. 111 Squadron, who used all 16 of the unit's aircraft. At the 1958 Farnborough Air Show, borrowing a few jets from another unit, the team put up a total of 22 Hunters and memorably performed a loop with all of them, a feat unlikely to be bettered. The Fleet Air Arm's No. 768 Squadron at one time also had a team called the Rough Diamonds.

The T.7, with a widened forward fuselage containing side-by-side seating for student and instructor, was the main trainer variant. Some were built by converting single-seaters with a new nose section. Some of the last RAF Hunters were T.7s used as conversion trainers for the Buccaneer strike aircraft, which had no dual-control version. The Royal Navy's Fleet Requirements and Development Unit (FRADU) used Hunters mainly for simulating antiship missiles in mock attacks on warships.

The Hunter was one of the great postwar British export successes, the first orders coming in

Right: *Some of the RAF's last T.8Bs were painted black in a matt version of the scheme used by the famous "Black Diamonds" aerobatic team of the 1950s.*

***Left:** Kuwait bought 11 Hunters in the 1960s, five of which were T.67s, mainly refurbished from ex-RAF and Dutch aircraft.*

1954 from Sweden, Denmark, and Peru. Other countries that acquired Hunters (some of them indirectly) were Abu Dhabi, Belgium, Chile, Denmark, India, Iraq, Jordan, Kenya, Kuwait, Lebanon, the Netherlands, Oman, Peru, Qatar, Rhodesia/Zimbabwe, Saudi Arabia, Singapore, Somalia, Sweden, and Switzerland. Belgium and the Netherlands built Hunters under license. Some aircraft were actually exported twice, having been returned to the manufacturer (renamed Hawker-Siddeley Aviation), rebuilt, and sold again.

Several national aerobatic teams used Hunters, including Belgium's Diables Rouges, Jordan's Hashemite Diamond, Sweden's Acro Hunters, India's Thunderbolts, and Switzerland's Patrouille Suisse.

Israeli fighters destroyed most of Jordan's Hunters on the ground at the beginning of the Six Day War, and Jordan's pilots flew with the Iraqi Hunter squadrons. Nine Hunters were claimed by Israeli fighters in the 1967 conflict, but the Hunter pilots scored several victories in return, one pilot being credited with four victories over Israeli Defense Force (IDF) aircraft, comprising a Mirage III, a Vautour, and two Mystères. Some of the successful Jordanian Hunter pilots were actually on loan from the Pakistan Air Force. In 1973, Iraq's Hunters claimed 12 air-to-air kills for five losses.

Lebanon's few remaining Hunters played little part during the Israeli invasion in 1982. The following year, however, they made a number of sorties during the ongoing civil war. These resulted in the loss of at least five to ground fire and accidents. Iraqi Hunters may have seen some action in the early part of the Iran–Iraq War. Hunters also flew ground-attack sorties in the Rhodesian civil war, Chile's 1973 coup, and in Omani raids against guerrillas in South Yemen.

Switzerland was one of the last major operators, in latter years using its F.58s in the ground-attack role with AGM-65 Maverick missiles. India took well over 100 Hunters, and some were still in service beyond 2000 in the target-towing role.

Perhaps the Hunter's final war role was during the 2003 Iraq War, when at least one long-retired decoy aircraft was destroyed on the ground by an AC-130 gunship.

In civilian life, the Hunter has become an extremely popular warbird. Currently, a total of more than 50 examples are found on the civil registers of the United Kingdom, France, Switzerland, the United States, Canada, Australia, New Zealand, and Brazil.

***Below:** Singapore's Hunters served from 1970 to 1992. These FGA.74s served with No. 141 Squadron at Paya Lebar.*

Convair F-102 Delta Dagger and F-106 Delta Dart

Convair's F-102 was the first delta-winged fighter in service. Once initial troubles were overcome it became a stalwart of the Cold War. The revised F-106 became the so-called "ultimate interceptor," and saw over 30 years of service.

***Right:** Problems with the original YF-102 were resolved on the F-102A by "wasp-waisting" the fuselage in accordance with the area-rule theory.*

The most famous series of delta-winged combat aircraft arose from a factory in San Diego not previously known for producing high-performance aircraft. As well as the two fighters described together here, the Convair company built the moderately successful B-58 Hustler bomber and the XF2Y Sea Dart floatplane fighter prototypes, also tailless deltas.

The Convair name came about as a contraction of Consolidated Vultee Aircraft, the result of one of the first large mergers in the aircraft business. Consolidated was known for its large, multi-engined aircraft, such as the B-24 bomber, and a series of flying boats, the most famous of which was the PBY Catalina. Vultee had mainly built dive-bombers such as the Vindicator and trainers such as the BT-13. Neither company had experience with building either jets or fighter aircraft when they began studies based on captured German documents in the late 1940s.

CONVAIR F-106B DELTA DART

Crew: two

Powerplant: one Pratt & Whitney J75-P-17 turbojet rated at 17,200lb (76.50kN) of static thrust and 24,500lb (108.98kN) with afterburner

Maximum speed: 1,328mph (2,137km/h)

Combat radius: 575 miles (925km)

Service ceiling: 57,000ft (17,380m)

Weight: 39,195lb (17,779kg) loaded

Armament: one MB-1 Genie nuclear-tipped AAM and four AIM-4 Falcon radar or IR-guided AAMs

Dimensions: span 38ft 4in (11.67m); length 70ft 9in (21.56m); height 20ft 4in (618 m)

USAF

The company's ambitious rocket/ramjet-powered XP-92 proposal of 1945 was a radical design, being little more than a tube with delta wing and tail surfaces, the pilot sitting in the intake cone. The Pentagon was interested, but deemed it necessary to build a less complex jet-powered experimental aircraft with a conventional cockpit first. This XF-92 research aircraft first flew on September 19, 1948 and was the first pure delta-winged aircraft to fly. It proved that delta-winged aircraft presented no particular control problems.

At the same time as this aerodynamic research was going on, great strides were being made in systems for radar, missiles, and fire control. The US Air Force decided to combine the basic aerodynamics of the XF-92 with a new Hughes fire-control system and internal carriage of the AIM-4 Falcon missile (the aircraft was then known as the GAR-1, and before that it was designated as the F-98) to create a new aircraft designated F-102. As well as these innovations, the US Air Force (USAF) wanted to speed the development and service entry by building "hard" tooling from the outset, assuming that there would only be minor changes between the first aircraft and production models. This "Cook-Craigie Plan," named after the two generals who devised it, fell apart when the YF-102, which was flown by Dick Johnson for the first time on October 24, 1953, resolutely refused to go supersonic in level flight.

Below: *An F-102A of the 57th Fighter Interceptor Squadron (FIS), based at Keflavik in Iceland.*

Various changes were tried, including a cambered wing surface, but these did not help the basic problem until the principles of Dr. Richard Whitcomb's

PILOTING THE CONVAIR F-106 DELTA DART

Above: *Aircraft 59-0061 was the last F-106 to fly and was retired on 6 July 1990. It was subsequently shot down as a QF-106.*

Unlike the F-102, the F-106 never saw actual combat, but Lieutenant Colonel Mike "Buddha" Nelson recalls what it was like to fly in mock dogfights. "In air-to-air combat with another fighter, the 'Six,' due to its low combat wing loading, exhibited quick turning, quick recovery of energy, and outstanding 'nose authority.' Nose authority allowed the pilot to employ lag maneuveres to gain position to fire the [infrared] AIM-4Gs directly at the tailpipe [of the enemy], then pull the nose into a lead position to employ the AIM-4Fs and/or the gun. The responsiveness of the airplane, its capabilities of turn, speed, and altitude, and its honesty in feedback, were the seeds of a life-long love affair. The F-106 never surprised me.... there have been many comments about the F-106 being a forgiving airplane. I disagree. Many a ham-handed aviator has come to grief with the airplane. However, in the hands of a skilled pilot, a pilot who listened when the airplane spoke, it was a real thoroughbred and an absolute joy to fly."

Above: The first F-106A is seen in high visibility markings during an early test flight from Edwards Air Force Base.

new "area rule" were implemented. Broadly speaking, this rule states that the best drag coefficient is achieved when a plot of a body's—in this case, an aircraft's—cross-section from nose to tail produces a smooth curve. To compensate for the wing, the fuselage should be slimmer along the wing root. It being impossible to slim the fuselage much, a similar effect could be achieved by lengthening the nose and adding bulged surfaces on the rear fuselage. Working day and night, Convair's engineers revised the design thoroughly, also repositioning the intakes, enlarging the fin, and completely redesigning the canopy. The new "Hot Rod" YF-102A flew on December 20, 1954 and had no trouble reaching Mach 1.2 the following day. Despite needing a further fin enlargement, the design remained much the same for the 873 F-102As that followed. The only variant was the TF-102A trainer, which had an unusual side-by-side canopy in a widened fuselage. As such, the "T-bird" remained essentially subsonic, but retained its weapons capabilities.

The Delta Dagger, as it was officially dubbed, was the first fighter designed to have an internal missile bay. This could house up to six examples of only one type of missile, the AIM-4 Falcon, albeit in semiactive radar homing (AIM-4A) and infrared guidance (AIM-4C or G) versions. Later the AIM-26A Nuclear Falcon was issued to some units. A battery of unguided rockets was fitted in the missile bay doors of early examples, but there was no internal gun.

The Delta Dagger was powered by a single Pratt & Whitney J57-P-23 turbojet rated at 17,200lb of thrust (76.50kN) with afterburner. This gave it a climb rate of 13,000ft (3,961m) per minute and a top speed of Mach 1.25 at 40,000ft (12,190m).

Service began with the 327th Fighter Interceptor Squadron (FIS) of Air Defense Command (ADC) in April 1956. The F-102 soon became the mainstay of the ADC squadrons and was deployed to Iceland and Europe, as well as to many bases in continental United States. The F-102 also served with Pacific Air Forces (PACAF)

Left: Originally called the F-102B, the Delta Dart became the F-106A by the time the first aircraft flew in San Diego in 1956.

***Right:** The tandem two-seat F-106B was fully combat capable, unlike the TF-102B, which had side-by-side seating and reduced equipment.*

***Above:** The original F-102 design refused to go supersonic until revised with a longer "Coke-bottle" fuselage and many other changes.*

in Japan and Alaska. "Deuces" intercepted many Soviet "Bears" making probing flights in northern latitudes. Surprisingly, this sophisticated interceptor was deployed to South Vietnam and Thailand, where there was little actual bomber threat. One F-102A was, however, surprised and shot down by a MiG-21 in February 1968. The F-102 crews took to using the aircraft's infrared sensor to hunt for Vietcong campfires and on one occasion reputedly put one out by firing an IR Falcon into it. TF-102As acted as observers for B-52 raids, and F-102As had a limited ground-attack role with rockets used against structures and rivercraft.

The F-102 was supplied to both Turkey and Greece, and it is believed that at least one Deuce-vs.-Deuce dogfight took place during the Cyprus conflict in 1974. Turkish F-5As are believed to have shot down two Greek F-102s, and a Greek F-102's Falcon destroyed one Turkish F-5A.

Even as F-102s were still being used to equip the ADC squadrons in 1960, they began a long career with the Air National Guard (ANG), often regarded unfairly as a home for "hand-me-down" equipment. President George W. Bush was a sometime F-102 pilot with the Texas Guard in 1970. In 1977, the last F-102s were retired from manned service, but more than 200 were converted to PQM-102 pilotless drones to be shot down in missile tests and in training of crews, including those of its successor, the F-106.

Even before the first F-102As were beginning to roll off Convair's San Diego production line, the company was working on a replacement. The F-102 was always regarded as the "interim interceptor," and the USAF had hoped to replace the various types in ADC (including the F-86D, F-89, and F-94) with the so-called "1954 ultimate interceptor," reflecting its proposed (and overly optimistic) in-service date. Even more so than the F-102A, the new aircraft was to be regarded more as a platform for a weapons system than a "fighter" in the conventional sense. Convair's proposal for an F-102B to carry the Hughes MA-1 system was the chosen solution and a greatly revised aircraft, soon redesignated the YF-106A, appeared in 1956, flying on December 26 that year. The development of the F-106 Delta Dart was much smoother than its slightly smaller predecessor, and service entry began

Left: *One of the last roles for the F-106 was as chase planes for the B-1B bomber program.*

with the 539th FIS in May 1959. Recognition points included a larger fin with a squared-off tip, a "Coke-bottle" fuselage without rear bulges, and completely reshaped intakes. The "Six" had a similar weapons bay for AIM-4s, but could also carry the MB-1 Genie. This rocket with a nuclear warhead was an unguided weapon and had a range of about 6.2 miles (10km) and a flight duration of 12 seconds. The MA-1 fire-control system guided the F-106 to a firing position on a formation of bombers, and the blast of the 1.5-kiloton warhead made up for any slight inaccuracy. The Genie was retired as late as 1985. The F-106 also had an inflight refueling receptacle and an arrester hook for runway use. A number of updates were made to the "Six" in later years of its service, including a "bubble" canopy, an infrared search-and-track (IRST) sensor, and a M61 Vulcan cannon in the weapons bay, installed under project "Six Gun."

Sixty-three of the 340 F-106s were F-106B two-seaters, which had a tandem cockpit layout and thus retained the performance of the single-seater. With its refined aerodynamic shape and larger J75 engine, the F-106 could reach Mach 2 and climb at 42,800ft (13,045m) per minute.

The Delta Dart was not exported and not as widely deployed as the F-102, but F-106s were rotated to South Korea to bolster local air defense during the 1968–70 period of tension with North Korea over the capture of the intelligence ship USS *Pueblo*. The "Six" finally retired from ANG service in August 1988, but continued to serve as an unmanned drone, with NASA and in the B-1B bomber program. The QF-106 program ran from 1989 to 1998 and saw 173 conversions, most of which were shot down in trials of missiles such as the Stinger SAM and the AIM-120 AMRAAM.

Left: *For many years the F-102A was flown by fighter-interceptor squadrons of the Air National Guard, many taking on the South-East Asia camouflage scheme.*

Vought F-8 Crusader

The F-8 Crusader was the last of its breed, designed with cannon rather than missiles as its primary armament. Crusader pilots were fond of saying, "When you are out of F-8s, you are out of fighters."

VOUGHT F-8 CRUSADER

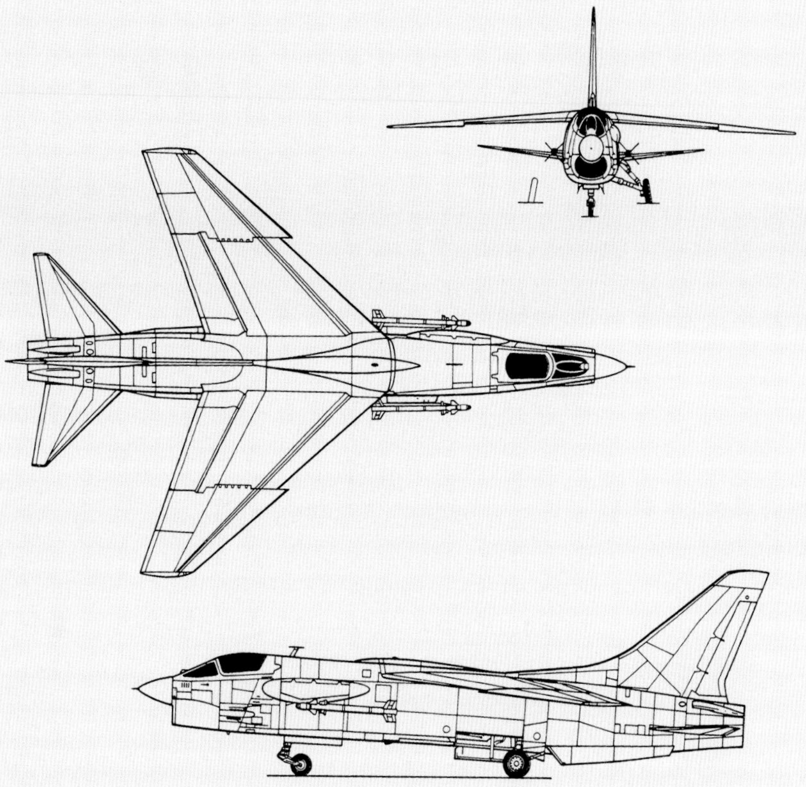

Crew: one

Powerplant: one Pratt & Whitney J57-P-20A turbojet rated at 10,700lb of thrust (47.61kN) dry and 18,000lb of thrust (80.07kN) with afterburner

Maximum speed: 1,135mph (1,827km/h)

Combat radius: 1,425 miles (2,293km)

Service ceiling: 58,000ft (17,680m)

Weight: 34,100lb (15,467kg) loaded

Armament: four 0.79-in (20-mm) Colt Mk 12 cannon, four AIM-9 Sidewinder air-to-air missiles, up to 5,000lb (2,270kg) of bombs or rockets

Dimensions: span 35ft 8in (10.87m); length 54ft 3in (16.53m); height 15ft 9in (4.8m)

Right: *An early F8U-1P comes aboard the USS* Forrestal. *Crusaders were the main fighters on the smaller "Essex" ships.*

Vought's Crusader is regarded as the "last of the gunfighters," being designed to use cannon as its primary armament. Like the Mitsubishi Zero, it was a rare example of a naval fighter that outperformed its land-based counterparts and received the nickname "MiG Master" for its combat exploits in Vietnam.

A US Navy request for a new supersonic carrier-based day-fighter was issued to industry in September 1952, and eight manufacturers responded with a variety of proposals. These included a navalized version of the North American F-100 and a twin-engined version of the McDonnell F3H Demon. Vought Aircraft of Dallas, Texas, submitted several designs.

Vought's previous projects had both been failures: the underpowered F6U Pirate and the oversophisticated and unreliable F7U Cutlass. There was a lot of opinion in the US Navy and elsewhere that it might be a better idea not to give the company another one. Fortunately the decision to procure the F8U was taken on the

GA
904
NAVY

Below: *This RF-8G photo Crusader belonged to reserve squadron VFP-306 at Andrews Air Force Base, Maryland.*

Right: *The only dual control "Two-sader" served for many years before it was lost in an accident.*

basis of the proposal offered, not past performance. Chief engineer John Russell (Russ) Clark had worked on the F6U and the F7U. This time his design, with the company designation V-383, was less radical, but offered enough promise to be selected as the winner in May 1953.

The design and testing process went marvelously quickly, albeit with a few delays before the first flight due to the late completion (and delivery by road from Texas to California) of some vital components, including the wing. Test pilot John Konrad made the first flight at Edwards AFB on May 25, 1955, taking the unpainted jet past Mach 1.0—the first time this had been done with any fighter on a maiden flight. The name "Crusader" was bestowed soon afterward.

Carrier qualifications took place in April 1956, and the first fleet Crusader squadron was VF-32 "Swordsmen," which stood up in March 1957 and went to sea later that year. The first Marine unit, VMF-122, was equipped by the end of 1957. Rarely has any postwar, high-performance combat aircraft program proceeded so rapidly, with operational service beginning four and a quarter years after release of the initial requirement. Reconnaissance models were in service almost as quickly as the fighters. The first version was the F8U-1P (RF-8A), with no armament and four camera stations. Reconnaissance Crusaders played an important role in the Cuban Missile Crisis of 1962. US Navy and Marine photo Crusaders flew almost constantly over the island photographing the construction of Soviet tactical missile sites and associated surface-to-air missile (SAM) batteries.

The exceptional level speed of the Crusader was used in several record-breaking flights, mainly to demonstrate its superiority to the US Air Force as much as to the Soviets. On July 16, 1957, under the code name Project Bullet, Marine Major John Glenn flew from Los Angeles to New York in 3 hours 28 minutes in an F8U-1P, photographing the land beneath him the entire way. Another record-breaking dash saw two Crusaders fly from one aircraft carrier off California to another off Florida in just under three and a half hours. These flights required several refuelings from AJ Savage tankers en route.

Probably the most unusual feature of the F8U was the variable-incidence wing. The whole wing

Right: *France's Crusaders were the last in service, finally retiring in late 1999 after nearly 40 years' service.*

PILOTING THE VOUGHT F-8 CRUSADER

Above: *An F-8J roars off the deck of the "Essex"-class carrier Oriskany in June 1969.*

One of the few victories to earlier Crusaders, and one of only two gun kills, fell to Lieutenant Commander Robert Kirkwood of VF-24 flying off the old wooden-decked "Essex"-class carrier *Bon Homme Richard* in July 1967. He was flying an F-8C on combat air patrol (CAP) over the target for a strike group of 15 A-4 Skyhawks when a group of up to 10 MiG-17s appeared.

"We only saw the first four MiGs initially: the second four got behind us undetected. I lit my burner, put my nose on a MiG, and selected a [Sidewinder] missile. In my excitement, I had buck fever, didn't wait for a tone, and fired. The missile went ballistic. I settled down a little, got a good solid tone on another MiG, and fired a second Sidewinder. But another F-8's missile got there first [that of Commander Marion Isaacks]. There was another MiG, though, and after some gentle maneuvering and 180 degrees of turn, I fired a third missile. It ran hot and true, but after it detonated, the MiG was still flying. The pilot reversed his turn to the right. I cut him off and charged my guns. I was in good position at his 6 o'clock, and not pulling much *g*. I wanted to shoot from close in.

"I resisted the temptation to fire until I was at about 600 feet. I squeezed the trigger and closed to 300 feet. I could see my shells hitting the MiG's fuselage—patches of skin appeared to dissolve and bright, white fire seemed to fill the fuselage and leak out of the lacy skin.

"I broke left to avoid a collision, then dropped my right wing to look at the MiG. I didn't think there was much chance he would turn to attack me, but I couldn't turn my back on him. The pilot ejected after I passed him."

tilted upward at the leading edge to give a better angle of attack for carrier takeoffs. On landing, it was also used to keep the fuselage in a level attitude. Armament consisted of four 0.79-in (20-mm) Colt Mk 12 cannon in the forward fuselage and racks for two or four AIM-9 Sidewinders on the fuselage sides. Early versions had a tray of folding-fin aircraft rockets (FFARs), intended mainly as an air-to-air weapon. The F8E had a secondary attack capability and was used for close-support missions in Vietnam with bombs and rockets, mainly by the US Marine Corps. Most Es could also launch the AGM-12B Bullpup air-to-surface missile. The conical nose cone originally housed the APG-30 gun-sight radar, later replaced with various models of fire-control radar.

Left: *Early F8U-1s of test squadron VX-3 line up for launch on the USS* Franklin D. Roosevelt.

The F8D's radar could guide the rare radar-guided AIM-9C version of the famous Sidewinder.

The intake trunk began with a fixed-geometry inlet under the nose and ran over 25ft (7.6m) to the compressor of the Pratt & Whitney J57 engine. The rear fuselage around the jet pipe and afterburner was largely made of titanium. Performance was superior to the US Air Force's F-100 Super Sabre in almost every respect, despite both types having the same engine. In fact, the Crusader was the only US fighter with better performance than the MiG-21 at the time of its debut. As well as having high speed and climbing ability, it was extremely maneuverable for its era and was able to hold its own in a dogfight with any of its contemporaries.

The initial day-fighter version, the F8U-1 (which became the F-8A in the tri-service redesignation of September 1962), was followed by the all-weather F8U-1E (F-8B) and the F8U-2 (F-8C) with ventral fins and four AIM-9s. The F8U-2N (F-8D) had the uprated J57-P-20 of 18,000lb of thrust (80.07kN) in afterburner, better radar, and no rockets.

The most important model was the F8U-2NE (F-8E) with its all-weather APQ-92 radar and multirole capability. It was the most successful against the North Vietnamese MiGs, scoring 11 kills out of a total of 18 Crusader victories, all in the 1966–8 period. Twenty-one F-8s were lost to enemy action in Vietnam, three of them to MiGs.

In all, 1,261 Crusaders were built, but there were several remanufactured versions, including the F-8J (rebuilt from F-8Es), F-8K (F-8B), and F-8L (F-8C). Only one two-seat TF-8A Crusader was built. This "Two-sader" first flew in 1962 and was used for various tasks until it was lost in a crash in Texas while a Philippine pilot was under instruction in 1978. It is unclear why the US Navy never ordered the two-seater to ease transition training for new pilots.

The XF8U-3 Crusader III was a highly modified version with a J75 engine of 29,500lb of thrust (131.22kN) with afterburning, a new intake, and large ventral fins. Three Sparrow missiles could be carried in recesses under the fuselage. Although capable of Mach 2.2, and having longer range, the F8U-3 was rejected in favor of the two-seat F4H-1 Phantom as the new US Navy interceptor. It was said by some that the F8U-3 was the best airplane the US Navy ever canceled, but the rationale at the time was that running a radar interception and firing missiles

***Below:** The Crusader could operate from the smaller "Essex"-class carriers, such as the USS* Intrepid, *seen here with an F8U-1E of VF-33 and Douglas F4D-1 aboard.*

***Right:** The Philippine Air Force operated a fleet of refurbished Crusaders, but the tropical climate reduced their serviceability. They were retired in the 1990s.*

***Left:** The XF-8U3 Crusader III was an improved high-performance version. It lost out to the F4H-1 Phantom as the Navy's main fighter of the 1960s and 70s.*

were becoming too much for one person. Pilots were to realize that "having a radar operator in the back is just like having a wingman who doesn't get lost," according to one later Phantom pilot.

The last active-duty fighter Crusaders were retired by the US Navy in 1975. The last RF-8Gs were retired in 1987. A total of 517 of the 1,261 US Crusaders were lost in accidents of one kind or another.

The Crusader was exported to two air arms, the French Navy (*Aéronavale*) and the Philippine Air Force. The Philippines received 25 F-8H models, rebuilt by Vought in 1977. The tropical climate caused deterioration of those components made of Metalite (an aluminum-balsa hybrid material) and other parts, and serviceability declined fairly quickly. By 1991, the last survivors had been retired, although several made a static appearance as RF-8As in the 2000 film about the Cuban missile crisis, *Thirteen Days*.

In 1962, France ordered 42 Crusaders designated the F-8E(FN) for use on its two aircraft carriers the *Foch* and *Clemenceau*, and they equipped two flotilles or squadrons from 1964. The French carriers were shorter at 870ft (265m) than even the "Essex"-class ships, which were 968ft (295m) and longer. As a result, the French F-8s were modified with greater maximum wing incidence, larger tailplanes, and boundary-layer control (BLC), which diverted engine bleed air to blow over the flaps and give extra lift on takeoff.

As well as the Mk 12 cannon, armament was the Matra R.530 infrared or radar-guided air-to-air missile or Matra Magic or Sidewinder short-range air-to-air missiles. The closest the French Crusaders came to combat was in 1983 flying cover over Super Etendard strikes on Lebanese guerrilla positions. The numbers slowly dwindled over the years, but replacement in the form of the Rafale M was a long time coming, and the French Crusaders were rebuilt in the late 1980s using parts from US Navy aircraft stored in the Davis-Monthan "boneyard." As such, 17 aircraft soldiered on for another decade as the F-8P (for *Prolonge*, or "prolonged"). Despite some hopes that they would fly the F-8 into the new Millennium, the *Aéronavale* retired the last "Crouze" in December 1999.

***Below:** This Crusader was tested by NASA with a highly modified supercritical wing in the 1980s. It was a simple matter to replace the original wing.*

Mikoyan-Gurevich MiG-21 "Fishbed"

The MiG-21 was the most numerous and widely spread fighter of the Cold War. Extremely efficient for its intended interceptor role, many users pushed its capabilities to and beyond the limit. Large numbers are still in service today.

MIKOYAN-GUREVICH MIG-21MF

Crew: one

Powerplant: one Tumansky R-13-300 turbojet rated at 8,972lb of thrust (39.92kN) dry and 14,307lb of thrust (63.66kN) in afterburner

Maximum speed: 1,385mph (2,220km/h)

Combat radius: 342 miles (550km)

Service ceiling: 59,711ft (18,200m)

Weight: 20,723lb (9,400kg) loaded

Armament: one GSh-23L 0.90-in (23-mm) cannon and four K-13 IR-guided air-to-air missiles

Dimensions: span 23ft 6in (7.15m); length 51ft 9in (15.76m); height 13ft 6in (4.10m)

Right: This Hungarian MiG-21PF shows the unusual forward-hinged canopy of this and other early "Fishbed" versions.

The classic MiG-21 series of fighters stemmed from a 1954 design program to develop a lightweight interceptor capable of Mach 2 and altitudes of more than 65,600ft (20,000m). Although the MiG-15/17 had led to the broadly similar MiG-19, this time the Mikoyan design team started with a clean sheet of paper. Debate about the merits of different wing configurations led to the swept-wing Ye-2 and delta-wing Ye-4 test aircraft in 1955. Each had a nose intake and a slender fuselage ending in a swept fin and all-moving tailplane. The bubble canopy used on each consisted of a single-piece unit, which hinged forward and provided a blast screen in the case of ejection.

Evaluation of further prototypes saw no great advantage of one wing over the other, but the delta Ye-5, first flown on January 9, 1956 by G.K. Mosolov, was chosen for further development. Further, more representative prototypes followed, and a modified one, the Ye-66, took the world air speed record at 1,484mph (2,388km/h) in October 1959.

The first full production version was the MiG-21F-13, known to the West as the "Fishbed-C." By the time it entered service in 1959, it was in time to take advantage of the new technology of guided air-to-air missiles (AAMs), acquired by various means. The R-3S (AA-2 "Atoll") was a copy of the AIM-9B Sidewinder infrared guided missile, and the early MiG-21s carried two of them, along with a 0.90-in (23-mm) rapid-firing revolver cannon.

503

Above: India remains the largest MiG-21 user. They have recently suffered a high accident rate. These are MiG-21FLs, of which about 240 entered Indian service.

Below: Many of India's MiGs and SEPECAT Jaguars were built locally by HAL. This Indian MiG-21bis is seen with a British-built Jaguar.

The MiG-21 was designed to reach interception altitude as fast as possible, directed by ground controllers to the enemy aircraft. When there, it was to use its cannon or short-range missiles to down the intruder, and then return. As such, there was little superfluous equipment on board or, indeed, fuel capacity in the slim fuselage. The mission time was typically 30 to 45 minutes, depending on whether or not external fuel tanks were carried.

Despite its impressive performance on paper, the first-generation MiG-21F has been called a "supersonic sports car," with little capability outside good weather conditions and a positive ground-control environment. The first major development to improve the "Fishbed's" capabilities was the MiG-21P, with its side-hinged canopy faired into a fuselage spine. The variable intake cone contained a new RP-21 radar, and cannon was deleted on early production models. A less capable model, the MiG-21FL, was built for export. The first-generation MiG-21s were supplied to many countries including China, Romania, India, and Finland.

India built many MiG-21s under license, and China built many more, mostly without Soviet approval, as the Chengdu J-7, which was subject to much local development after the Sino-Soviet split. The export F-7M Airguard had a rear-hinged canopy, two cannon and up to four air-to-air missiles. Much western equipment was fitted, and the type was exported to Pakistan, Iran, Zimbabwe, and other countries. MiG-21s were introduced in Vietnam in April 1966, initially the limited capability F-13, but later also the PF and PFM.

The second-generation "Fishbeds," lead by the reconnaissance MiG-21R and the MiG-21S fighter, increased in sophistication, fuel capacity, and armament. Identification of different models depended largely on subtleties of the size and shape of the fuselage spine, which contained fuel or avionics, or both. The Tumansky R-13 engines in this series varied, reaching 8,972-lb thrust (39.92kN) dry and 14,307-lb thrust (63.66 kN) in afterburner in the MiG-21MF.

PILOTING THE MIKOYAN-GUREVICH MIG-21 "FISHBED"

The leading ace of the Vietnam War was MiG-21 pilot Nguyen Van Coc of the 921st Regiment, who was credited with nine victories. A further 12 pilots reached ace status in western terms by achieving the destruction of five or more US aircraft. On May 7, 1968, Van Coc and another pilot were ordered to meet an incoming attack by US Navy aircraft based on carriers in the Tonkin Gulf. "My leader, Dang Ngoc Nhu, and I took off from Tho Xuan. A second pair of MiGs acted as our escorts. Because of poor co-ordination with local air defense forces, our MiGs were mistaken for American fighters and the AAA opened up on us. This was not the only mistake—even Dang Ngoc Nhu initially mistook the escorting MiGs for Americans and dropped his fuel tanks in preparation for an attack, but he soon recognized them as North Vietnamese.

"We flew three circuits over Do Luong before being told of fighters approaching from the sea—this time they were real Americans. Dang Ngoc Nhu noticed two F-4 Phantoms five kilometers to starboard. There was a lot of cloud and he was unable to get into a firing position. I wanted to follow him, but I noticed I was running low on fuel. I was planning to land back at Tho Xuan when suddenly I spotted a Phantom ahead of me at an altitude of 2,500 meters. I went after him and fired two missiles from 1,500 meters. The Phantom crashed in flames into the sea."

Van Bay's victim was an F-4B of VF-92 from USS *Enterprise* which had suffered radar failure and become separated from the rest of its flight. The crew of two, Lieutenant Commander E.S. Christensen and Lieutenant (junior grade) W.A. Kramer ejected over the sea and were rescued. This was the seventh of Van Coc's nine kills. Ngoc Nhu was also to become an ace, with six kills.

***Above:** MiG-21 pilots were trained to rigidly obey ground control to achieve a successful interception.*

The most capable production version was the third-generation MiG-21bis. This had enhanced weapons options, including the R-60 (AA-8 "Aphid") air-to-air missile, bombs, rockets, and even nuclear weapons. The R-25-300 engine had a special emergency rating that could be used (for three minutes only) above Mach 1 and below 13,125ft (4,000m) that boosted thrust to 21,825lb (97.12kN). Use of this of course consumed fuel at a prodigious rate. As the bis—and, in fact, any MiG-21—does not have aerial refueling capability, endurance was commensurately short.

The MiG-21bis could be found in

***Left:** This Czechoslovakian "Fishbed" was a MiG-21R reconnaissance version, first of the "second-generation" Mig-21s.*

***Above:** From the MiG-21PFM onward, a side-opening canopy was introduced, as seen on these Soviet Air Force machines.*

***Below:** A Soviet Air Force MiG-21PF gets airborne with the assistance of auxiliary booster rockets.*

the air forces of many Third World nations and others friendly to the Soviet Union. A non-exhaustive list would include Afghanistan, Algeria, Angola, Bulgaria, Cuba, Hungary, India, Laos, Nigeria, Yemen, and Yugoslavia. Other operators of various "Fishbed" models have included Bangladesh, Bulgaria, Burkina Faso, Cambodia, Congo, Croatia, Czechoslovakia (and the air forces of the divided Czech Republic and Slovakia), Egypt, Ethiopia, East Germany (and, briefly, the Federal Republic after reunification), Finland, Guinea Republic, Indonesia, Iran, Iraq, Kazakhstan, Mongolia, Mozambique, North Korea, Poland, Romania, Somalia, Sudan, Syria, Uganda, Ukraine, Vietnam, and Zambia. Chinese-made F-7s also serve with Bangladesh, Egypt, Iran, Myanmar (Burma), Pakistan, Sri Lanka, Tanzania, and Zimbabwe.

Hindustan Aeronautics Limited (HAL) of India built many MiG-21s up until the late 1980s. With more than 830 delivered, they are still the most numerous combat aircraft in Indian service, although more than 100 have been lost in accidents. In 2003, India finally agreed to purchase BAE Systems Hawks to partially replace the MiGs in the training and light-attack roles. Its indigenous Light Combat Aircraft (LCA) program continues to make slow progress.

In various Middle East conflicts, the MiG-21 usually came off second best in combat, with Israeli Mirages, Phantoms, F-15s, and F-16s claiming more than 380 destroyed, although Egyptian and Syrian "Fishbed" pilots have claimed more than 100 kills in return.

The two-seat trainer version, also exported in large numbers, is the MiG-21U "Mongol" with individual canopies. Subvariants include the MiG-21UM and MiG-21US, usually with cannon pods and two weapons pylons.

With as many as 5,000 MiG-21s still in service around the world in the 1990s, eastern and western aerospace firms vied to replace or upgrade them. The MiG-21-93 was proposed by MiG (then MiG-MAPO, now Russian Aircraft Corporation (RAC) MiG) in 1993 and adopted by India under the designation MiG-21bis Upgrade. This is proceeding slowly on 125 aircraft, most of them reworked by HAL. RAC MiG's MiG-21-98 upgrade is intended for older versions of the

fighter. Both offer new multimode radar and the ability to carry modern air-to-air missiles and precision-guided air-to-ground weapons.

The most ambitious and successful upgrade program is Romania's Aerostar MiG-21 Lancer. A total of 110 Romanian Air Force aircraft have been converted to one of three configurations. The project encompasses 75 ground-attack Lancer A models, 25 Lancer C air-defense fighters, and 10 Lancer B trainers. Fitted with Israeli electronics, the upgraded MiGs can operate both eastern and western weapons and have fully modernized cockpits with multifunction displays (MFDs), a helmet-mounted sight (HMS), and a hands-on throttle and stick (HoTaS) control system. The first Lancer was flown in 1995 and the last in 2003.

Aerostar is offering to upgrade MiGs for other customers without input from the parent company. The market for upgrades has diminished, however, with many nations acquiring western aircraft or retiring their MiG-21s without replacement. In 2002, it was estimated that about 1,000 remained in service around the world.

Above: *Some Indian "Fishbeds," such as this MiG-21bis, adopted unusual colored areas to help identify them during air combat training.*

Left: *The Slovak Air Force operated this MiG-21MF "Fishbed J" after the separation of the Czech Republic and Slovakia.*

Dassault Mirage III and 5

The Mirage III was the most successful French warplane and spawned a series of variants, official and unofficial, in France, Israel, and Argentina. Dassault deltas have achieved an enviable combat record in many conflicts.

DASSAULT MIRAGE IIIC

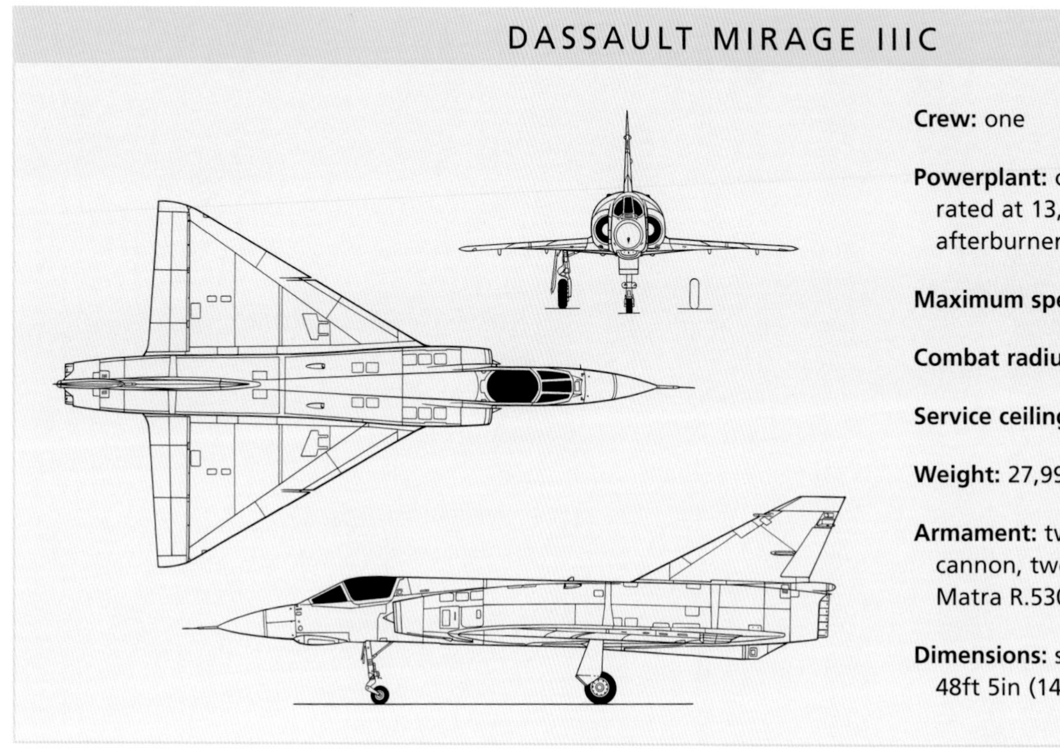

Crew: one

Powerplant: one SNECMA Atar 9C turbojet rated at 13,228-lb thrust (58.84kN) in afterburner

Maximum speed: 1,320mph (2,112km/h)

Combat radius: 180 miles (290km)

Service ceiling: 65,615ft (20,000m)

Weight: 27,998lb (12,700kg) loaded

Armament: two 1.18-in (30-mm) DEFA cannon, two AIM-9 Sidewinders, and one Matra R.530 air-to-air missile

Dimensions: span 27ft (8.22m); length 48ft 5in (14.75m); height 14ft 9in (4.5m)

***Far right:** The Mirage Milan was a version with canard foreplanes offered for export in the early 1970s.*

***Right:** A Mirage IIIEA of the Fuerza Aérea Argentina Grupo 8 de Caza at Rio Gallegos in April 1982.*

Dassault's classic Mirage family has been one of the most widely used and combat-tested modern warplanes. From the deserts of the Middle East to the South Atlantic, variants of Dassault's delta have fought many battles and continue to serve with several nations.

Like a number of fighters, the French Mirage series originated in the early 1950s, influenced by jet combat experiences in the Korean War. In January 1953, the French air staff called for a supersonic, missile-armed aircraft powered by one or more turbojets, liquid or solid-fuel rockets, or a mixture of these. The French aircraft industry responded with half a dozen designs. Three of these were ordered as prototypes: the mixed turbojet/rocket Sud-Est Durandal and Sud-Ouest Trident, and the Dassault Mystère Delta, a jet with rocket boost.

Although named for Dassault's successful swept-wing Mystère fighter, the tiny Delta shared almost nothing with its predecessor by the time Roland Glavany took it on its maiden flight on June 25, 1955. The MD.550 Mystery Delta had a pointed nose, side-mounted intakes, a delta wing controlled by large flaperons, and a large, triangular tailfin. These basic features remained on all of the Mirage delta fighters up to the Mirage 4000.

As built, a single non-afterburning 1,653-lb thrust (7.35-kN) Armstrong Siddeley MD30 Viper turbojet powered the MD.550. After initial tests, the MD.550 was reconfigured with a smaller fin and re-engined with two afterburning MD30R Vipers, each with 2,160lb of thrust (9.61kN). Extra boost at altitude came from a 3,300-lb thrust (14.7-kN) SEPR liquid-fuel rocket motor. In its new form the name was changed to Mirage I.

The Mirage I was too small to be an operational fighter, and the slightly larger Mirage II was canceled in favor of a version able to take the new SNECMA Atar engine. This was the initial Mirage III. It flew for the first time on November 17, 1956. It was also modified during testing to have moveable intake center-body cones and a fixed SEPR rocket under the tail. Very quickly a contract was awarded for a developed version to be known as the Mirage IIIA, being slightly longer with an enlarged wing. Phillipe Ambiard led the redesign that brought the aircraft closer to becoming an operational fighter. The first IIIA flew in May 1958 with the Atar 09B of 13,230lb of thrust (58.9kN). It also had cannon and could carry a single Matra R.530 or R.511 or a Nord 5103 AAM on the centerline. An unusual weapon was a rocket pack built into the nose of each external fuel tank (although it could also be described as rocket launcher with a fuel pod attached).

After 10 IIIAs were built as a preproduction batch, the design was further revised as the Mirage IIIC, which became the first version to enter *Armée de l'Air* service, in July 1961. The IIIC was slightly longer than the IIIA and omitted the rocket. The nose contained Thomson CSF Cyrano radar. Ninety-five Mirage IIICs and 26 Mirage IIIB two-seaters entered French service and were used up to 1988 in the interceptor role. Nearly as many were exported, most of them to Israel. Other users were South Africa and Argentina, which received surplus Israeli aircraft.

Israel's first Mirage IIIs arrived in 1962 and were

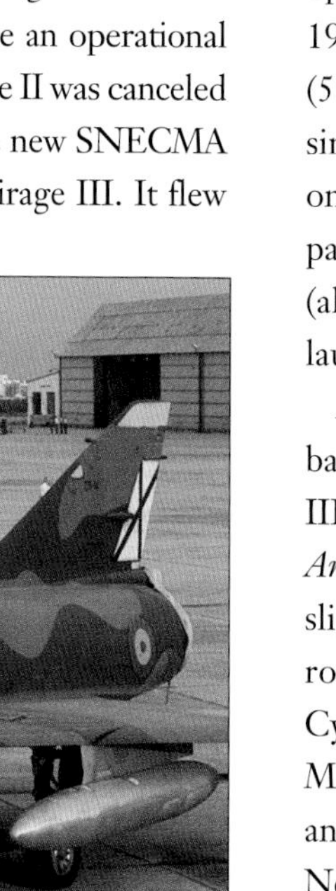

Below: *Spain bought 24 Mirage IIIEEs and six IIIDEs in 1970. These examples served with 112 Escuadron of Ala 11 at Valencia.*

Right: *The Mirage IIIC was the initial interceptor version and was usually armed with a single largely ineffective R.530 missile.*

PILOTING THE DASSAULT MIRAGE III AND 5

On May 21, 1982, the Argentines launched over 50 sorties against Royal Navy warships in San Carlos Water, an inlet off Falkland Sound, and the channel between East and West Falkland. "Raton" flight, the second of three flights of Daggers, took off from the small southern airfield of San Julian just before midday. Flight leader Captain Guillermo Donadille describes events from when they crossed the mountains at low level and heard a chilling warning from his wingman: "Sea Harriers at three o'clock!"

"The tense voice of Jorge Senn almost stopped my heart. I turned my head and to our right I could see the unmistakable silhouette of a Sea Harrier about 300 meters above our flight. I had the strange feeling that his wingman was behind us. At almost the same moment the British pilot saw us and started a diving turn toward us.

"'Eject bombs and tanks, break right, go!' I ordered, and at the same time I did the same in order to engage the Sea Harrier head-on. One of my wingmen hesitated, so I repeated the order. I saw his underwing stores separate from his aircraft, which, without all that drag, leaped like a frightened rabbit and crossed in front of me.

Above: *Nearly half of Argentina's Daggers were lost over the Falklands. The Mirage IIIs were less heavily used and only two were shot down.*

"The British pilot maintained a convergent heading to my aircraft in a shallow dive. I pressed the gun trigger from a distance of 700 meters and I think the flashes of my guns surprised him. My burst went high over his cockpit without doing any harm.

"I made a 90-degree bank and initiated a rudder dive, lowering the nose and trying to avoid losing the Sea Harrier beneath me. I fired again. The ground was approaching very quickly indeed, and my windshield was completely filled by a dark gray fuselage flanked by two big intakes and a pair of short wings.

"Stick to the stomach, careful with the yaw, I felt the *g* forces pressing me against the seat, and the anti-*g* suit inflated to prevent the blackout. I saw one of my wingmen passing over my left side in a hard level turn. I half rolled the Dagger and, while upside down, I saw that aircraft going away from me with a bright flame pouring from the tailpipe, indicating he was in full afterburner.

"Then I heard a small detonation, not very loud, as if somebody had crushed a paper bag beside my ear. My aircraft went out of control, first pointing into the clouds above, then started a frightening pitching motion that flattened me against the seat or made me float with all the dirt rising from the cockpit's floor. Suddenly the Dagger started a series of fast rolls—parallel to the ground—and the control stick felt soft.

"I ejected when the Dagger was almost upside down, but the chute opened and, and seconds later I made a very hard landing. I concealed my parachute and got away from the landing area, all the time hearing the 30-mm rounds cooking off in the fire of the unfortunate Dagger, which had crashed about 300 meters from where I had landed."

Donadille's aircraft had been brought down by an AIM-9L fired by Lieutenant Steve Thomas. Thomas then shot down Major Piuma, and Lieutenant Commander "Sharkey" Ward completed the destruction of "Raton" flight, bringing down Jorge Senn's Dagger with another Sidewinder. All three pilots survived and joined up with Argentine ground forces.

Right: *The Mirage 5 series was exported far and wide. This was a 5DM two-seater for Zaïre, one of three delivered along with eight 5M single-seaters.*

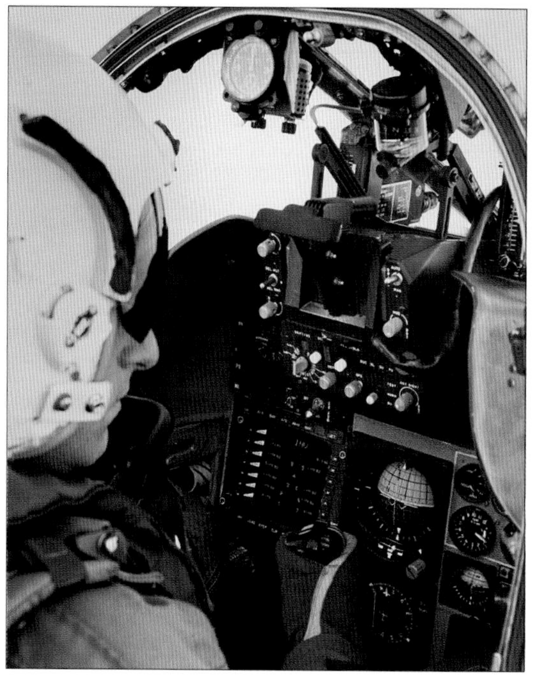

Right: *This Israeli Mirage has been modernized with a head-up display and a multifunction display, replacing many of the original dial instruments.*

given the Hebrew name *Shahak* ("Skyblazer"). At first issued to only the most experienced pilots, the *Shahak*'s first kill was scored during border skirmishes in August 1966. In the Six Day War of June 1967, Israeli Defense Force/Air Force (IDF/AF) *Shahak* pilots shot down about 60 Egyptian, Syrian, Jordanian, Iraqi, and Lebanese aircraft for seven known losses to fighters or a combination of fighters and antiaircraft fire. Many other Arab aircraft were destroyed on the ground, with No. 101 Squadron claiming 35 plus nine probables in one day. In total, Israeli Mirages claimed up to 250 kills up to 1974, mostly with cannon and, later, AIM-9Bs rather than the unreliable R.530 missile. The top Israeli Mirage ace was Abraham Shalmon with 13 kills.

Further French development led to the dual-role Mirage IIIE with greatly enhanced ground-attack capability. *Armée de l'Air* IIIEs were tasked with nuclear strike, battlefield air superiority, and defense suppression. The IIIE was an export success, going to Abu Dhabi, Argentina, Brazil, Egypt, Lebanon, Pakistan, South Africa, Spain, Venezuela, and Zaire. Australia tried out a version with the Rolls-Royce Avon, but then built all its Mirage IIIOs under license with the Atar 09C. Switzerland built the Mirage IIIS, later updating them with small canard foreplanes.

The Mirage 5 arose from Israeli requests for a cheaper, simplified version that was suitable for longer range low-level attack missions. All-weather navigation systems and radar were not needed, so a slimmer nose was used and a fuel tank was fitted in place of avionics behind the cockpit. Two more hardpoints were added at the rear wing roots. After the first flight of the Mirage V prototype on May 19, 1967, Israel was due to receive 50 examples of the Mirage 5J, but Charles De Gaulle put an arms embargo on arms sales to Israel following the Six Day War, and they were never delivered.

The *Armée de l'Air* had to take these aircraft as the Mirage 5F, but the type was

Right: *Belgium's Mirage 5BR reconnaissance aircraft served into the 1990s before replacement by F-16s with podded camera units.*

eagerly bought by a number of nations. These included Abu Dhabi, Belgium, Egypt, Colombia, Egypt, Gabon, Libya, Pakistan, Peru, Venezuela, and Zaire. Some aircraft identified by Dassault as Mirage 5s are closer to Mirage IIIs, having Cyrano radar. Many Mirage 5s had EMD Aïda ranging radar and radar warning receivers (RWRs). Simplicity of maintenance was a factor in the Mirage 5's sales success, particularly with less developed nations. A Mirage 5 needed about 15 maintenance man hours per flight hour, whereas an F-104 required 50.

The Mirage 50 was another export variant with the Atar 09K-50 engine. It was offered with the Agave radar or Cyrano IV, which contains elements of the radars used in the Mirage F1 and Mirage 2000. The Mirage 50 served only with Chile and Venezuela.

Denied the Mirage 5, Israel acquired the manufacturing plans by cloak-and-dagger means, possibly with covert assistance (or at least a blind eye) from Dassault. The result was the Nesher (Eagle), which was an unlicensed copy produced from 1969 with some local avionics, provision for Shafrir air-to-air missiles and other new weapons, and a Martin-Baker seat. This version was extremely successful in the 1973 war, with many kills, one pilot scoring 10. From 1978–80, 35 of the Neshers were sold on to Argentina as the Dagger, joining Mirage IIIs. Both types were heavily involved in the Falklands War, but fared badly against the Royal Navy's Sea Harrier.

In total, two Mirages and 11 Daggers were lost in action, mostly falling to the combination of Sea Harrier and AIM-9L. Some of the surviving Daggers were later upgraded in Argentina as the Finger.

***Above:** From 1966 to 1973 this Israeli* Shahak *(Mirage IIICJ) shot down 13 Syrian and Egyptian aircraft. It was sold to Argentina but was later returned to Israel.*

Further foreign developments of the Mirage III/5 included the Israeli IAI Kfir series with General Electric J79 engines, the Chilean ENAER Pantera, and the South African Atlas Cheetah. All of these have a longer, slimmer nose with an Elta ranging radar and canard foreplanes on the intake sides. The story of these variants is really outside that of the basic Mirage family.

Space precludes detailed description of the various experimental models such as the Milan with its "mustache" canards, the sophisticated Mirage 3NG, and the vertical takeoff Balzac V and Mirage IIIV. Two-seat trainer variants were built of every basic model, and there were many reconnaissance models with camera noses. Although now gone from Europe, aircraft of the Mirage III family still serve around the world, particularly in Latin America and the Middle East.

***Below:** Now in storage, Libya's Mirage 5DDs provided conversion training for the five squadrons of this type once operated by the Libyan Arab Air Force.*

English Electric Lightning

The Lightning performed spectacularly in the interceptor role and was no slouch as a dogfighter, either. Constantly expected to retire "next year," the Lightning stayed in service until 1988, but retained its 1950s-era avionics and weapons.

***Right:** The F Mk 6 was the definitive version of the Lightning. This formation is from No. 5 Squadron, based at Binbrook, in Lincolnshire, England.*

In 1947, W.E.W. "Teddy" Petter of the English Electric company submitted a proposal for a supersonic aircraft with highly swept wings to the British Ministry of Supply. Impressed by the concept, and spurred by US success in breaking the "sound barrier" earlier that year, the ministry issued a requirement for a supersonic research aircraft based on the English Electric (EE) P.1. An order for two flying prototypes was not issued until April 1950, by which time Teddy Petter had gone to work for Folland (where he designed the Gnat), so much of the P.1's development was done by F.W. Page.

The P.1 had a long oval-section fuselage, beginning at a single intake and ending with the exhausts of two 8,100-lb thrust (36-kN) Armstrong-Siddeley Sapphire engines stacked one above the other. The parallel chord wings were swept at 60 degrees, as was the tailplane, which was mounted below the plane of the wing, another novel feature. A stalky undercarriage with very thin large-diameter wheels retracted outward into the wing. The nose intake was oval and did not contain the radar of later versions. The fuel tanks were concentrated in the wing box, giving a somewhat less than adequate supply.

The P.1 was preceded by the Shorts SB.5 aerodynamic testbed, which was flown in late 1952. The SB.5 came about because the Royal Aeronautical Establishment (RAE) did not trust Petter's calculations for the P.1 and was

ENGLISH ELECTRIC LIGHTNING F.6

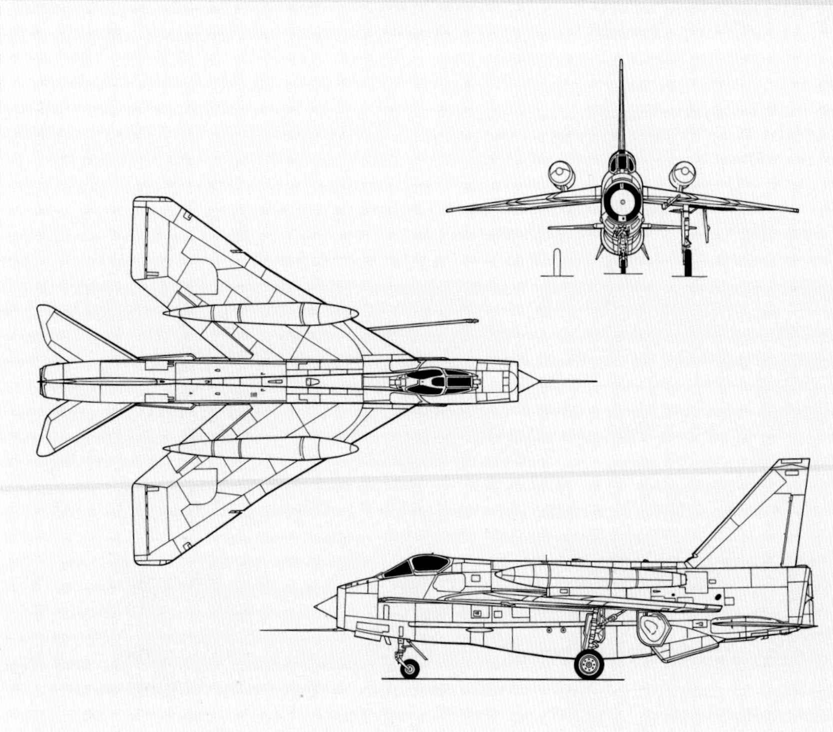

Crew: one

Powerplant: two Rolls-Royce Avon 301 turbojets rated at 16,360lb of thrust (72.76kN) in afterburner

Maximum speed: 1,320mph (2,112km/h)

Combat radius: 348 miles (560km)

Service ceiling: 55,000ft (16,770m)

Weight: 40,000lb (19,047kg) loaded

Armament: two Red Top or Firestreak IR-guided air-to-air missiles or up to 44 2-in (50-mm) unguided rockets; two 1.18-in (30-mm) Aden cannon in a ventral pack

Dimensions: span 34ft 10in (10.62m); length 55ft 3in (16.84m); height 19ft 7in (5.97m)

J
K
XR762

PILOTING THE ENGLISH ELECTRIC LIGHTNING

Above: *The Lightning cockpit was the most coveted position in the 1960s RAF. These are F.1s of No. 74 "Tiger" Squadron.*

Practicing the low-level interception role was great fun in the Lightning F.3, as then Flying Officer Tony Paxton recalled: "The Lightning was very good in these low-level hassles, with its big wing and lots of power. It would turn with anything. The Phantoms were no problem. Normally you'd nip in and out fairly quickly because they'd be in pairs or fours, while we'd generally operate singly or with a second aircraft if you were lucky. On a big exercise we'd usually set up a line of CAPs [Combat Air Patrols] from the Austrian border right up to the Baltic, and the Lightnings would take a stretch of that line, in the center, with US Phantoms or Eagles further north.

"Basically our job was to operate low down, behind the SAM [surface-to-air missile] belt. I remember having some great scraps with F-4s. You'd engage a Phantom, then see his wingman. 'Oh Christ! There's two of them!' and you'd be shouting to people in the next adjacent CAP. You'd get some amazing Battle of Britain type chat over the radio: 'Come on, come up and help me!' 'Where is he?' 'You see that little lake? We're just over there. Oh hang on, I've got another one!' 'Right, I've got you. Keep turning!' 'Oh God, there's a Harrier in there as well!' It was amazing, really good fun.

"The Ginas (Fiat G.91s) probably gave us the most trouble because they were so small and difficult to see. The F-104s were difficult, too, just catching them. I remember chasing one down past the Möhne Dam (you know, the 'Dambusters' and all that!) at about 300 feet doing Mach 1.1 at half past seven in the morning, and I was only just catching him! We never had any noise complaints then, though. It was amazing. We used to do combat down to a base of 10,000 feet, and quite often you'd go supersonic in combat but no-one ever complained.

"The F-15 was just beginning to make its presence felt when I left Germany. The Eagle was pretty new then and the pilots weren't that wonderful. I mean, straight one-to-one we didn't stand a chance, but using good tactics, two Lightnings could always see off one F-15, and we could usually deal with two without too much trouble. They tended to stick in pairs, so we'd get them to commit one way or another then we'd split. We'd give each other mutual support and pick one off, leaving us with one F-15 against two Lightnings.

"Trying to get a 'guns kill' on someone at low level is hard work. If you could persuade him to turn in some way, that helped; you'd halved your problems, you could fire across the corner. If he just stayed very low and very fast you'd be bouncing around all over the place, and getting a gun on him could be almost impossible."

Right: *Wearing the green camouflage adopted for low-level operations in the 1970s, a No. 92 Squadron Lightning lands at Gutersloh, Germany.*

particularly skeptical of his low-set tailplane. The SB.5 had a fixed undercarriage and could only explore low-speed handling. It was tested with several wing configurations and either a low-set or a T-tail. Eventually it validated Petter's original layout, but had little direct influence on the design of the P.1.

Roland Beamont flew the P.1 on August 4, 1954 and took it past Mach 1.0 a week later. Remarkably, this was done without afterburners, achieving what was later to be called "supercruise." The second aircraft was the P.1A, armed with twin cannon. By the time it flew in July 1955, the Air Ministry had decided to procure a dedicated fighter version, designated P.1B. The P.1B had a larger vertical fin and a circular intake containing AI.23 Airpass radar in a central cone. The radar could fly the aircraft to within range of the target and fire the missiles, although the system was not as sophisticated as on contemporary US fighters such as the Convair F-106. Power was supplied by Rolls-Royce RA.24 Avon engines of 14,430lb of thrust (64kN) in reheat (afterburner).

The intended armament was the Blue Jay infrared homing missile, later renamed Firestreak. This came as a modular pack of two missiles with a pair of 1.18-in (30-mm) Aden cannon. Alternatively a pack with 22 rockets and two cannon could be fitted. The Firestreak was later supplemented by the Red Top, originally known as Firestreak Mk IV. The F.2 could have two additional cannon instead of Firestreaks.

The day the P.1B first flew, April 4, 1957, was the same day that the Minister of Defence announced cancellation of all other manned combat aircraft projects. Duncan Sandys declared that the day of the (surface-launched) missile had come, and fighters would no longer be necessary. The P.1B had progressed "too far to be canceled." In July 1957, the P.1B unofficially broke the world air speed record of Mach 1.72. Actual top performance was much higher, but the British government was reluctant to reveal the true capabilities. Mach 2.0 was surpassed in November 1958.

Above: *An F.2 of No. 19 Squadron, armed with Firestreaks, shows the rounded fin tip used on the F.1 and F.2 Lightnings.*

Below: *The T.5, a training version of the Lightning, served with many units, including the Lightning Training Flight (LTF).*

Above: For a brief period the RAF's Lightnings outdid the brightly-marked biplane fighters of the 1930s for color. From the top this stack features Lightnings of Nos. 92, 111, 56, and 19 Squadrons.

The P.1B was renamed Lightning in October 1958, and the initial production Lightning F Mk 1 entered service with No. 74 Squadron in July 1960. This was the first of eight RAF frontline squadrons to fly Lightnings over the next 28 years. UK Lightning squadrons were based on the East Coast to intercept Soviet bombers coming down from the Baltic Sea or around the Kola Peninsula. As such, they encountered many "Bear" and "Badger" aircraft probing NATO defenses.

As well as their home defense tasking, RAF Lightnings were deployed to West Germany, Cyprus and Singapore. RAF Germany (RAFG) Lightnings were tasked with low-level patrols against possible "sneak attacks" from the east. Despite not being designed for such operations, the Lightning had superb low-level handling and a high thrust-to-weight ratio, and made an excellent dogfighter in this regime. In their later years, RAFG Lightnings adopted an overall green camouflage scheme. UK Lightnings also changed from natural metal to a gray and green pattern, and then overall gray.

The Lightning F.1 was followed by the F.1A with aerial refueling capability and UHF radios and the F.2 with a better navigation system and improved fully variable afterburner. The F.3 had no cannon, improved radar, Red Top missiles, and a larger fin.

A two-seat T.4 with side-by-side seating entered service in 1962; the T.5 with a different cockpit layout was closer in configuration to the F.3. The final RAF model was the F.6 with a variable camber "kinked" wing, large ventral fuel tank and overwing hardpoints. The last F.6 was delivered to the RAF in August 1967, but redeliveries of F.2s upgraded to similar F.2A standard continued a while longer.

The location of the undercarriage prevented the use of regular underwing fuel tanks, so, from the F.6 model hardpoints were added to allow tanks to be mounted above the wing. These proved more

Right: An F.6 of No. 56 Squadron arrives at RAF Akrotiri, Cyprus. The boarding ladder bent out to clear the missile and in to avoid the refueling probe.

useful on low-level flights, as their weight and drag tended to cancel out the extra fuel by the time the aircraft reached high altitude. The low-drag ventral tank increased range by around 20 percent without drag or handling penalties. A removable refueling probe could be fitted under the port wing, improving endurance and effectiveness, but complicating pilot access as he had to squeeze between the ladder and the probe to get in or out.

Without aerial refueling, the Lightning F.6 had an endurance of only about 50 minutes, and unrefueled flying seldom went further than 100–150 miles (160–243km) from base. Shutting down one engine and use of a particular descent profile could stretch endurance. Pilots bragged of flying 90-minute or even two-hour sorties. Its climb performance was spectacular, with an initial climb rate of 50,000ft (15,240m) per minute. From brakes off to 36,000ft (10,972m) took two and a half minutes.

The Lightning was exported to only two nations, Saudi Arabia and Kuwait. After the loan of seven F.2 and T.4 models in 1966, Saudi Arabia took delivery of 35 F Mk 53s and six Mk 55s from 1969 to counter Yemeni incursions and Egyptian air attacks. These could carry bombs and air-to-ground rockets on underwing pylons and were used in action in the border areas from late 1969. One was lost to Yemeni ground fire in May 1970. The Saudi two-seaters were better equipped than the RAF's T.5, having the large ventral fuel tank and the enlarged variable-camber wing of the F.6.

Kuwait had less success with their 14 aircraft, also designated F.53 and T.55, which arrived in 1969–70. Not having contracted with BAC for support, the Kuwaitis found maintaining the complex aircraft difficult. They were put up for sale in 1973 and retired in 1977.

The Saudi Lightnings stopped flying in 1986 and were repurchased by British Aerospace (Bae) as part of the Al-Yamamah arms deal. There were hopes that Austria might buy these aircraft, but they chose Saab Drakens instead. Nigeria also briefly showed an interest in the ex-Saudi Lightnings.

Despite its spectacular performance, the Lightning was increasingly outdated in the modern air combat environment, having no countermeasures either electronic or disposable (chaff and flares). The radar was very basic, and the single pilot was something of a "one-armed paper hanger" in managing the intercept while trying to fly the aircraft accurately and not run out of fuel. The radar itself had an effective range of no more than 25 miles (40km), and, at supersonic speeds, the closing rate between fighter and target might be 18 miles (29km) per minute.

The Firestreak missile had a short range and would not work in cloud. More importantly, perhaps, the Lightning could only carry two of them, and then it was down to cannon. Plans to equip the Lightning with Sidewinders were never carried out as retirement was always "around the corner."

The Lightning was finally retired from frontline RAF service in 1988 and replaced by the Tornado F.3, but several aircraft were retained by BAe as radar calibration targets until 1993. Despite the enthusiasm of a number of groups, the airworthiness authorities in the United Kingdom have not permitted such a complex aircraft as the Lightning to fly in private hands, but a collector in South Africa has two T.5s and an F.6 airworthy, with another F.6 under rebuild. The two-seaters are available for joyrides by the well-heeled tourist.

Above: *Saudi Arabia's Lightning F.53s were the only Lightnings to see (limited) action. This is actually an RAF F.6 painted in Saudi markings.*

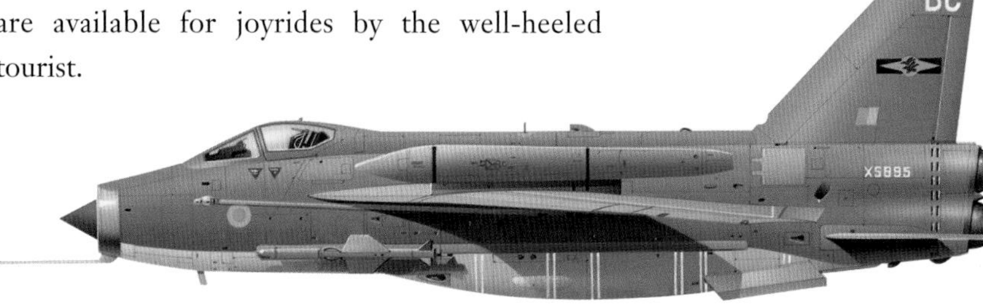

Below: *A Lightning F.6 of No. 11 Squadron at RAF Binbrook in the 1980s. In their latter years the Lightnings mainly adopted gray camouflage.*

McDonnell Douglas F-4 Phantom II

Designed for the US Navy's fleet defense role in the 1950s, McDonnell's fabulous Phantom soon adopted other missions and appeared in many specialized versions and the colors of a dozen air arms.

MCDONNELL DOUGLAS RF-4E PHANTOM II

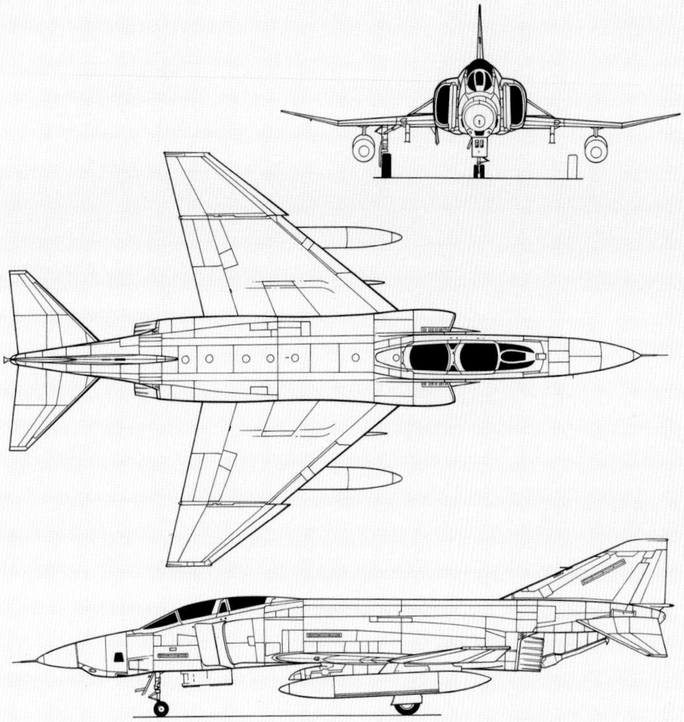

Crew: two

Powerplant: two General Electric J79-GE-17A turbojets rated at 17,900lb of thrust (79.62kN) in afterburner

Maximum speed: 1,485mph (2,390km/h)

Combat radius: 594 miles (958km)

Service ceiling: 62,250ft (18,975m)

Weight: 61,795lb (28,030kg) loaded

Armament: none (fighter versions normally carry four AIM-7 Sparrow and four AIM-9 Sidewinder air-to-air missiles)

Dimensions: span 38ft 5in (11.71m); length 63ft (19.2m); height 16ft 5.5in (5.03m)

Far right: *Among the last Phantoms in British service were the FGR.2s of No. 74 "Tiger" Squadron, based at Wattisham, in the UK.*

Right: *An F-4J Phantom of VF-31 "Tomcatters," based on the USS* Saratoga *during the Vietnam War.*

Seeing more combat than most of its contemporaries, the F-4 Phantom was the most numerous western jet fighter after the F-86 Sabre. Even today, nearly 50 years after its inception, hundreds of Phantoms continue to serve with air forces around the world, many of them the subject of sophisticated upgrade programs.

The McDonnell company's initial work on what would become the Phantom commenced in 1953, beginning as a single-seat cannon-armed twin-engined development of the F3H Demon. By May 1955, when the US Navy ordered two prototypes, McDonnell's Model 98 had evolved to having two General Electric J79 engines, two crew, and armament of up to eight air-to-air missiles. The outer wings had an upward tilt (dihedral), while the tailplanes swept down with considerable anhedral.

The prototype, designated F4H-1 under the pre-1962 system, first flew on May 27, 1958, in St Louis, with

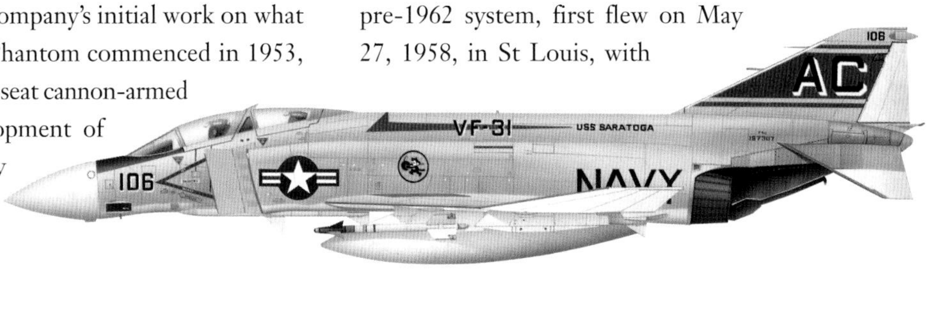

PILOTING THE MCDONNELL DOUGLAS F-4 PHANTOM II

Right: *An F-4B crew from the "Rock Rivers" of VF-161 scored the last US Navy kill in Vietnam.*

A US Navy Phantom crew had the honor of scoring the final aerial victory of the Vietnam War, on January 12, 1973. Flying from the USS *Midway*, an F-4B of VF-161 "Rock Rivers" was launched on a routine BARCAP (barrier combat air patrol) mission to patrol the likely approach route of any attacking North Vietnamese aircraft. Pilot Lieutenant Victor Kovaleski and his radar-intercept officer (RIO) Lieutenant (junior grade) James Wise, together with another Phantom, were directed by the airborne controller code-named "Red Crown" to a radar contact to the northeast. The two aircraft assumed a combat spread formation, the wingman flying 1,500ft (458m) higher and 3,000ft (916m) abreast of "Rock River 102."

As the range to the MiG closed, Kovaleski and Wise descended to 3,000ft (916m) and accelerated to approximately 515mph (830km/h). At a range of four nautical miles (7.4km), Kovaleski called a visual contact on a dark-colored MiG-17, heading north at 500ft (153m). Obtaining clearance to fire, the section closed to less than one mile of the MiG's seven o'clock. At that moment, the Vietnamese pilot broke hard to the left, then into Kovaleski and Wise. The section slid into the MiG's six o'clock blind spot, but, anticipating an overshoot, the MiG pilot reversed hard to his right.

Still maintaining good nose–tail separation, Kovaleski and Wise reversed right with the MiG, placing it within the gunsight pipper. Kovaleski triggered a Sidewinder, which detonated behind the MiG, knocking off a section of its tail, but the MiG kept flying. Kovaleski triggered a second Sidewinder, this one at a range of 3,000ft (916m). The missile guided well, and just before impact the F-4 crew saw the North Vietnamese pilot eject. The MiG then exploded in a huge fireball and careened into the water. No parachute was seen.

Two days later, Kovaleski and another RIO were shot down near Than Hoa by antiaircraft fire. This was the last American aircraft to be brought down over North Vietnam, but fortunately the crew were able to eject over water and were rescued by a US Navy helicopter.

Right: *The front cockpit of the F-4E was typical of its era, having a large radar scope and a multitude of "clockwork" instrument dials.*

McDonnell test pilot Robert C. Little at the controls. The F4H-1 was named Phantom II in July 1959. The original McDonnell FH-1 Phantom had been the US Navy's first carrier-based jet in 1946. Early Phantoms were used to set a variety of records. Project Top Flight set a new absolute altitude record of 98,560ft (30,041m), Project Skyburner an absolute speed record of 1,606.347mph (2,585.299km/h) and Project Sageburner a low level speed record of 902.760mph (1,452.902km/h).

The 45 F4H-1Fs (redesignated F-4A from September 1962) were not considered fully operational and did not see regular fleet service. Late production F4H-1Fs established the shape of most subsequent Phantoms, with a raised rear canopy and a much larger radome, containing the APQ-72 radar with an 32-in (81-cm) reflector. They were soon replaced by the F4H-1, or F-4B, which had full weapons provisions, revised intake ramps, and slightly more powerful J79s. This model entered service in early 1961, VF-74 "Bedevilers" becoming the first operational squadron later that year.

In 1961, the US Air Force evaluated the F-106 against the F4H-1 and was so impressed by the performance, radar, and weapons capabilities of the Phantom that it made plans to acquire its own version of the F-4B. To this end a batch of 29 was loaned to the US Air Force under the designation F-110. An unarmed reconnaissance model, the RF-110, was also planned. These air force models were later redesignated the F-4C and RF-4C, respectively. They retained such naval features as arrester hooks and folding wings, but added dual controls for the rear-seat crewman, who was known as a weapons systems operator, or WSO, in air force parlance. Thicker lower-pressure tires were fitted for runway use, and these necessitated a bulged upper wing surface to accommodate them. A receptacle on the spine for the boom system used by air force tankers replaced the navy's retractable

***Below:** Before they disbanded or re-equipped with Tornado F.3s, several RAF Phantom squadrons marked aircraft in various colors, as with this No. 56 Squadron.*

***Left:** Spain was the only export user of the F-4C. The similar F-4D was supplied to South Korea and Iran.*

__Above:__ The F-4G was the dedicated "Wild Weasel" version of the Phantom, converted from F-4Es and tasked with destroying enemy missile-guidance radars.

__Below:__ The Phantom FG.1 or F-4K was the last fixed-wing Royal Navy fighter. No. 892 was the only operational RN squadron.

refueling probe. The F-4C was followed by the F-4D with improved bombing capability.

Both early US Air Force Phantom models could fire the AIM-4 Falcon, as well as the AIM-9 Sidewinder and AIM-7 Sparrow missiles. The F-4D and later models could mount an M61 0.79-in (20-mm) cannon on the centerline pylon; however, as with other first-generation Phantoms, there was no internal gun.

The F-4J was an improved navy version with J79-GE-10 engines, stronger undercarriage, more fuel, slotted tailplanes, better ground-attack capability, and APG-59 radar with a new fire-control system. The surviving F-4Bs were rebuilt as F-4Ns in the early 1970s with improved radar warning and ECM equipment, slotted tailplanes, and a datalink. In a similar fashion, remaining F-4Js became the F-4S model with slatted outboard wing sections, giving improved turning ability.

The US Navy, Air Force, and Marine Corps units used the Phantom throughout the Vietnam War in the bomber, fighter, and reconnaissance roles. Just under 150 kills were scored against North Vietnamese MiGs between 1965 and 1973.

In 1969, the US Air Force introduced the F-4E, which was the first version to have an internal gun, an M61 Vulcan cannon mounted in a fairing under an elongated nose. The E also had extra fuel and APS-107B radar. It was the most numerous model, with nearly 1,400 built. Related models included the F-4G "Wild Weasel" defense-suppression version and the RF-4E reconnaissance model for export.

The Phantom was supplied to 11 nations, one of which, Japan, built its own aircraft under license. The roster of users is Spain (F-4C and RF-4C), United Kingdom (F-4K, F-4M and F-4J), Israel (F-4E and RF-4E), West Germany (F-4F and RF-4E), Korea (F-4D, F-4E and RF-4C), Egypt (F-4E), Greece (F-4E, RF-4E), Iran (F-4D, F-4E, RF-4E), Japan (F-4EJ and RF-4EJ), and Turkey (F-4E and RF-4E). Australia leased F-4Es while awaiting F-111 deliveries.

Britain's F-4K and F-4M Phantoms were unique in having Rolls-Royce Spey turbofans. These required wider intakes, the drag of which negated much of the extra thrust offered. The F-4K (Phantom FG.1) flew from Royal Navy carriers before transfer to the Royal Air Force alongside that service's F-4Ms (FGR.2s). After the Falklands War, a batch of ex–US Navy Phantoms was acquired as the F-4J(UK).

Israel's requests for the supply of Phantoms were finally granted in 1968, and the first of an eventual 238 Phantoms were delivered in September 1969 during the War of Attrition. The F-4Es and RF-4Es gave Israel its first true long-range strike and reconnaissance capabilities, as well as an interceptor with greater combat persistence (with its eight missiles and cannon) than any fighter in the region. Many were lost to

***Left:** An F-4EJ of the 305th Hikotai of the Japanese Air Self-Defense Force (JASDF), a unit that now flies F-15J Eagles.*

ground defenses during the 1973 Yom Kippur War, and more than 50 were supplied from US Air Force stocks under the emergency Operation Nickel Glass. Israel Air Force Defense Force/Air Force (IDF/AF) F-4Es have been credited with 116 kills over Lebanon against their Arab neighbors between September 1969 and June 1982. About 60 F-4Es were modified from 1987 as the *Kurnass* ("heavy hammer") 2,000 with APG-76 multimode radar, a HUD, new weapons, and hands-on throttle and stick (HoTaS) controls. A more ambitious Super Phantom proposal with new PW1120 turbofans did not proceed past the prototype stage.

Iran was the second-largest export user, taking delivery of 225 examples, mostly F-4Es, between 1971 and 1979. Further deliveries were embargoed after the Islamic revolution, but Iran managed to maintain a substantial force of Phantoms during the 1980–88 war with Iraq. More than 20 kills, including a number of helicopters, are known to have been scored by Islamic Republic of Iran Air Force (IRIAF) F-4 crews, with a dozen or so Phantoms lost to Iraqi fighters. More were shot down by ground defenses, but a full and accurate accounting for this war will probably never be known.

The Phantoms of a number of operators have been upgraded. Japan's F-4EJ-Kais have APG-66J radar and Germany's F-4Fs have been given AMRAAM capability under the F-4F ICE program. Greece's F-4Es and Turkey's F-4Es have both gone through similar upgrades to Israel's, the latter being sometimes called the "Terminator 2020." Generally speaking, the modifications have all involved new multimode radar, HoTaS controls, HUDs, and integration of new precision weapons.

The last of 5,201 Phantoms was built in 1981. The United Kingdom and Spain are the only export operators to have completely retired their Phantoms. The last Phantoms in US Air Force service are F-4Es used for training *Luftwaffe* aircrew, and some QF-4E and QF-4G drones. The US Navy still flies a handful of QF-4Js and QF-4Ns at Point Mugu, California. Apart from a few F-4s operated by defense contractors, only one Phantom, an F-4D, has been operated as a purely civil aircraft.

***Below:** A US Air Force F-4E in the toned-down markings adopted in the 1980s and equipped with the TISEO television camera in the port wing.*

SAAB Viggen

Saab's Viggen, a massive design and engineering challenge for a small nation, gave Sweden a fighter suited exactly to its defensive needs. The Viggen carried on the tradition of the innovatively designed Saab fighters built since the 1940s.

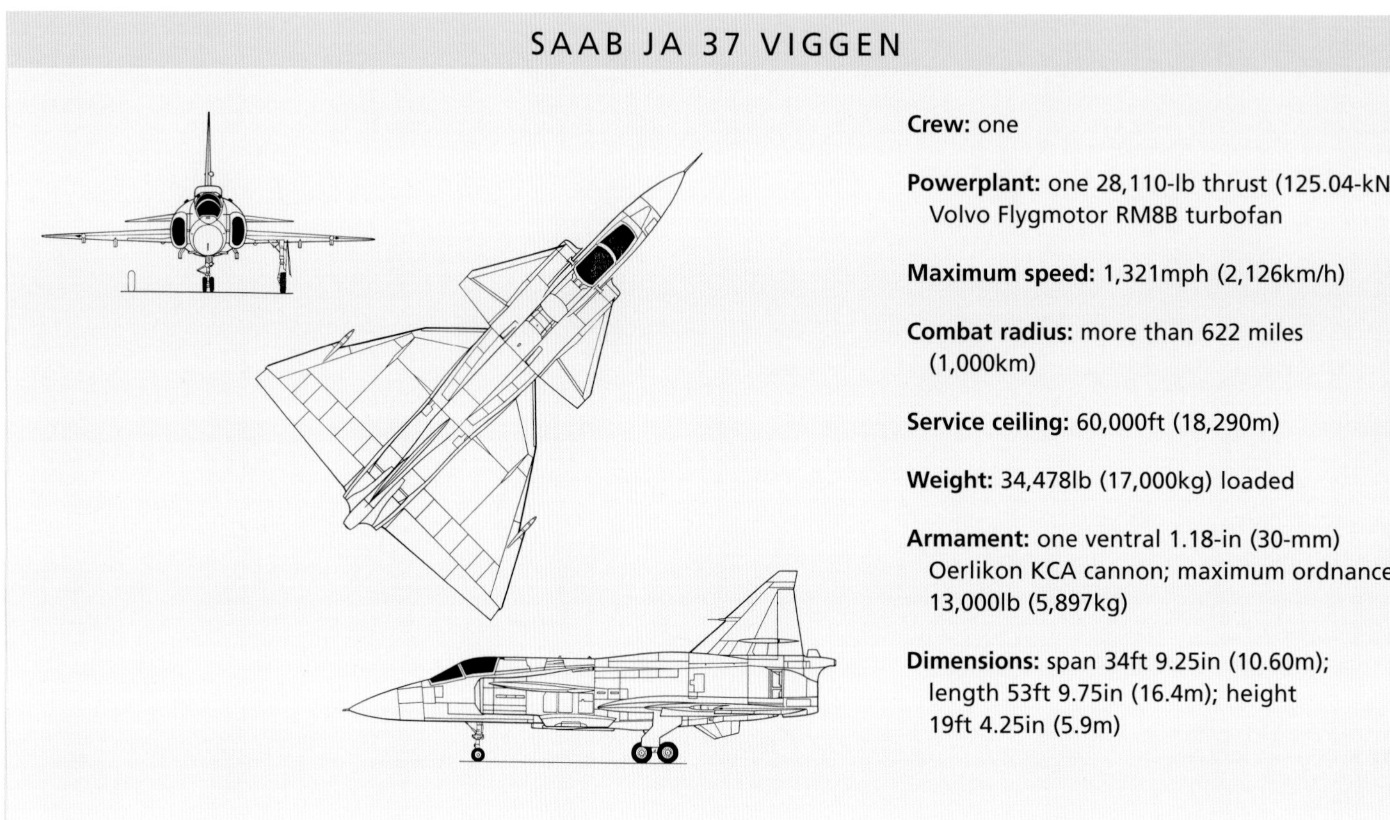

SAAB JA 37 VIGGEN

Crew: one

Powerplant: one 28,110-lb thrust (125.04-kN) Volvo Flygmotor RM8B turbofan

Maximum speed: 1,321mph (2,126km/h)

Combat radius: more than 622 miles (1,000km)

Service ceiling: 60,000ft (18,290m)

Weight: 34,478lb (17,000kg) loaded

Armament: one ventral 1.18-in (30-mm) Oerlikon KCA cannon; maximum ordnance 13,000lb (5,897kg)

Dimensions: span 34ft 9.25in (10.60m); length 53ft 9.75in (16.4m); height 19ft 4.25in (5.9m)

Right: *With its delta wing and canard foreplanes, the Viggen is one of the most distinctive modern combat aircraft in service.*

Named in Swedish after the thunderbolt of the Norse god, Thor, the Saab Viggen was one of the most distinctive and innovative combat aircraft of the 1970s. Studies began as early as 1954 on a fighter and attack aircraft to replace the J35 Draken and J32 Lansen under various designations in the Project 1300 series. Swedish defense planners were coming to the realization that fixed airbases were vulnerable to attack in the first hours of any war, and they developed the concept of dispersing fighters to road bases either preceding conflict or when they returned from their first combat sorties. Straight stretches of road were widened and modified with turn-off areas to support aircraft and mobile teams of technicians.

The aircraft component of what was called System 37, the Flygplan 37 or Aircraft 37, was designed both to be capable of short field operations and to be serviced by teams of conscripts with little specialized training. As such, Saab's team, led again by Erik Bratt, considered using additional lift engines to reduce the landing speed. This was rejected due to control problems caused by downwash. The design team had already chosen to use the then-fashionable delta wing, but added to it a delta foreplane, or canard, with large trailing-edge elevators. This double-delta configuration was the first such to be seen on a fighter, and the large area of the canards caused some to suggest that the Viggen was a modern biplane. On landing,

13
13
39
323

PILOTING THE VIGGEN

***Above:** As Viggen units disband or transition to the Gripen, a number of special color schemes, such as this red AJS 37 of F10, have appeared.*

Major Bengt Eriksson, then an AJ 37 pilot with the now-disbanded F6 wing, recalls standing five-minute alert at the Visby base during one summer in the mid-1980s. The message came through that an intruder had been detected east of Gotland and that two pilots were to be ready to start up in 10 minutes with no further radio signals. The datalink system was not installed in the "attack" Viggen, and in these Cold War days it was assumed that some conscript airmen or other observers might be sympathetic to the "other side" and pass on timings to a potential enemy. For the same reason, the pilots walked rather than ran to the aircraft. At the appointed time, the Viggens took off and headed to the north before turning east and proceeding at a speed of Mach 0.9 just 164ft (50m) above the sea to a predetermined climb point. The Viggen is one of the most stable aircraft at low level and can easily reach Mach 1.2 at 1,000ft (330m).

This was Eriksson's first "live" intercept, and he was hoping to be the first in his squadron to see a MiG-29, particularly as there were no good pictures of them at the time. The Viggens climbed and broke radio silence to receive directions from ground radar for an interception. The surprised intruder turned out to be a Soviet Tu-16 "Badger" and was duly photographed with hand-held cameras. The honor of netting the first "Fulcrum" fell to the squadron commander a few weeks later. Bengt Eriksson had to wait several more years before he saw one himself. Fortunately the interceptions flown by the AJ squadrons (who rotated alert duties with the JA squadrons) never resulted in an actual dogfight, as the AJs were only armed with cannon and would have been no match for a MiG-29, either inside or outside gun range.

the canard flaps, wing flaps, and elevons combined to force the nose down and reduce the landing roll.

The engine was a license-built Pratt & Whitney JT-8D, as used on the Boeing 727. As the Volvo Flygmotor RM8A, the engine had both afterburner and thrust reverse, the first time these had been combined. Together, the control services and thrust reverser helped to reduce the required landing distance to 1,640ft (500m). An unusual tandem main landing gear design reduced landing shock and worked better in snowy conditions. It was also slimmer than a single, thick wheel and could fit within the thin wing when retracted. The steerable double nosewheel unit allowed the aircraft to turn around at the end of the landing strip, ready to taxi back to the takeoff point.

The first Viggen flew at Linköping on February 8, 1967, piloted by Erik Dahlstrom. A tragic accident happened early in the test program when another pilot inadvertently ejected himself at low speed during takeoff and was killed. The SAAB-

***Right:** An SF 37 reconnaissance Viggen of F21 wing based at Luleå in northern Sweden.*

designed seat was only effective above 43mph (70km/h). Late production models had a zero-zero seat, which was retrofitted to all surviving aircraft. Eight Viggen prototypes were tested, including a two-seater, before deliveries of the first production AJ 37 (Attack-Jakt) or attack fighters began in 1971. Almost simultaneously with the AJ 37 deliveries, Flygvapnet accepted two reconnaissance variants, the SH 37 and SF 37. The SH (Spanings Havsövervakning, or reconnaissance coastal surveillance) version looked much like an attack Viggen, concealing powerful surface-search radar within a standard radome. The SF (Spaning Foto, or photo-reconnaissance) model had a chisel-ended camera nose, crammed with seven cameras of various focal lengths. Additional reconnaissance equipment could be carried in underwing pods.

The first unit to become operational with the Viggen was the second squadron of the 7th Wing, or Flygflottilj 7 (F7), at Såtenäs, which had previously operated six earlier Saab fighter-bomber designs, but not the Draken. As with all operational Viggens, the F7 aircraft wore the wing number on the nose and an individual number on the tail. The attack Viggens could carry rocket pods and up to 16 265-lb (120-kg) bombs, although Swedish-designed

***Above:** This AJ 37 displays its armament of Sidewinder and Skyflash missiles and a centerline drop tank, which was almost always carried by Viggens.*

***Left:** A group of AJ 37s involved in the early testing of the Viggen. After they entered service, Viggens adopted the distinctive splinter markings.*

Right: In later years, many Viggens, such as this JA 37 of F16, have adopted a gray color scheme with high-visibility identification markings.

Above: This early Viggen has three Sidewinders, two Skyflash, and a fuel tank on one shoulder pylon.

air-to-surface missiles were the main weapon. These included the heavy Rb 04 and Rb 04 (where "Rb" stands for "robot") and the Rb 75, a licensed version of the AGM-65 Maverick.

The prototypes and early production deliveries were in unpainted metal finish, but soon the air force started painting their Viggens in the elaborate "Fields and Meadows" camouflage, consisting of a "splinter" pattern of tan, light green, olive green, and black over light gray undersides. Soon all sorts of Flygvapnet equipment, vehicles, and particularly uniforms adopted the same pattern. After experiments that included trials of an all-white aircraft, the JA 37s and some of the trainers and photo aircraft adopted a two-tone light gray pattern. Otherwise there were few variations until the late 1990s, when some spectacular special schemes were permitted, including an all-red AJS of F10 and another of F17 in the blue and yellow of the Swedish flag.

The last SH 37 was delivered in 1980. Production of the second-generation Viggen continued for another 10 years. Production numbers were once something of a secret, but are believed to amount to 329 Viggens, consisting of 108 AJ 37s, 17 Sk 37s, 28 SF 37s, and 27 SH 37s, as well as 149 JA 37s. About 115 AJS 37s were created by upgrading AJ, SF, and SH models to AJS, AJSF, and AJSH models, respectively.

The true fighter Viggen is the JA 37 Jakt Viggen (Fighter Viggen), developed in the early to mid-1970s as a dedicated interceptor. It introduced a new pulse-Doppler look-down/shoot-down PS-47 radar, new avionics, an uprated and modified RM8B engine and a 30-mm Oerlikon cannon in a ventral installation. The main armament was two Rb 71 (BAe Dynamics Sky Flash) semiactive radar-homing AAMs, together with two Rb 24s (AIM-9B/J Sidewinders) or Rb 74 (AIM-9Ls). A modified AJ 37 was flown as the JA 37 prototype on September 27, 1974, and production JA 37s entered service in 1978. A number of aircraft have now undergone the JA 37 Mod D upgrade, giving them AIM-120 AMRAAM (Rb 99) capability and many of the avionics and displays of the JAS 39 Gripen.

Force cuts during the 1990s saw the retirement of many AJ 37s, as squadrons were disestablished and aircraft were scrapped. The advent of the Gripen brought about a rationalization of the

Viggen fleet. The retirement of the Saab J 32E Lansen from the electronic warfare (EW) training role saw a small number of two-seat Viggens converted to Sk 37E "Erik" electronic aggressors. These have a rear instrument panel that can be exchanged between a basic instructor's panel and an EW control panel as required.

At the time the Viggen program was launched, production was forecast to reach up to 831 aircraft, with considerable export potential. The Viggen was offered for the Nato Starfighter replacement requirement of the 1970s in competition with versions of the F-16, F-18, and Mirage F1. Unfortunately Sweden's neutrality and Saab's relative lack of sales experience worked against them. The potential customers were put off by the possibility that the spare parts supply would be cut off in the event of war or at times of high political tension. Due to the huge orders placed for the US Air Force, General Dynamics was able to offer the F-16A/B at very low unit cost, and in 1975 Belgium, the Netherlands, Norway, and Denmark ordered F-16s in the so-called "sale of the century."

Above: *The AJ 37 was the original attack Viggen. Many were upgraded to AJS 37 standard.*

More recently, Saab has offered the lease or loan of surplus Viggens to nations contemplating purchase of the JAS 39 Gripen such as Poland and the Czech Republic. Draken operator Austria was seen as the most likely to take up this offer, as many of its pilots have flown the Viggen on exchange tours, but in the end Austria settled on the Eurofighter Typhoon. Thus it appears that Sweden will be the only Viggen operator, and this distinctive fighter will disappear from Nordic skies, bar one or two preserved for the historic flight, sometime around 2005.

Left: *The Viggen (this is an AJ37 of F17) was as distinctive for its "fields and meadows" camouflage as it was for its configuration.*

Grumman F-14 Tomcat

Designed to destroy Soviet long-range bombers, the F-14 saw action against Libya, over the Balkans, in both US-Iraq wars, and in the Iran-Iraq conflict. The Tomcat is now in its twilight years with the US Navy.

With its powerful radar and suite of long-, medium-, and short-range missiles, the F-14 Tomcat has been the most capable carrier-based fighter since the early 1970s. In the 1990s, when its career was waning, another string was added to the Tomcat's bow with the integration of precision strike capability.

The F-14's genesis was in the US Navy's stillborn Douglas F6D Missileer project of the early 1960s and the US Air Force's TFX (Tactical Fighter eXperimental) requirement. By 1961, US Defense Secretary Robert McNamara and his staff insisted that aircraft for the US Air Force (USAF) and US Navy had as much "commonality" as possible to save development costs. To this end, it was directed that the new tactical fighter-bomber for the USAF's and the US Navy's fleet defense interceptor were to be versions of the General Dynamics F-111. To cut a long story short, the F-111B for the navy was canceled in May 1968 having suffered massive cost overruns and having proved incapable of being reduced in weight or complexity in order to be able to perform the required mission.

Right: *Already blessed with long range, the Tomcat's reach can be extended further by air refueling, as seen here, with an Air Force KC-135 as the provider.*

In July 1968, the US Navy issued a request for proposals for an all-new aircraft and Grumman responded with its Design 303, which, like the F-111, was of variable-geometry (swing-wing) configuration, but had tandem rather than side-by-side seating. Normal wing sweep range was from 20 to 68 degrees with a 75-degree

GRUMMAN F-14D TOMCAT

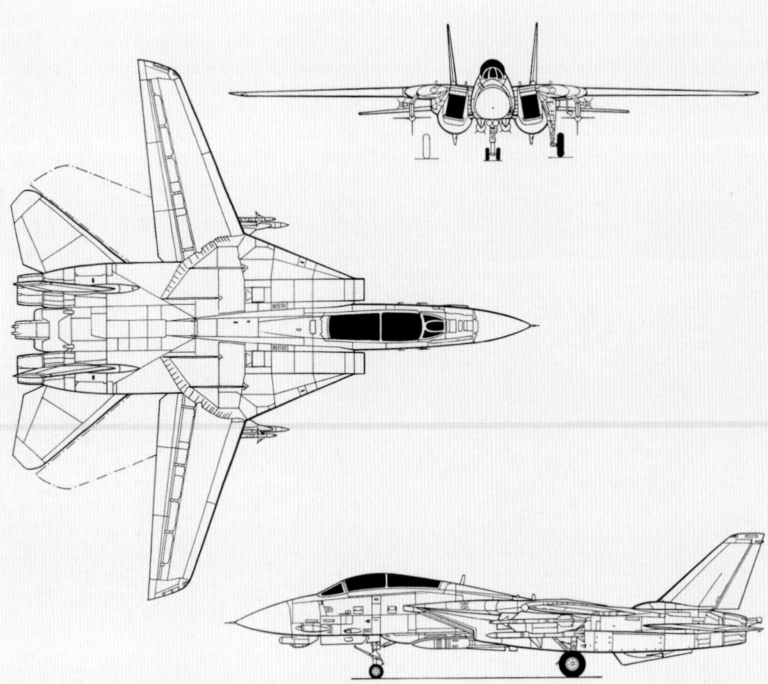

Crew: two

Powerplant: two General Electric F110-GE-400 turbofans rated at 23,100lb of thrust (102.75kN) in afterburner

Maximum speed: 1,544mph (2,470km/h)

Combat radius: 1,239 miles (1,994km)

Service ceiling: more than 53,000ft (16,150m)

Weight: 74,349lb (33,724kg) loaded

Armament: one M61 Vulcan 0.79-in (20-mm) cannon; maximum ordnance 14,500lb (6,577kg), including two AIM-9, four AIM-7 Sparrow, and four AIM-54 Phoenix air-to-air missiles

Dimensions: span (spread) 64ft 1.5in (19.54m); length 62ft 8in (19.10m); height 16ft (4.88m)

103

"oversweep" position for shipboard parking. An automatic system adjusted sweep to the optimum angle during combat. For roll control below 57 degrees sweep, wing spoilers are used in conjunction with its all-moving tailplanes, which operate differentially; above 57-degree sweep, the tailplanes provided the only roll control. Originally the Design 303 had a single fin, but this was later changed to twin canted vertical tails. The engines were the same Pratt & Whitney TF30 turbofans rated at 20,900lb of thrust (94.2kN) with afterburning as intended for the F-111B.

Grumman's proposal was selected as the winner over the McDonnell 225D in January 1969 and designated F-14. The company named it "Tomcat" in line with the feline theme of its previous fighters

PILOTING THE GRUMMAN F-14 TOMCAT

Above: The AIM-54 Phoenix missile gives the Tomcat long-range killing power, although all US kills have been scored with other weapons.

On two occasions in the 1980s, US Navy Tomcats fought conclusive dogfights with Libyan fighters over the Gulf of Sidra. In August 1989, two VF-41 F-14As shot down two Sukhoi Su-22 'Fitters' with AIM-9Ls. On January 4, 1989, the *John F. Kennedy* battle group was exercising its freedom of navigation, or violating Libyan territorial waters, depending on one's point of view, when two patrolling F-14As of VF-32 "Swordsmen" were alerted to the takeoff of a pair of MiG-23 "Floggers" from Al Bumbah airfield near Tripoli. The Tomcats picked up the MiGs on their own radar at a range of about 72 miles (116km). The Tomcats started the engagement at 20,000ft (6,095m), while the MiGs were descending from 10,000ft (3,050m) to 8,000ft (2,440m). The Tomcats made a left turn and descended rapidly so that their radars could look up at the MiGs with no surface clutter. The MiGs turned toward the Tomcats to prevent themselves from being outflanked. The Floggers and Tomcats made several more turns toward each other, and the F-14s were given authority to fire if directly threatened.

"The bogies have jinked back at me for the fifth time. They're on my nose, now inside of 20 miles," reported the lead F-14's RIO Lieutenant Commander Leo Enright. His pilot, Commander Joseph Connelly, fired a Sparrow at 12.9 miles (20.7km), followed quickly by another. Both missiles failed to guide. The two Tomcats then made 30-degree turns, splitting left and right before turning back in to bracket the MiGs, which then came into visual range. Lieutenant Hermon "Munster" Cook, pilot of the second F-14, called "Tally-ho! Eleven o'clock high. They're turning into me," and fired a Sparrow at a range of seven miles (11km). It flew into the right intake duct of the second MiG, which exploded in a huge fireball. The pilot ejected, but was not rescued by the Libyans. Both F-14s turned after the second MiG in a 4.5 *g* turn and fired a Sidewinder, which arced into the MiG, hitting just behind the cockpit, the pilot ejecting just after the hit. "Splash two Floggers, two good chutes in the air," reported Connelly as he dived to low level and led his wingman back to the carrier, low on fuel.

Right: VF-11 "Red Rippers" is one of the oldest fighter squadrons in the Navy. It can trace its lineage all the way back to the biplane era.

Left: The "Diamondbacks" of VF-102 were one of the first Tomcat squadrons to transition to the F/A-18F Super Hornet.

from the F4F Wildcat to the F11F Tiger. The first Tomcat flew in Calverton, Long Island, New York, on December 21, 1970, flown by Robert Smythe and Bill Millar. On its second flight nine days later, it was lost in a crash caused by hydraulic failure, but both Smythe and Millar ejected safely.

The F-14 was designed around the Hughes AWG-9 weapons system, including the AIM-54 Phoenix missile, both of which were originally intended for the F-111B and which had proved the most successful part of the original program.

By this time, the US Navy had learned an important lesson from Vietnam: close-in dogfighting was not dead and a gun therefore still had a place in a modern fighter. Hence a 0.79-in (20-mm) cannon was specified. Filling the gap between the cannon and the long-range Phoenix were the short-range AIM-9 Sidewinder (up to four on wing glove pylons) and the medium-range AIM-7 Sparrow III, of which four could be carried semirecessed under the belly and two on the pylons. The Phoenix could be carried on pallets under the fuselage and on the wing pylons, but a "John Wayne" load-out of six AIM-54s would never be carried in fleet service, as it made the total aircraft weight greater than could be safely brought back to the ship.

After testing of no fewer than 20 prototype and preproduction models, the F-14A entered fleet service with VF-1 "Wolfpack" in July 1972 and made its first operational cruise in 1974. F-14s covered the evacuation of Saigon in 1975, but saw no combat at this time. Eventually they equipped 29 regular and reserve squadrons, as well as test units and others such as the Naval Fighter Weapons School, better known as "Top Gun."

Left: The F-14A's cockpit reflects the state of high technology in the late 1960s when it was designed.

Problems with the TF-30 turbofan were a key factor in the development of re-engined and upgraded Tomcat variants. One airframe was fitted with F401-PW-400s and tested as the F-14B as early as 1973–74. This aircraft later re-emerged as the F-14B Super Tomcat with F101-DFE engines. This engine was developed into the GE F110-GE-400, which was selected to power improved Tomcat variants. Two re-engined variants were proposed: the F-14A (Plus) was to be an interim type, while the F-14D would introduce improved digital avionics. Subsequently, the F-14A (Plus)

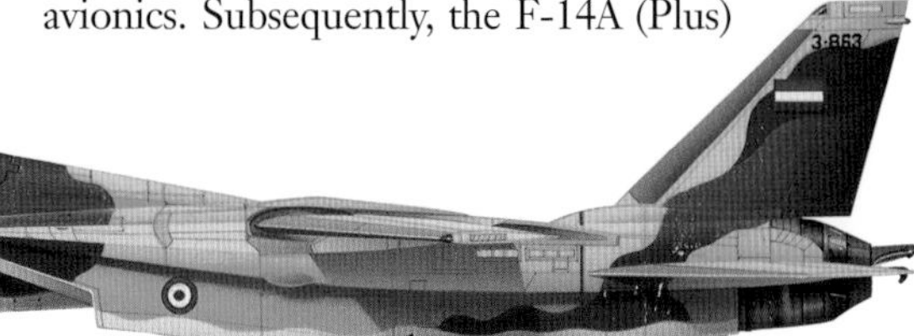

Left: Iran was the only export user of the Tomcat. Despite sanctions and war they have kept a good proportion of their F-14As in service.

***Above:** The Tomcat became one of the best-known modern fighters with help from the 1986 movie* Top Gun. *This F-14 wears ficticious film markings.*

***Below:** With three types of missile and a cannon, the Tomcat could deal with air threats over a wide range. AIM-7, AIM-9, and AIM-54 missiles can be seen here.*

was redesignated as the F-14B, 38 new-build examples being joined by 32 F-14A rebuilds by 1988. These incorporated some avionics changes, including a modernized fire-control system, new radios, upgraded radar warning systems, and various cockpit changes. The B/D has the power to make catapult takeoffs without using afterburner and has carefree handling compared to the more temperamental F-14A.

The first new-build F-14D made its initial flight on February 9, 1990. The F-14D added digital radar processing and displays to the AWG-9, resulting in a designation change to APG-71 and a dual undernose TV/infrared sensor pod. Other improvements include new ejection seats and radar warning equipment. Defense cuts resulted in the service receiving only 37 new-build aircraft, with deliveries beginning in 1990. Deliveries of rebuilt F-14D rebuilds finished at 110, in 1995. A proposed Tomcat 21 strike-fighter lost out against the F/A-18E/F Super Hornet.

In the 1991 Gulf War, one F-14A destroyed an Iraqi Mi-8 helicopter with an AIM-9M Sidewinder, but otherwise there were no kills for the Tomcat. During the long period of Operation Southern Watch over Iraq, there were several inconclusive engagements. On one occasion, an F-14 fired a Sidewinder, then a Sparrow, and finally a Phoenix against a retreating Iraqi MiG, all without success.

The only export customer for the Tomcat was Iran, which ordered 80 F-14As in 1974 mainly to stop unrestricted overflights by Soviet MiG-25 reconnaissance aircraft. Deliveries of F-14As began to the Imperial Iranian Air Force (IIAF) in 1976 and, within a year, the MiG-25 incursions finished. One Iranian Tomcat was retained in the United States for testing, but the remainder were in service at the time of the 1979 Islamic revolution, as were a total of 284 AIM-54s. The revolution and subsequent purging of most of the officers during the creation of the Islamic Republic of Iran Air Force (IRIAF) were thought to have reduced the useable Tomcat force to almost nothing. In fact, however, Iran was able to keep up to 30 F-14s operational throughout the 1980s and 1990s. Nearly 40 kills were scored by Iranian Tomcats during the Iran–Iraq War of 1980–88, using all weapons from cannon to Phoenix. Five or six IRIAF Tomcat pilots became aces by western standards, scoring five or more victories. The most successful of them and probably the leading non-Israeli ace of the post-Vietnam era was Major Jalal Zandi, who was credited with nine kills and three "probables." In return, Iraqi MiG-21, MiG-29, and Mirage F1 pilots claimed 10 F-14s destroyed.

The F-14 had always had a residual air-to-ground capability, but this was not exploited until the mid-1990s. Legend has it that the plan to use the F-14 as a precision-strike platform was hatched by squadron commanders one evening in the Oceana Officers' Club. Whatever the case, an F-14 first dropped a GBU-16 laser-guided bomb (LGB) in May 1994, and the first combat use was over Bosnia in September 1995. Initially, F/A-18s were needed to designate the targets, but later LANTIRN targeting pods were integrated with the F-14, as were other weapons including the JDAM satellite-guided bomb. In this new role as the US Navy's longest-ranged and most accurate strike platform, the US Navy's F-14s have seen more actual combat than ever before, over Serbia and Kosovo, Afghanistan, and Iraq. In Afghanistan in late 2001, US Navy Tomcats used their cannon for the first time in combat (officially) in strafing runs against Taliban forces.

With the arrival of the F/A-18F Super Hornet, the Tomcat is gradually disappearing from the fleet, with the last expected to leave service in 2007.

***Above:** Wings fully swept, an F-14 of VF-84 "Jolly Rogers" makes a high-speed flyby between its carrier and escorting destroyers.*

***Left:** VF-33 is one of the F-14 squadrons that have already been disbanded. Most of the remainder will transition to the two-seat version of the Super Hornet.*

McDonnell Douglas F-15 Eagle

America's F-15 Eagle has achieved an impressive tally of air combat victories in US hands. Israeli and Saudi pilots have added to this total with no admitted losses, making the Eagle the most successful fighter of its generation.

MCDONNELL DOUGLAS F-15C EAGLE

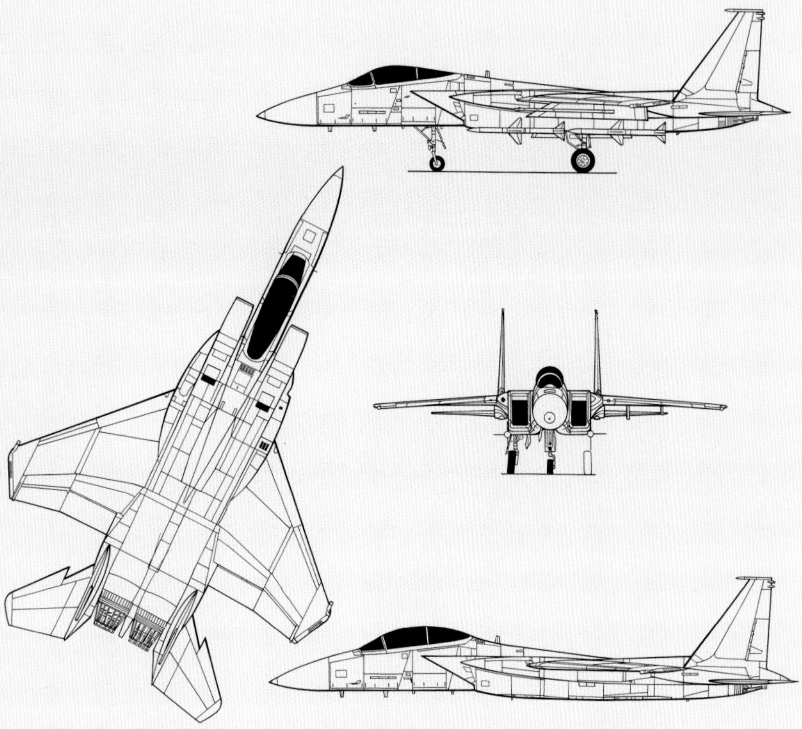

Crew: one

Powerplant: two Pratt & Whitney F100-P-220 turbofans rated at 23,830lb of thrust (106.0kN) in afterburner

Maximum speed: 2,125km/h (1,321mph)

Combat radius: 1,222 miles (1,967km)

Service ceiling: 60,000ft (18,290m)

Weight: 68,000lb (30,844kg) loaded

Armament: one M61 0.79-in (20-mm) cannon, maximum ordnance 16,000lb (7,247kg), including four AIM-7 or AIM-120 and four AIM-9 air-to-air missiles

Dimensions: span 42ft 10in (13.05m); length 63ft 9in (19.43m); height 18ft 6in (5.63m)

Far right: *An F-15C of the 390th Fighter Squadron, based at Mountain Home, Idaho, refuels from a KC-135 tanker.*

Even as the Vietnam War was hotting up in 1965, the US Air Force was beginning to look for a replacement for its F-4 Phantoms, new versions of which were then still being developed. The FX (Fighter eXperimental) requirement was further refined in 1968 with a formal request for proposals from industry. This called for a long-range tactical "air superiority" fighter with both BVR (beyond visual range) and close-in dogfight capabilities. The fighter was to be able to reach a maximum speed of Mach 2.5 and to fly to Europe from the United States without tanker support. Unlike the F-4 and (originally) the F-111, it was not to be multirole. The mantra of the US Air Force program office was "Not a pound for air-to-ground," meaning that

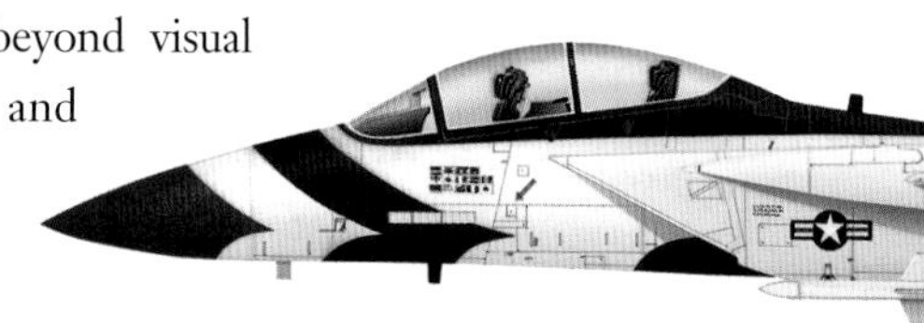

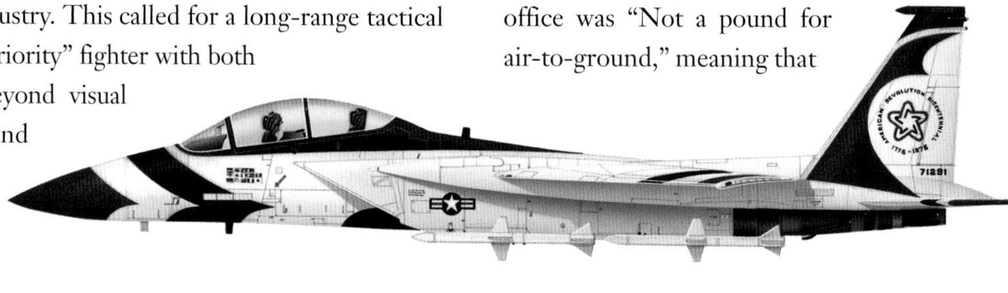

Right: *Here wearing a special Bicentennial color scheme, this F-15B was used for many test programs.*

GUNFIGHTERS
MO
59 498
MO
390FS

***Right:** The F-15D is the fully capable two-seat version of the Eagle. Here it wears the codes of the 6512th Test Squadron at Edwards AFB.*

there be no additional structural weight added to give the fighter a secondary ground-attack capability.

McDonnell Douglas beat designs by North American Rockwell, General Dynamics, and Fairchild Republic to win the FX competition in 1969. Irving Burrows flew the first F-15A Eagle on July 29, 1972 at St. Louis, Missouri. The two-seat version was originally called TF-15A, but was later renamed F-15B. A total of 730 of the two models was planned, but this was cut back to 355 production aircraft. These models were replaced in production from 1979 with the F-15C and D, which had improved versions of both the APG-63 radar and the Pratt & Whitney F100 turbofan engines, although the latter remained rated at the same 23,830lb of thrust (106.0kN) in afterburner. Other changes increased the takeoff weight, the maximum *g*, and the fuel capacity by the use of conformal fuel tanks, or CFTs. Like the F-4E

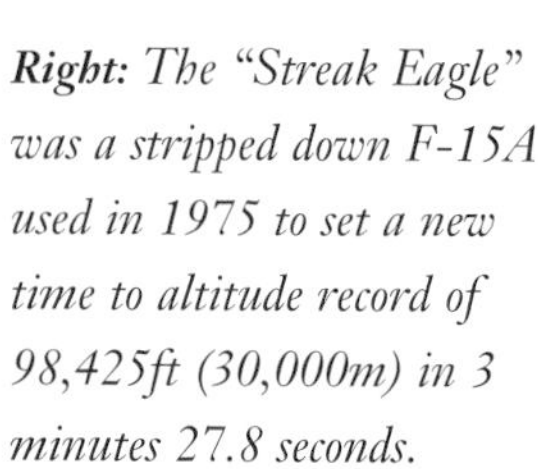

***Right:** The "Streak Eagle" was a stripped down F-15A used in 1975 to set a new time to altitude record of 98,425ft (30,000m) in 3 minutes 27.8 seconds.*

PILOTING THE MCDONNELL DOUGLAS F-15 EAGLE

Above: *F-15Cs of the 493rd Fighter Squadron scored four of the USAF's six kills over Kosovo, all with AMRAAMs.*

On March 26, 1999, during Operation Allied Force, two pilots of the 493rd Fighter Squadron, the "Grim Reapers" flew a mission over Bosnia. The two "Eagle Drivers," call signs "Boomer" and "Claw" (Jeffery Hwang) were flying as "Dirk 21" flight and told their story to Captain Lawrence Spinetta in *Jets* magazine. An abridged version appears here.

"Initially, there was no Serbian air activity. A defensive counter air mission can be painfully dull if no one comes out to play. After a few turns in the CAP, a 'brick' (radar contact) appeared on Boomer's scope. Surprised, he called it out to wake up the AWACS.

"Boomer: 'Dirk Two, group east of Bullseye for 30 miles, ten thousand.' [Bullseye is a previously-agreed fixed reference point]

"AWACS: 'Copy. I'm showing that contact as well.'

"Claw: 'Dirk One same ... Dirk Flight push it up [increase airspeed] ... looks like trouble.'

"AWACS: 'Copy, contact hostile. You are cleared to kill.'

"Claw's blood pressure instantly tripled. He said he could hear the sound of his own heartbeat as he pressed out of the CAP for this mortal combat. His mind raced as he calculated his intercept geometry. He realized that his original intercept plan would have put him over Serbian territory, so he elected to turn away from the threat, despite his fighter pilot's instincts to continue the attack.

"Claw: 'Dirk cold right.' [He directed the flight to turn west, away from the threat.] The enemy aircraft, now identified as a MiG-29, continued its aggressive behavior and continued its flight into Bosnian airspace.

"Claw: 'Hot right. Tapes on.' He selected the system that recorded the HUD image for later analysis. 'Picture single group Bullseye 090/10. Dirk Two target there.' He said, directing Boomer to lock on to the target. 'Combat jet One.' The two Eagles dropped their external fuel tanks, which jumped upward due to the sudden reduction in weight. There's a point in air combat when you know that someone is going to die from an engagement. It's either you or him. You don't have an option to turn and run because the bandit's missile will run you down.

"Boomer: 'Fox!' His voice was steady and confident as he hurtled an AMRAAM at the MiG.

"Claw: 'There's a trailer. Fox trailer!' (Pause) 'Additional Fox leader!'

"The single contact turned out to be two MiGs flying in close lead-trail formation. Claw shot the trailer and decided to target forward to back up Boomer's shot on the lead MiG. Missiles streaked off both Eagles like bottle rockets. The AMRAAM is an extremely fast missile. US Army soldiers at their base far below saw the contrails and thought they were under attack, sounding the alarm and diving for foxholes.

"Claw: 'Pure pursuit for the Tally-Ho.' Both fighters pointed at the MiGs, placing the bandit's radar contacts in the center of their HUDs so as to keep them in sight. Both targets burst into flames right above a scattered cloud deck.

"Claw: 'Splash two MiGs!' Claw was almost shouting into the radio. Later that night he said he wished he'd sounded a little cooler. The two F-15s had to stay on station until their replacements showed up. When they were finally relieved, they did victory rolls the entire 400 miles back to Cervia [Italy]. Claw was eventually credited with both the MiGs. Even though Boomer shot slightly earlier, a review of the videos showed that Claw's missiles were the ones to make lethal impact."

The two Serbian pilots ejected and made it back to their territory. The MiGs fell in Bosnia, and to this day the pancaked wreckage of one remains a local landmark.

Top: *This colorful F-15 demonstrated short takeoff and high maneuverability with its canard foreplanes and thrust-vectoring engines.*

Phantom, the Eagle's basic armament is four Sidewinder and four Sparrow (later AMRAAM) missiles and an internal M61 cannon.

The F-15 achieved its dogfighting ability by having a very large wing (which has often been likened to a tennis court due to its area). The twin tails gave the required lateral stability without an excessively large single fin. The bubble canopy marked a return to the all-round vision of the F-86, which had been lost on most subsequent US fighters. The F-15 met the Mach 2.5 requirement, but only with great effort and expense. The maximum speed can only be achieved by flipping a special "VMAX" switch on the cockpit sidewall, and the engines need to be removed for inspection afterward. In practical terms, an armed Eagle is limited to Mach 1.78.

The first operational F-15 unit was the 1st Tactical Fighter Wing (TFW), which received F-15As and Bs from January 1976. The first C and D models went to the 18th TFW in Okinawa in September 1979. A total of 408 F-15Cs and 62 F-15Ds was built for the US Air Force, and they were also supplied to Saudi Arabia, to Japan as the F-15J (built under license by Mitsubishi) and F-15DJ, and to Israel. Israel took delivery of its first F-15A in late 1976, with the bulk of an eventual total of 105 Eagles following from 1978. The A, B, C, and D models are known locally as the *Baz* ("Buzzard"), and some have been upgraded locally to give ground-attack capability with precision-guided weapons, unlike other "fighter" Eagles. Since June 1979, Israeli Eagles, both single- and two-seat models, have destroyed a total of nearly 60 Syrian MiGs of various types.

In the 1991 Gulf War, F-15Cs destroyed 32 Iraqi aircraft in air combat. Two of these fell to a Saudi pilot. One F-15E destroyed a hovering helicopter with a laser-guided bomb. US Air Force F-15C pilot Cesar Rodriguez was credited with a MiG-23 and a MiG-29 over Iraq in 1991 and a MiG-29 during Allied Forces operations over Serbia and Kosovo in 1999, making him the top-scoring US Air Force Eagle pilot to date.

Above: *Israel has used its two-seat F-15Bs and Ds in combat. This F-15D scored victories against three Syrian MiGs in June 1982.*

Right: *Eagles, such as this F-15C seen flying over Lake Mead, Nevada, are widely used for tests.*

Left: *A pair of Eagles from Bitburg, Germany, leave a slick runway at Bodo, Norway, during Exercise Alloy Express in March 1982.*

Despite the initial reluctance to give the Eagle an "air-to-mud" role, provisions were made in the design to allow ground-attack missions, at least theoretically. The dual-role two-seat F-15E began as the privately funded Strike Eagle demonstrator in 1982. The F-15E "Beagle" has led to further export versions, including the F-15S, a slightly downgraded model for Saudi Arabia. The Israeli Air Force took delivery of the first F-15I Ra'am ("Thunder") in 1998. The F-15I is Israel's primary strike aircraft; tasked with the nuclear-strike role, although it has a significant air-to-air capability as well, with Python 4 and 5 air-to-air missiles. It has many local modifications, including a sophisticated electronic warfare suite, helmet-mounted sight capability, and Israeli cockpit displays.

Following the attacks on the United States on September 11, 2001, F-15s were launched with the previously unthinkable mission of shooting down, if necessary, a civilian airliner. Under Operation Noble Eagle, F-15s and F-16s flew many hundreds of thousands of hours on patrol over US cities in the following months.

In the Iraq war of 2003, the F-15Cs again dominated the skies, but the Iraqi Air Force chose to make no sorties, and thus preserved the lives of their pilots, and most of their aircraft, so no aerial combats took place. F-15Es used their unequaled night-attack capability to good effect. A surface-to-air missile fired by Iraqi troops shot down an F-15E, possibly using a man-portable weapon abandoned by a retreating Coalition special forces team.

F-15 production looked as if it was to end by the turn of the century; however, small repeat F-15E orders from the US Air Force and success for the F-15K (an improved-capability F-15E) in South Korea's F-X competition in 2001 will keep the St. Louis line open for a few years to come. The first of 40 F-15Ks (with a possible further 40 options) will be delivered in 2007.

Below: *This AIM-120 AMRAAM, seen on a 91st FS Eagle, was one of the first to be fired as part of a pair, during a test in 1987.*

General Dynamics/Lockheed Martin F-16 Fighting Falcon

Regarded as the standard by which all modern fighters are judged, the F-16 has seen a quarter of a century of worldwide service. Even now it is being further developed to fulfill new roles and meet the needs of new customers.

Right: *The F-16 offered unprecedented performance and maneuverability when it appeared in the 1970s. This is one of the first production F-16As.*

The F-16 Fighting Falcon was conceived as a lightweight "no frills" fighter for air-to-air combat, but has evolved into a sophisticated multirole combat aircraft that has grown in capability and been exported to 20 nations. It still retains considerable growth potential even as it enters its fourth decade.

A program to acquire a lightweight fighter for the US Air Force (USAF) began in 1971 with a request for proposals for a small and maneuverable aircraft able to tackle the sort of threat encountered in Vietnam, namely the MiG-17, MiG-19, and MiG-21. When General Dynamics of Fort Worth, Texas, was eliminated from the FX competition (which produced the F-15 Eagle), it formed a new design team, headed by Harry Hillaker, to work on concepts for a lightweight fighter. This was a concept promoted by an influential group of USAF officers (including Major, later General, John Boyd), Pentagon analysts, and aircraft engineers, who came to be collectively known as the "Fighter Mafia." They opposed the trends for increasingly large, heavy, complex, and expensive fighters and favored a single-engined design optimized for turn rate, range, and acceleration, rather than top speed.

The Lightweight Fighter (LWF) was initially funded as a technology demonstrator, partly as a

LOCKHEED MARTIN F-16C BLOCK 52

Crew: one

Powerplant: one General Electric F110-GE-129 IPE turbofan rated at 29,100lb of thrust (129.4kN) in afterburner

Maximum speed: more than 1,320mph (2,125km/h)

Combat radius: 340 miles (547km)

Service ceiling: 50,000ft (15,240m)

Weight: 27,099lb (12,292kg) loaded

Armament: one internal M61 Vulcan 0.79-in (20-mm) cannon; maximum ordnance 15,591lb (7,072kg)

Dimensions: span 31ft (9.45m); length 49ft 4in (15.03m); height 16ft 8.5in (5.09m)

AF
80
543

back-up in case difficulties arose with the FX. For the first time in many years, the USAF held a competitive "fly-off" evaluation with the Northrop YF-17 to choose a winning design. The General Dynamics and Northrop designs were selected for fly-off evaluation in April 1972. The first YF-16 service-test prototype first flew on February 2, 1974, although it had made an unofficial flight on January 20 during a high-speed taxi test. In both cases the pilot was Phil Oestricher. The first aircraft was followed by nine others, most of which were subsequently used to trial new engines and

PILOTING THE F-16 FIGHTING FALCON

Above: By far the most numerous aircraft in the USAF inventory, the earlier F-16A and F-16B have been supplanted by the F-16C and F-16D, respectively.

In the 1991 Gulf War, the USAF's F-15 Eagles took the air-to-air glory, while the F-16s were mainly used for bombing and close air support. At that time, the Falcons were largely equipped with nonprecision or "dumb" weapons. In January 1991, Major Dick "Disco" Naumann of the 157th TFS, South Carolina ANG, flew a SEAD (suppression of enemy air defenses) mission over Kuwait, ahead of a strike package of F-16s, RAF Tornadoes, and French Jaguars:

"As we came across the border, everything seemed quiet. We were carrying 2,000-lb Mk 84s, equipped with radar fuses designed to detonate the ordnance about 15 feet off the ground. [Suddenly] ... all hell broke loose. We started getting triple-A fire and many, many SAM launch indications, both visually and on sensors. Everybody was talking on the radio at once, but we proceeded onto our targets. Some guys couldn't get to theirs because of the cloud cover or the SAM defenses: they came back and dropped on El Salimyah.

"We had one pilot up at Kuwait City who dodged one SAM, and as he rolled back to acquire his flight leader he saw another flash by close enough to see that the wings were camouflaged. Fortunately it was clear above his plane before it exploded.

"Everyone delivered their ordnance, then headed back to the IP [initial point]. Counting heads we had all made it, which seemed a miracle because the SAM fire was so thick.

"We were supposed to have been the third people to visit this area, but looking at the way they threw things at us we were the first airplanes in that sector of sky since the war started. We'd convinced ourselves that it would be like a walk in the park. What we didn't know was that it was going to be a walk in Central Park at midnight."

***Right** With its reclined seat, sidestick, and multifunction displays, the F-16A was radical for its time. Later versions have much larger, full-color displays.*

configurations. In 1975, the F-16 was selected as the USAF's new fighter to complement the F-15 and replace Phantoms and the remaining "Century Series" fighters in Tactical Air Command (TAC) and in Reserve and Air National Guard service.

Although a number of later fighters adopted similar configurations to the F-16, at the time of its rollout it was quite radical. The fixed ventral intake and the blending of the wing and fuselage were novel features, but more importantly the F-16 was the first "fly-by-wire" fighter, commanded by a sidestick in the cockpit, rather than having conventional mechanical control linkages from cockpit to control surfaces. The control inputs were routed through flight control computers, able to keep the aircraft in constant trim regardless of pilot input. As such, the airframe was designed with "relaxed static stability," meaning it was inherently unstable (and thus extremely maneuverable) and could not be flown without the computers.

The low-swept wing offered the best combination of good maneuverability, high acceleration, and maximum lift for good altitude performance. Computer-controlled leading-edge flaps kept the wing at maximum efficiency. The F100-PW-200 turbofan, rated at 23,830lb of thrust (106kN) in afterburner, as used on the F-15, gave a lightly loaded F-16 a thrust-to-weight ratio greater than one-to-one. The only framing on the teardrop canopy was behind the pilot, giving unequaled visibility. The production F-16A Fighting Falcon had an enlarged wing, greater fuel capacity, and a deeper nose to house the APG-66 radar.

F-16s entered service with the USAF's 388th TFW at Hill AFB, Utah, in January 1979. The same month, the Belgian Air Force received its first examples. Even while only the YF-16s were flying, the F-16A and the two-seat F-16B had been selected as the winner of a European-wide competition to replace the F-104 Starfighter with Nato air forces in June 1975. The so-called "fighter sale of the century" saw Belgium, the Netherlands, Denmark, and Norway order an initial 348 aircraft. Assembly lines were set up in the two former countries, with component manufacture set up in several others. Later Turkey set up its own production line, as did South Korea. Israel received the first 67 of an eventual 260 F-16s in 1980. In June 1981, eight Israeli F-16s attacked and destroyed Iraq's Osirak nuclear reactor, seriously denting Saddam Hussein's weapons program. Over Lebanon's Beka'a Valley in 1982, more than 40 Syrian fighters fell to Israeli F-16s, the basic models of which are known as the *Netz* (Falcon) in IDF/AF service.

Above: *This F-16 is equipped with AGM-88 HARM missiles, mounted inboard of Sidewinders, and AMRAAMs, to suppress enemy air defenses.*

Left: *The 8th TFW "Wolf Pack" was one of the first USAF units based overseas to equip with the F-16. It was based at Kunsan in South Korea.*

***Right:** Norway specifically asked for braking parachutes on their F-16As and Bs. This upgraded aircraft bristles with AMRAAMs and Sidewinders.*

***Below:** Greece has been a major F-16 buyer.This Block 50 model wears the unique blue and gray camouflage chosen by the Hellenic Air Force.*

Although the majority of F-16s are outwardly similar, the compact airframes hide many differences in engine, avionics, and capabilities. A system of production block numbers tells more about an F-16 than does the traditional suffix letter.

The equivalent of the first USAF F-16As, Block 5, and 10 F-16A/Bs, were exported to Belgium, Denmark, Israel, the Netherlands, and Norway. The F-16A/B Block 15 introduced the larger "big tail" fin and wider tailplanes. The APG-66 radar was improved and new electronic warfare (EW) and identification friend or foe (IFF) systems were fitted. Export sales were made to Belgium, Denmark, Egypt, Israel, the Netherlands, Norway, Pakistan, and Venezuela. The F-16 Block 15 OCU added some features of the F-16C/D, including the F100-PW-220E engine and have been delivered to Belgium, Denmark, Indonesia, Netherlands, Norway, Pakistan, Portugal, and Thailand. A specialist USAF interceptor version, armed with the AIM-7 missile, was developed as the F-16 Block 15 ADF (Air Defense Fighter).

The F-16C and the two-seat F-16D were introduced to give a measure of beyond-visual-range (BVR) air combat capability with AIM-7 or AIM-120 missiles guided by the Hughes AN/APG-68 (V) multimode radar with better range, sharper resolution, and expanded operating modes. The F-16C/D Block 32 was powered by

***Right:** The USAF's Flight Demonstration Squadron, the "Thunderbirds," have flown the F-16 since the early 1980s.*

an uprated F100-PW-220 engine and delivered to Egypt and Korea. From Block 30/32 on, a major block designation ending in "0" signifies a General Electric engine; one ending in "2" signifies a Pratt & Whitney engine. The F-16C/D Block 40 and Block 42 Night Falcons are dedicated night-attack models supplied to the USAF, Bahrain, Egypt, Israel, and Turkey. Israel's F-16Cs are known as *Barak* (Lightning), and the F-16D is known as *Brakeet* (Thunderbolt). The Block 50/52 F-16C/D incorporates all the improvements of the Block 40 and more powerful engines, and also integrates the AGM-88 HARM missile. Export customers include Korea, Singapore, and Turkey.

Israel has developed a "big spine" version of the Block 30/40 F-16D, with a dedicated defense-suppression role. Similar aircraft have been delivered to Singapore. The European F-16s are now undergoing the F-16 MLU (midlife update), bringing them up to F-16C Block 50 standard, with AIM-120 AMRAAM and precision weapons capability.

F-16Cs equip the USAF's Thunderbirds demonstration team. Indonesian and Singaporean aerobatic teams have also flown Fighting Falcons. The most recent export customer is Italy, which in 2003 took delivery of the first of 34 F-16A ADF models under a five-year lease deal while it waits for full deliveries of the Eurofighter. In 1992, Lockheed (later Lockheed Martin) bought the General Dynamics aircraft division at Fort Worth.

Although the F-16 scored no aerial victories in the 1991 war, one Iraqi MiG-23 was destroyed by an F-16D over the northern "no-fly-zone" in December 1992. This was the first kill for a USAF F-16 and for the AIM-120 AMRAAM. USAF pilots scored five kills over Serbian jets in 1994 and 1999. A Dutch F-16MLU pilot also destroyed a MiG-29 during Operation Allied Force. Lockheed Martin claims that a total of 71 kills have been scored worldwide by F-16 pilots, although has not given a full breakdown. The great bulk of these are by Israeli Falcons, but Pakistan's F-16s downed about nine Afghan Air Force aircraft that crossed into Pakistan's airspace during the 1980s. One F-16 pilot also shot down his wingman by mistake—one kill not counted in Lockheed's total. Also probably omitted are encounters between Greek and Turkish F-16s and other fighters, a number of which have been lost on each side, mainly in crashes while maneuvering. During an attempted coup in Venezuela in 1992, F-16s shot down three propeller-driven aircraft.

To date, more than 4,000 F-16s have been built, with production expected to continue until the F-35 JSF comes on stream. The next important variant is likely to be the Block 60 for the United Arab Emirates fitted with conformal fuel tanks and advanced sensors including an infrared search-and-track system.

Above: *A General Electric F110-GE-100 or Pratt & Whitney F100-P-220 turbofan powers the F-16C.*

Below: *Armed with Sidewinders and cluster bombs, a USAF F-16 draws away from a tanker before crossing the Iraqi border on a Desert Storm mission.*

Mikoyan-Gurevich MiG-29 Fulcrum

The MiG-29 represented a new generation of Soviet "super fighters" when it appeared in the 1980s. Supplied to many Warsaw Pact and other nations, the MiG-29 is showing its age. Most will require upgrading to remain competitive.

MIG-29 FULCRUM

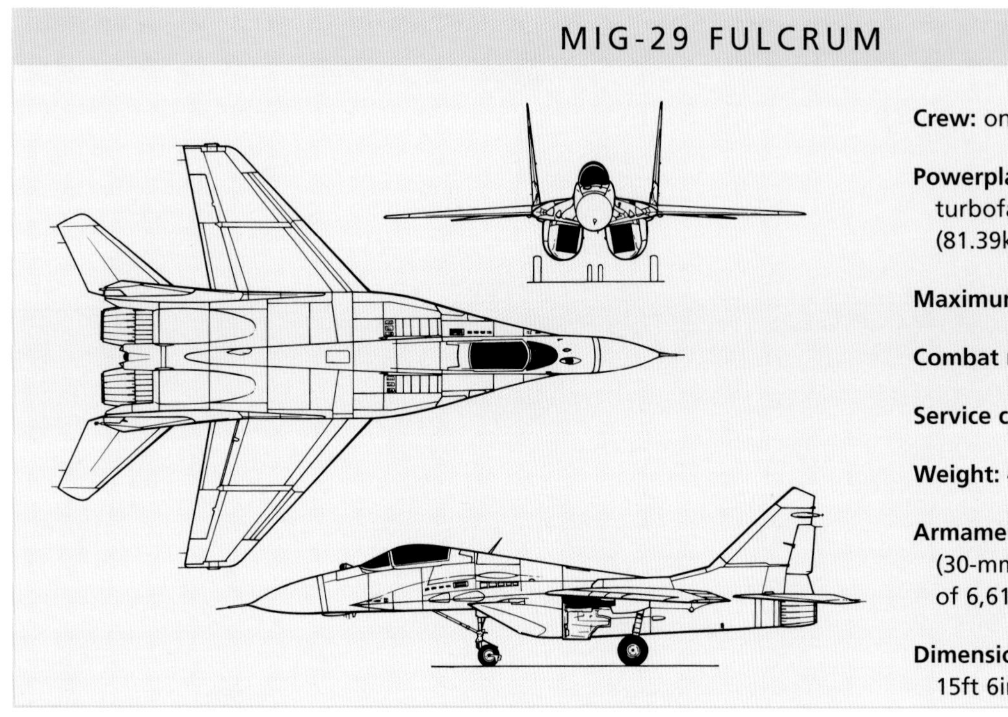

Crew: one

Powerplant: two Klimov/Leningrad RD-33 turbofans rated at 18,298lb of thrust (81.39kN) in afterburner

Maximum speed: 1,519mph (2,445km/h)

Combat radius: 466 miles (750km)

Service ceiling: 55,775ft (17,000m)

Weight: 40,785lb (18,500kg) loaded

Armament: one GSh-301 1.18-in (30-mm) cannon, maximum stores of 6,614lb (3,000kg)

Dimensions: span 37ft 3in (11.36m); length 15ft 6in (4.73m); height 15ft 6in (4.73m)

Far right: *The "Swifts" are one of several Russian aerobatic teams to have emerged recently. They have appeared outside Russia.*

Below: *The MiG-29M was one of several proposed new versions that never actually entered production.*

The Mikoyan-Gurevich MiG-29 was designed to meet a Soviet air force requirement for a "light frontline fighter" with ground-attack capability. The fighter that emerged was to prove one of the best dogfighters of the modern era and shook off western perceptions of Russian fighters as crude and not as capable as their US and European counterparts.

Design work on the MiG-29 began in 1974 led by Rostislav Belyakov. The brief was to replace the MiG-21, MiG-23, and Su-15 in service with Frontal Aviation. MiG's 9-12 design bore a superficial resemblance to several US "teen-series" fighters, having a planform similar to the F-15, a general configuration not unlike the F/A-18, and widely separated engines as on the F-14 Tomcat. The pilot's vision was less encumbered by the heavy cockpit framing usually previously found on Russian fighters, and weapons aiming was aided by a HUD and a helmet-mounted cueing system (HMCS), which allowed missiles to be launched at targets up to 45 degrees off boresight.

Alexander Fedotov made the first flight in the 9-12 on October 6, 1977 in Zhukovsky, near Moscow. After the first flight, ventral fins were fitted at the base of the tailplanes. Subsequent prototypes and

Right: Poland has been one of the most enthusiastic "Fulcrum" users, adding ex-Czech and ex-German aircraft to its original fleet.

production aircraft had the main leg of the nose landing gear moved aft and shortened, which significantly lowered the nose. Smaller tires were also used, and there were many detail changes.

Early MiG-29s were first spotted in 1979 by US spy satellites on the ramp at Zhukovsky, which was usually referred to as Ramonskoye by western analysts after the airfield's nearest village. They gave the type the code name RAM-L (the Sukhoi Su-27 was the RAM-K). Later the reporting name "Fulcrum" was assigned. The MiG-29 entered service with the Soviet Air Force in 1983 and was issued to the 16th Air Army in East Germany in 1985.

Below: Folding wings identify the MiG-29K, which did not enter Russian Navy service, but is likely to be supplied to India.

It was only in 1985 that western pilots first made intercepts of MiG-29s and brought back photographs. In August 1986, six MiG-29s made a goodwill visit to Finland and gave western observers their first detailed look at the Fulcrum, including a display of its incredible agility. Two years later at the Farnborough Air Show, and at the subsequent Paris Salon, the MiG-29 demonstrated its turning ability, high angle-of-attack performance, and one maneuver not practiced in the west, a tail-slide. At the 1989 Paris Air Show, test pilot Anatoly Kvotchur suffered an engine failure at low level and ejected just before his aircraft crashed on the airfield in full view of the world's press. This and other airshow incidents proved the effectiveness of the Zvezda K-36 ejection seat, which has become standard in Russian combat aircraft and even some helicopters. The maneuverability of the basic MiG-29 is all the more remarkable given that it does not have fly-by-wire controls as found in the F-16 and F/A-18, previously regarded as setting the standard for fighter agility.

The MiG's construction is mainly conventional aluminum alloys with some use of composite materials. Surface finish and component fit are better than previous Soviet/Russian fighters, but not quite up to western standards. The MiG-29 is powered by two 18,30-lb thrust (81-kN) (in afterburner) Isotov RD-33 turbofans. These give a

PILOTING THE MiG-29 FULCRUM

Above: The MiG-29 was the only former East German Air Force combat aircraft retained by the reunified Luftwaffe.

Johann Koeck is a Western-trained *Luftwaffe* pilot who became commander of 1/JG.73, the reunified Germany's MiG-29 unit. He was realistic about the good and bad points of the Fulcrum in an interview with British writer Jon Lake. "The employment of the MiG-29 suffers from severe inherent constraints. The most obvious limitation is the aircraft's limited fuel capacity of 9,698 lb with a centerline tank. We have no air-to-air refueling capability, and our external tank is both speed and maneuver limited.

"Our navigation system is unreliable without TACAN updates and is not very accurate (I'd prefer to call it an estimation system). It relies on triangulation from three TACAN stations, and if you lose one you effectively lose the system. We can only enter three fixed waypoints, which is inadequate. For communications we have only one VHF/UHF radio.

"The radar is at least a generation behind the AN/APG-65 ... it has a poor display, giving poor situational awareness, and this is complicated by the cockpit ergonomics. The radar has reliability problems and look-down/shoot-down problems. There is poor discrimination between targets flying in formation, and we can't lock on to the target in trail, only onto the lead.

"We suffer from poor presentation of the radar information (which leads to poor situational awareness and identification problems), short BVR weapons range, a bad navigation system, and short on-station times.

"But when all that is said and done, the MiG-29 is a superb fighter for close-in combat, even compared with aircraft like the F-15, F-16, and F/A-18. This is due to the aircraft's superb aerodynamics and helmet-mounted sight. Inside ten nautical miles I'm hard to defeat, and with the IRST, helmet sight, and 'Archer' I can't be beaten. Period. Even against the latest Block 50 F-16 the MiG-29 is virtually invulnerable in the close-in scenario. On one occasion I remember the F-16s did score some kills eventually, but only after taking 18 'Archers.' We didn't operate 'kill removal' (forcing 'killed' aircraft to leave the fight) since they'd have got no training value, we killed them too quickly (just as we might seldom have got close-in if they used their AMRAAMs BVR!). They couldn't believe it at the debrief; they got up and left the room."

thrust-to-weight ratio of 1.2 for a "clean" MiG-29. The intakes have hydraulic doors that can be closed during rough-field operations to prevent foreign-object damage. Louvres over the leading-edge root extensions then open to provide airflow. Armament consists of a GSh-301 1.18-in (30-mm) cannon in the port wing root and up to six air-to-air missiles, usually four R-73 (AA-11 "Archer") medium-range IR-guided missiles and two R-27 (AA-10 "Alamo") medium- and long-range IR- or radar-guided missiles.

Left: Although it caused a sensation when it appeared, most MiG-29s are relatively unsophisticated and outclassed by modern Western fighters.

Above: *India received 70 MiG-29s, including eight two-seaters. They equip three Air Force squadrons.*

Below: *Slovakia's air force became the custodian of the MiG-29s belonging to the former Czechoslovakian Air Force.*

One of the less satisfactory aspects of the MiG-29 is its short maximum range, which is half that of the F-16. The MiG-29 was designed as a high-speed, high-altitude interceptor, emphasizing climb rate and acceleration rather than range, and it lacks aerial refueling in its standard form. The Su-27 was to fulfill the long-range fighter role.

Avionics on the early MiG-29 were unsophisticated, and there was no ECM provision at first. Radar and detection equipment were good, however. The pulse-Doppler RP-29 ("Slot Back") radar can track a higher altitude fighter at more than 50 miles (80km) and 30 miles (50km) in look-down/shoot-down mode. The radar was backed up by an infrared search-and-track (IRST) sensor and a laser rangefinder.

All basic single-seaters were known as "Fulcrum-As" to the western powers, but export models were indeed MiG-29As in the Soviet designation system. MiG-29A users included Poland, East Germany, Czechoslovakia, Bulgaria, and Romania. The two-seat trainer equivalent is the MiG-29UB, or Fulcrum-B, which lacks radar and requires a retractable periscope to give the instructor a forward view.

The MiG-29B was the late-standard Fulcrum-A supplied to those nations without a complete Soviet-style ground control system, such as Cuba, Iran, Iraq, India, North Korea, Syria, and Yugoslavia. Although Fulcrum-A's had a limited nuclear role, the Mig-29 Fulcrum-C had enhanced conventional and nuclear attack capabilities, as well as extra fuel and a jamming system in an enlarged "fatback" spine. Various other models, most of them demonstrators such as the MiG-29SE and MiG-29SM, are also known as the Fulcrum-C, or Model 9-13. A feature of the post-1992 Russian aircraft industry has been the proliferation of new projects, which offered much but failed to find orders. Only now is the Russian military taking delivery of upgraded Mig-29s based on the MiG-29SMT demonstrator with an even bigger spine, new single airbrake, and "glass" cockpit with color displays. A retractable refueling probe can be fitted.

The most radical version was the MiG-29K (*Korabelnyy*, or ship-based) with folding wings and a tailhook for use aboard the aircraft carriers that the Soviet Union planned in the 1980s. In the end only one ship, the *Admiral Kuznetzov*, was built, and the Su-27K was chosen to equip it, so only two MiG-29K prototypes were built.

The MiG-29 has seen considerable combat action with export customers and former Soviet republics. During the 1991 Gulf War, US Air Force (USAF) F-15s destroyed five Iraqi MiG-29s in air combat and no doubt others on the ground. About 21 of Iraq's 41 MiG-29s escaped to Iran to avoid destruction. Any hope that they might be returned later was dashed when Iran added them to

its own fleet of 14. Some were still in Iraqi service in early 2003, but played no part in the war.

Eritrea used its 10 new MiG-29s against Ethiopia in 1998–2000, but lost a large proportion to Su-27s. A small replacement batch has arrived since the conflict. After using them in a brief war against Russian forces in 1992, Moldova put many of its Fulcrums on the markets during the mid-1990s. It has been said that some of the Eritrean aircraft came from this source. In 1997, the US government purchased 21 MIG-29Cs from Moldova, along with 500 R-73 missiles. This was ostensibly to keep them out of the hands of "rogue states," but the USAF was also interested in studying this nuclear-capable version. The MiGs were delivered to Wright-Patterson AFB by C-17 transport and were dispersed to various sources. Several have since turned up in air force museums, but it is thought that none was flown by USAF pilots.

Seven of Yugoslavia's 14 MiG-29s were destroyed by US and Dutch pilots in Operation Allied Force in 1991. Others were bombed on the ground, but the Yugoslavs made effective use of realistic decoys, a number of which were targeted by NATO. In February 1996, a Cuban MiG-29B shot down one of two civilian Cessna 337s belonging to an exile group that aided refugee crossings to Florida. This is one of the few confirmed kills for the MiG-29.

Some upgrade programs are under way, with little or no help from the original manufacturer. EADS, Elbit, and Aerostar combined their talents to upgrade Romania's Fulcrums as the MiG-29 "Sniper," which is compatible with NATO weapons, communications and IFF systems. Funding problems prevented implementation of the program, but some of the modifications have been offered to Bulgaria and other MiG-29 operators. A limited upgrade was done on the German aircraft before they were given to Poland in 2003–04.

MiG continues to propose new versions and has some export success. In 2003, Yemen took delivery of its first MiG-29MT, a version of the SMT without the large spine. The two-seat equivalent of the SMT is the MiG-29UBT, which is the first two-seater to have radar and a "missionized" rear cockpit.

More than 450 MiG-29s still serve in Russia, and up to 800 are in service in former Soviet republics and elsewhere, including Bulgaria, Cuba, Eritrea, Germany, Hungary, India, Iran, North Korea, Malaysia, Moldova, Peru, Poland, Slovakia, Serbia, Syria, and Yemen. There is no replacement forthcoming in the near future from MiG, so many nations are likely eventually to take the upgrade route.

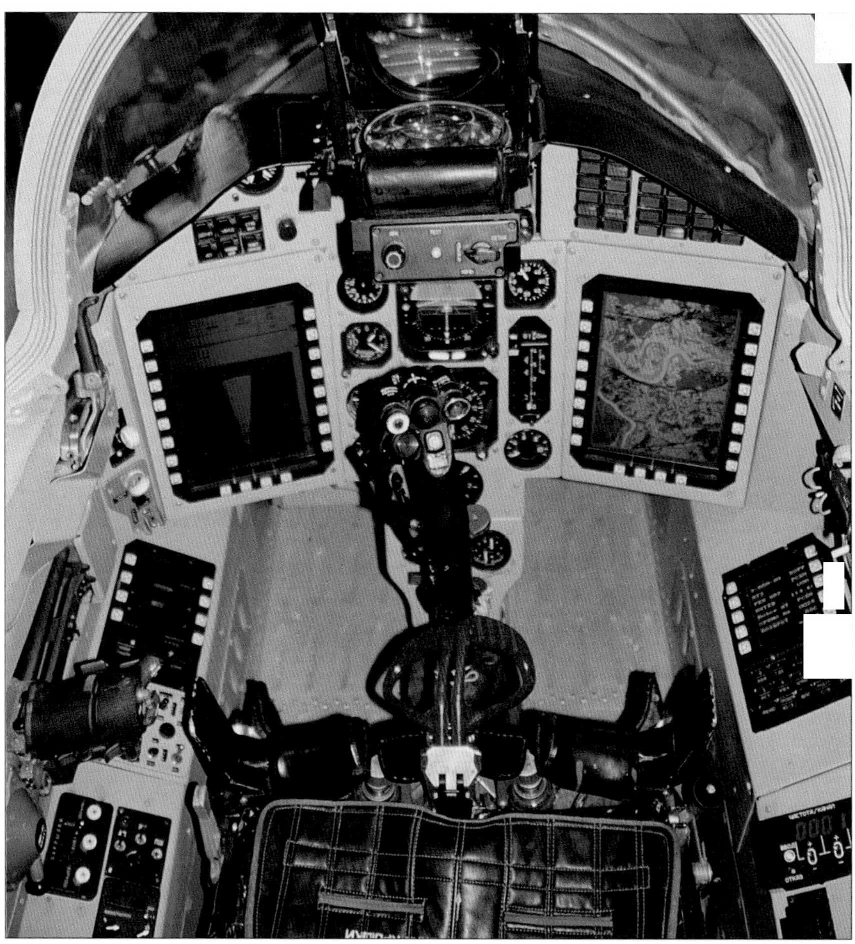

Above: *The MiG-29SMT cockpit has varied. But this early set-up is far ahead of the baseline "Fulcrum."*

Below: *The highly armed, maneuverable "Fulcrum" is a formidable dogfighter.*

McDonnell Douglas F/A-18 Hornet and Boeing Super Hornet

Developed from a design for a lightweight air combat fighter, the Hornet has evolved into an effective multirole combat aircraft. In its Super Hornet form, it will replace the F-14 and maybe even some more specialized naval aircraft.

The F/A-18 Hornet has become the backbone of US naval aviation and has proved its effectiveness in multiple roles in several conflicts. Its evolution into the Super Hornet will see new roles and no doubt further export success for a design that began three decades ago as a single-role air combat fighter.

Right: *This F/A-18C shows it can carry up to 10 AIM-120 AMRAAM and two AIM-9 Sidewinder missiles. It might prove to be too heavy for a carrier landing.*

In 1974, the US Air Force held a fly-off competition to choose a lightweight fighter (LWF) to complement the F-15 Eagle. At the same time, the US Navy decided that it needed a similar aircraft, albeit with greater multirole capabilities, to replace the A-7 Corsair II and F-4 Phantom II, and complement the F-14 Tomcat. As such they launched a fighter-attack experimental (VFAX) program, which later became the Naval Air Combat Fighter (NACF) when Congress essentially directed the US Navy to choose one of the contenders for the LWF, rather than develop a stripped-down F-14 or a version of the F-15.

Northrop offered its YF-17 Cobra for the US Air Force contest, powered by two YJ101-GE-100 turbofans of 14,400lb of thrust (64.5kN) in afterburner for the LWF contest. The Cobra was a highly agile fighter with twin canted tails and long leading-edge root extension (LERX) fairings,

BOEING F/A-18C HORNET

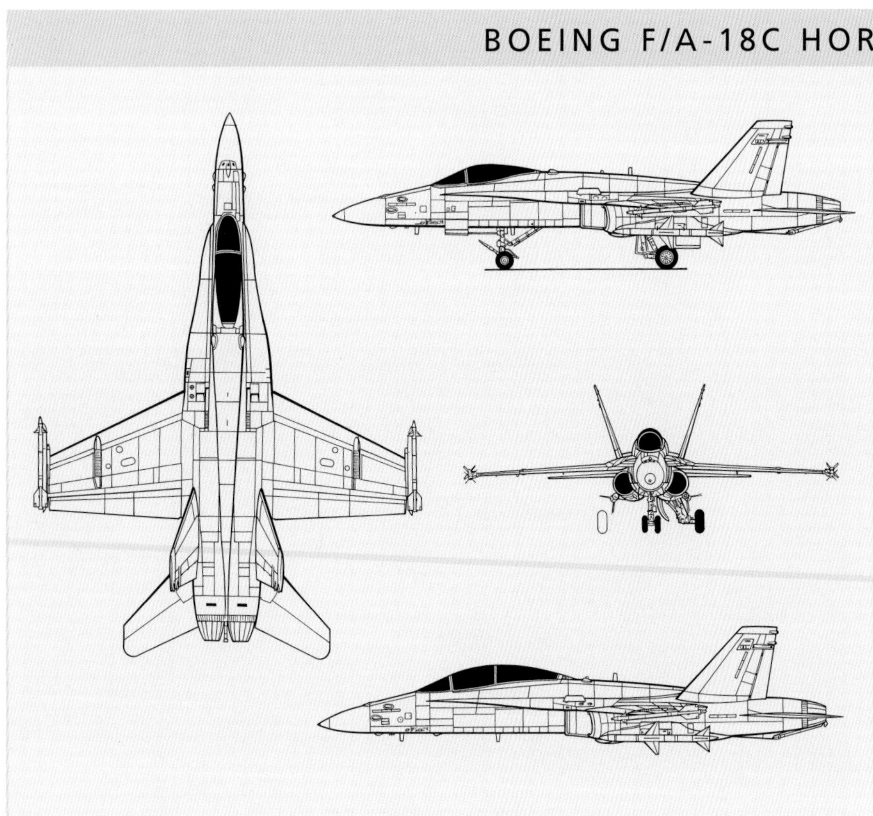

Crew: one

Powerplant: two General Electric F404-GE-402 turbofans rated at 17,700lb of thrust (78.73kN) in afterburner

Maximum speed: more than 1,190mph (1,915km/h)

Combat radius: more than 460 miles (740km/h)

Service ceiling: 50,000ft (15,250m)

Weight: 51,900lb (23,541kg) loaded

Armament: one M61A1 0.79-in (20-mm) cannon with 570 rounds; maximum ordnance load 15,500lb (7,031kg)

Dimensions: span (over wingtip AAMs) 40ft 5in (12.31m); length 56ft (17.07m); height 15ft 3in (4.66m)

16
16

which gave exceptional controllability at high angles of attack.

To better meet the US Navy's specific requirements, Northrop partnered with McDonnell Douglas, a company with considerable experience of carrier aircraft, to work on proposals for a navalized version of the YF-17; likewise General Dynamics and Ling-Temco-Vought (LTV) teamed up to develop a naval aircraft out of the YF-16. When the YF-16 was announced as the winner of the US Air Force's air combat fighter contest in January 1975, the US Navy quickly rejected it as unsuitable, announcing its preference for a developed version of the twin-engined

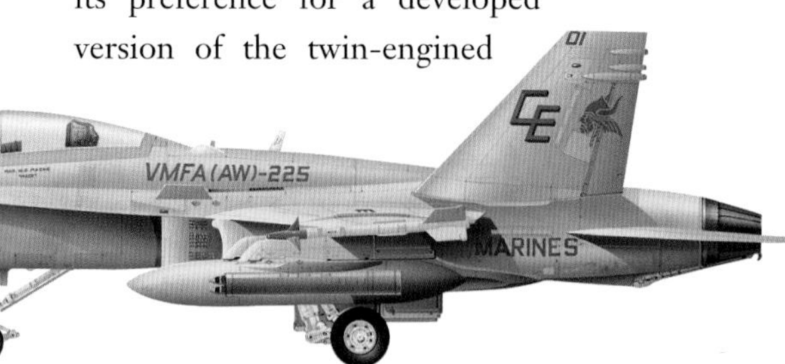

Right: *An F/A-18D of VMA(AW)-225. The Marines use the D model for forward air control and night attack missions.*

PILOTING THE F/A-18 HORNET

Above: *The Hornet, the US Navy's most numerous strike aircraft in Desert Storm, served with many land-based Marine Corps units.*

The 1991 Gulf War saw Hornets fly the bulk of the US Navy's attack missions over Iraq and Kuwait. On January 17, the first day of the war, four F/A-18Cs of VFA-81 "Sunliners" loaded with four Mk 84 2,000-lb (907-kg) bombs apiece took off from the USS *Saratoga* to attack H-3 airfield in Western Iraq. About 30 miles (50km) from the target they received warning from an E-2C Hawkeye that enemy aircraft were in the vicinity. "Hornets, bandits on your nose 15 miles!"

The pilots of the two leading Hornets, Lieutenant Commander Mark Fox and Lieutenant Nick Mongillo, changed their onboard systems from air-to-ground to air-to-air mode and selected missiles. As the flight looked for the oncoming MiGs, Fox got a lock-on at 10 miles (16km)—two MiG-21s in a left echelon, a standard Soviet formation. Fox recounts the mission:

"It all happened very quickly. I switched back to air-to-air and got a lock on one of them. I had the MiG on the right while the second Hornet in our formation, Lieutenant Mongillo, took the MiG on the left. The MiGs approached us, nose on, supersonic at Mach 1.2. Our relative rate of closure was more than 1,200 knots. They weren't maneuvering.

"I shot a Sidewinder first. It was a smokeless missile and I thought, at first, that I had wasted it because I couldn't see it tracking toward the MiG. I fired a Sparrow. The first missile actually did the job, and the Sparrow flew into the fireball. The whole event, from the E-2's call to missile impact took less than 40 seconds."

Lieutenant Mongillo fired a second Sparrow, which took out the second MiG-21. During the engagement, the Hornets had kept their bombs, all 800lb (3,632kg), with them. They went on to make a successful strike on the airfield. This mission perfectly illustrated the dual-role (what would later be dubbed "swing role") ability of the F/A-18 to carry out both air-to-air and air-to-ground functions on a single mission. These were the sole Hornet kills of the war, and in fact the only ones to date in any conflict. On the same mission, a VFA-81 Hornet was shot down by a MiG-25 for the only Iraqi kill of the war.

YF-17 in May 1975. One reason for the choice was the perceived greater potential for the Northrop/McDonnell Douglas to fulfill multiple missions. The original plan for the new fighter was to procure three distinct versions: an F-18 fighter, an A-18 attack bomber, and a TF-18 trainer. McDonnell was to be prime contractor on the navy version, with Northrop contracted to develop and market a land-based F-18L version. Eventually the two companies had a quarrel over this agreement, and later McDonnell Douglas was given the rights to all versions.

In its transformation to the F-18, the YF-17 was largely redesigned to meet the US Navy's needs, becoming larger and stronger to accommodate more fuel and avionics, and to withstand carrier launches and arrested landings. Engines were now 16,000-lb thrust (71.2-kN) F404-GE-400s. The undercarriage was totally redesigned, and hydraulic wing folding was added for carrier stowage. A larger nose contained the APG-65 radar with a 0.79-in (20-mm) M61 cannon firing from an aperture just above and behind the radome. Two pylons on each wing, two wingtip rails, and three fuselage stations allowed the carriage of a wide variety of ordnance, including AIM-9 and AIM-7 air-to-air missiles.

The first F-18, which was named Hornet in 1977, flew on November 18, 1978 in St. Louis, piloted by Jack Krings. Eight more single-seat development aircraft and two TF-18s were to follow. Advances in avionics and redesign of the weapons pylons allowed merging of the fighter and attack roles in the same airframe, and the plan to have separate squadrons for each version was dropped. It was not until 1984, however, that the somewhat cumbersome F/A-18A and F/A-18B designations (for fighter/attack) came into general use, preceded by the VFA and VMFA designations for US Navy and Marine Corps Hornet squadrons.

The Hornet entered operational service with a marine unit, VMFA-314 "Black Knights," in

***Above** The prototype Hornets appeared in this white color scheme with the blue and gold trim associated with naval aviation.*

***Above:** The F/A-18E Super Hornet is large and highly capable. This was the first flight of the Super Hornet in November 1995.*

***Left:** Spain was at one time planning to buy 144 Hornets but later halved this number. This EF-18A belongs to Ala 12 at Torrejon.*

Above: *Switzerland's F-18s have no stated ground-attack role, but are used purely as air defense fighters.*

August 1982, and with the US Navy's VFA-113 "Stingers" in March 1983. Problems arose in early service with cracking in the tail section brought about by fatigue from turbulent airflow, causing temporary grounding of the whole fleet. Beefing up of certain structures and later the addition of a fixed fence on each leading-edge extension (LEX) eventually cured this problem. In March 1986, the Hornet made its combat debut during tensions with Libya, attacking SAM sites with AGM-88 HARM missiles. Similar missions followed during the "El Dorado Canyon" operation a few weeks later.

Production switched to the F/A-18C (and two-seat F/A-18D) in 1987. There were no significant external differences, but the C/D model had new ejection seats, a self-protection jammer, and an improved mission computer. New weapons included the AIM-120 AMRAAM, AGM-84 antiship missile, and the AGM-65F infrared version of the Maverick air-to-surface missile. A new generation of weapons, including the JDAM (Joint Direct Attack Munition) GPS-guided bomb series, the JSOW (Joint Stand-Off Weapon) and the SLAM-ER (Stand-off Land Attack Missile-extended Range) have recently been integrated with the US Hornet fleet. Some earlier US Hornets have been upgraded to F/A-18A (Plus) standard with some of the features of the F/A-18C.

Below: *The US Navy's Flight Demonstration Squadron, the "Blue Angels" replaced its A-4 Skyhawks with the F/A-18A in 1986.*

In the US Marine Corps, the Hornet replaced the F-4 Phantom, A-4 Skyhawk, and A-6 Intruder. The precision night-attack role of the Intruder has been taken up by specially modified F/A-18Ds that have full weapons controls (but no flight controls) in the rear cockpit. Both cockpits are compatible with night-vision goggles (NVGs) and have color multifunction displays.

F/A-18A/Bs were exported to Australia and Canada (as the CF-188) and to Spain as the EF-18A and B. F/A-18C/Ds have gone to Kuwait, Finland, and Switzerland. The latter two countries more correctly operate F-18s, as their aircraft have no declared attack role. Malaysia only acquired F/A-18D models, built to the highest production standard of the time and supplied with air-to-air and air-to-surface weapons. The last of 1,479 Hornets was delivered in September 2000.

Canadian Hornets have seen combat over Iraq and Kuwait (in 1991), the former Yugoslavia, and Afghanistan. Australia's F/A-18As flew the Royal Australian Air Force's first combat missions since Vietnam when they took place in Operation Iraqi Freedom in 2003. Both Canada and Australia have been upgrading their Hornets to C/D standard, the latter adding ASRAAM (Advanced Short-Range Air-to-Air Missile) to the F/A-18's weapons options for the first time. Spain is also putting its EF-18s through a midlife update.

Efforts to promote a "Hornet 2000" for the French navy to bridge the gap between the Crusader and Rafale were unsuccessful, but the work done toward this proposal fed into the evolved version that was to become the F/A-18E and F Super Hornet.

In 1991, the US government canceled the A-12 Avenger II, a triangular-shaped stealthy replacement for the A-6 Intruder. The prospect of the US Navy and Marines being left without an all-weather strike capability when the Intruder retired in the mid-1990s saw several alternatives explored as a matter of urgency. One was a new production version of the F-14 called the Super Tomcat 21 that would have been capable of several roles, including long-range strike. McDonnell Douglas proposed a stretched version of the Hornet with a larger wing, and a single-seat F/A-18E version was chosen to replace the A-6 and the two-seat F/A-18F, the F-14, in 1992.

The Super Hornet, which first flew on November 29, 1995, is 2ft 10in (86cm) longer than the standard model, with a wing 25 percent greater in area. The wing has six underwing pylons and a "dogtooth" on the leading edge. New intakes and other features such as extensive use of radar-absorbent material (RAM) reduce the Super Hornet's radar cross-section. Engines are the 22,000-lb thrust (97.9-kN) General Electric F414-GE-400. The APG-73 radar is retained from the F/A-18C/D, but a new active electronically scanned array (AESA) radar is likely to be retrofitted in the future.

The Super Hornet offers longer range, easier maintenance, and a larger weapons load than its predecessor. It also has a higher "bring-back" load, meaning that it can land with more unexpended weapons, rather than having to jettison them or carry fewer to start with.

Above: *The F/A-18F is optimized for the fighter role and is replacing the F-14 Tomcat on the US Navy's carriers.*

During Operation Enduring Freedom, the Super Hornet made its first combat deployment and dropped bombs on Taliban and Al Qaeda forces, as did "regular" Hornets. In Operation Iraqi Freedom, some of the limited number of Super Hornets deployed were used as airborne tankers, supplementing the S-3B Viking in this role.

A two-seat Super Hornet version, unofficially called the F/A-18G "Growler," is likely to replace the EA-6B Prowler in the electronic warfare and defense-suppression roles. The Boeing Super Hornet (McDonnell Douglas merged with Boeing in 1997) has been offered to several nations including Australia and Singapore. Malaysia is likely to swap its small fleet of eight F/A-18Ds for Super Hornets.

Below: *Malaysia bought a handful of F/A-18D two-seaters for ground attack, and is a possible future Super Hornet customer.*

Hawker Siddeley Harrier/Sea Harrier McDonnell Douglas/BAe Harrier II

The original "Jump Jet," the Harrier is one of the few British or European aircraft acquired in large numbers by US forces. The US Marine Corps has been an enthusiastic user, and was the spur behind the Harrier II.

***Far right:** Early Harriers were limited but gave some nations a capability for naval strikes and air defense beyond their normal means.*

***Right:** The AV-8B Plus is the Marine Corps' latest version, with APG-65 radar and the ability to use a wide range of precision weapons.*

The Harrier was for many years a unique attack aircraft, having the ability to take off and hover like a helicopter, deliver bombs to the frontline, and then return to a hidden base in the woods to be rearmed and refueled. Over time, the vertical takeoff element became less important, and new variants appeared more geared to air combat and defense of naval forces. And while all Harriers can carry bombs, the "jump-jet" has evolved beyond its original remit to become one of the most effective small fighters in service today.

Vertical takeoff and landing (VTOL) combat aircraft were studied by many nations in the 1950s and 1960s, primarily as a means to ensure survival of retaliatory assets after the first hours of a European war. At the time it was accepted (by many, but not all) that fixed air bases would be quickly knocked out by Soviet air or missile attacks.

The path from 1957, when Ralph Hooper of Hawker Aircraft outlined a compact, high-winged, single-seat, single-engined jet with a "four-poster"

BRITISH AEROSPACE SEA HARRIER FRS.MK I

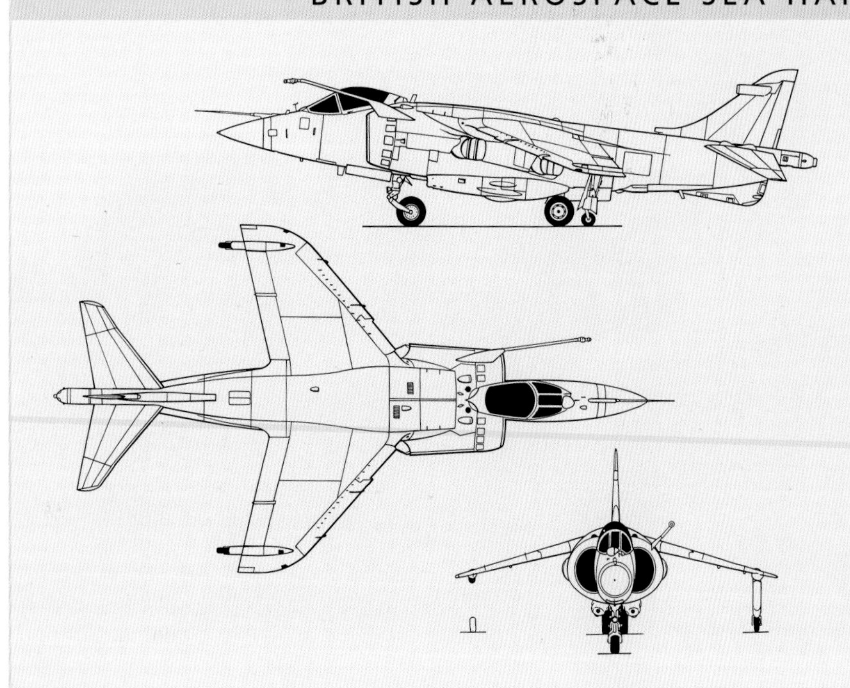

Crew: one

Powerplant: one 21,500-lb thrust (95.64-kN) Rolls-Royce Pegasus Mk 106 turbofan

Maximum speed: 735mph (1,183km/h)

Range: 980 miles (1,480km)

Service ceiling: over 50,000ft (15,240m)

Weight: 26,190lb (11,880kg) loaded

Armament: two 1.18-in (30-mm) ADEN cannon in under-fuselage pods, maximum ordnance 8,000lb (3,629kg), including Sea Eagle ASMs or AIM-9 Sidewinder missiles

Dimensions: span 25ft 3in (7.70m); length 47ft 7in (14.50m); height 12ft 2in (3.71m)

***Right:** Most models of Harrier have been able to carry AIM-9 Sidewinders for self-defense. Even the GR.5 version can be used as a fighter when needed.*

arrangement of thrust nozzles, through the trials of the P.1127 development aircraft and the introduction of the Harrier to Royal Air Force (RAF) service in 1969 is long and twisted. Suffice to say that Bill Bedford made the first tethered "hop" of the P.1127 on October 21, 1960, and a long (and sometimes troubled) test and development phase followed. This culminated in evaluation (by the United Kingdom, United States, and Germany) of the similar Kestrel and eventual purchase by the RAF and US Marine Corps (USMC) of the Harrier GR.1 and AV-8A, respectively.

Where Hawker's design succeeded above the many others was in its use of a single engine with swiveling nozzles that could direct the thrust from the vertical to the horizontal plane. This unique powerplant was the Rolls-Royce Pegasus, initially rated at around 11,000lb of thrust (49kN). Most other VTOL projects used multiple engines, the majority of which became excess baggage in the conventional flight mode. Vertical takeoffs imposed a severe weight penalty and burned large amounts of fuel, so the acronym quickly became V/STOL (vertical/short takeoff and landing). It was later changed to STO/VL (short takeoff and vertical landing), in recognition of the fact that much more ordnance and fuel could be carried from a short strip if the nozzles were set at an intermediate position, allowing a wing-borne rather than a thrust-borne lift-off.

***Below:** The USMC's AV-8As differed from the RAF's GR.1s in their radio fit and ability to carry Sidewinders.*

***Right:** All Harriers evolved from the original and very basic P.1127 of 1960.*

The USMC's AV-8A was license-built by McDonnell Douglas as a barely modified GR.1 Harrier with US radios and provision for two Sidewinders. The US Marines loved the AV-8A, but it suffered from a high accident rate, with nearly 50 of the 102 AV-8A and eight two-seat TAV-8As being lost. A US Marine pilot named Harry Blot was responsible for discovering the Harrier's potential to "VIFF," an acronym for "vectoring in forward flight." Soon Marines were exploiting the technique of swiveling the nozzles to rapidly change direction, climb, and slow down in simulated combat, forcing the adversary to "fly-through" and lose the advantage.

Eventually, some of the shortcomings of the first-generation Harriers were addressed when McDonnell Douglas collaborated with British Aerospace (Hawker Siddeley's successor) on the Harrier II. This retained the general configuration

PILOTING THE SEA HARRIER

Above: The Sea Harrier was instrumental in allowing Britain to retake the Falkland Islands from Argentina.

Commander Neill Thomas, the commanding officer of No. 899 NAS, was on combat air patrol (CAP) over Falkland Sound in company with Lieutenant Mike Blissett and controlled by the Type 22 frigate HMS *Brilliant,* which was part of the escort to the amphibious fleet. It was May 21, 1982, the first day of the landings on San Carlos Water. "We were at about 1,000 feet halfway down Falkland Sound, and *Brilliant* vectored us off West Falkland after a contact they'd got." The target was a lone A-4B Skyhawk of the Argentine Air Force's Grupo 5, which had just attacked HMS *Ardent.* "We headed off at a fair old rate of knots, and were approaching Chartres when we picked up four A-4s coming over the ridge." These were A-4Cs of Grupo 4, which had taken off armed with 500-lb (227-kg) bombs from San Julian 45 minutes before and refueled from a KC-130H tanker. They were heading northeast and, when picked out low and left by Thomas and Blissett, were about 35 nautical miles (65km)—four minutes—from the anchorage. The tracks of the attacking and defending aircraft crossed at right angles, and, as the Sea Harriers broke to starboard to get behind them, the A-4s also broke into a hard 180-degree turn to starboard.

"As soon as they saw us the A-4s turned tail, jettisoned their bombs and headed off to the south." Thomas and Blissett pulled harder into their turn, wheeling at full throttle through a 270-degree turn, which placed them directly in the Skyhawks' six o'clock position. "They must have lost a lot of speed, because we ended up about a mile and a half astern. Mike was nearer than myself, and fired; I couldn't see him until then. He got the man on the left, and having picked Mike up reasonably well to my left, about 40 degrees off, I got a very good growl from the target, so I just shot the missile and it went straight to it. The other two A-4s broke to starboard, with Mike close astern of them. I got a growl from my Second Sidewinder but couldn't fire, because I didn't know where Mike was. So we missed the other two." In fact, Mike Blissett damaged one of the other A-4s with cannon fire, although it returned safely to base. The two Skyhawks came down within 330ft (100m) of each other. Both pilots, *Teniente* (Lieutenant) Nestor Lopez and *Primer Teniente* (1st Lieutenant) Daniel Manzotti being killed.

and the Pegasus, albeit now producing 21,450 lb of thrust (95.42 kN) in Mk 105 form, but had a larger carbon-fiber wing, six wing pylons, and an all-new cockpit and canopy. No airframe parts in the RAF's Harrier GR.5 and the USMC's AV-8B were common with earlier Harriers.

While the US Marines waited for the AV-8B Harrier II, the surviving AV-8As were rebuilt from 1979–84 as AV-8Cs with chaff and flare dispensers, a radar warning receiver (RWR) and the lift-improvement devices (LIDs) developed for the Harrier II. Later called leading edge root extensions (LERXs), these are curved strakes between the wing root and fuselage, which improved turn rate and gave extra lift in the hover. The AV-8Cs were replaced by AV-8Bs in 1987. Spain and Thailand

Left: The Harrier II has extra pylons on each wing, allowing a wide range of weapons to be carried.

***Right:** The FA.2 Sea Harriers were mostly rebuilt from FRS.1s, although there were some newly built examples.*

also bought small numbers of AV-8As for their carriers. The RAF modified most of its Harrier GR.1s with a new laser range-finder and marked target seeker (LRMTS) in an elongated nose.

The Harrier was demonstrated aboard a Royal Navy carrier as early as 1963 when a P.1127 made landings aboard HMS *Ark Royal.* Trials were conducted on the flight decks of US and British helicopter carriers and a variety of other warships in the late 1960s before the USMC began shipboard operations in 1971. As the last conventional British carriers neared retirement, in favor of land-based fleet air defense, the Royal Navy concocted the "through-deck cruiser," which was a small aircraft-carrier in all but name, able to operate Harriers but not conventional jets. Three were built and one older ship, HMS *Hermes,* was converted with a "ski-jump" ramp (another British innovation like the steam catapult, angled deck, and mirror landing system), which allowed rolling rather than vertical takeoffs, saving fuel and permitting a greater useable load of fuel and weapons.

The Navy's Sea Harrier FRS.1 (fighter, strike, reconnaissance) was essentially a GR.1 airframe with a new nose containing Blue Fox radar, a raised cockpit, and an oblique camera. The first operational squadron (No. 899 Naval Air Squadron) was commissioned in April 1980, and two units (Nos. 800 and 801 NAS) were subsequently deployed to the South Atlantic during the Falklands War, where they served with distinction, scoring 23 confirmed victories. RAF Harriers also flew attack missions from carriers and rough strips ashore.

***Below:** Training on the RAF's Harriers is conducted with the T.10, which has all of the mission equipment of the single-seaters. This trio is from No.4 Squadron.*

Above: With its Sea Vixen radar, the Sea Harrier FA.2 can fire the AIM-120 AMRAAM, giving it a beyond visual range that was lacking in the FRS.1.

Post-Falkland attrition replacements and further orders subsequently took total Royal Navy procurement up to 57 FRS.1s and four trainers (including three T.4Ns). Improvements included revised wing pylons for carriage of four AIM-9Ls (on twin launch rails), larger capacity drop tanks, and installation of improved radar and RWR. In 1978, the Indian Navy had become the only export Sea Harrier operator, ordering a total of 24 FRS.51s and four T.Mk 60 trainers.

A midlife update was initiated in 1985 to refine the Sea Harrier as a more capable interceptor. BAe (now BAE Systems) converted two FRS.1s to serve as FRS.2 prototypes, with the first flying in September 1988. A recontoured nose houses Blue Vixen multimode pulse-Doppler radar, which gives compatibility with the AIM-120 AMRAAM and is regarded by many as one of the best fighter radar in service today. The cockpit introduces new multifunction CRT displays and HoTaS controls. The FRS.2 designation was changed to F/A.2 in May 1994, and then to the current FA.2 in 1995. FA.2s were used in action over the former Yugoslavia in the mid-1990s, one being lost to a surface-to-air missile. Plans for a "Joint Force Harrier" of RAF Harriers serving as the attack component aboard Royal Navy carriers in partnership with Sea Harriers were shelved when it was announced the Sea Harrier would be retired in 2007. A future RAF GR.9 model (without radar) will take over the shipboard role until deliveries of the F-35 JSF to the Royal Navy from about 2012.

The RAF's Harriers have been upgraded as the GR.7 and two-seat T.10, which retain a primary attack function. Their combat debut came over Kosovo in 1999. The USMC has also improved some of its AV-8Bs as the Night Attack Harrier II and transformed others by fitting APG-65 radar, giving true fighter capability with the AIM-120 AMRAAM, as well as Sidewinders and cannon. These models are known as the AV-8B Plus. Most US Harriers have been or will be converted to Plus standard. Spain and Italy bought AV-8Bs from American production. The very last new-build Harrier was an AV-8B delivered to the US Marines in October 2003.

In the 1991 Gulf War, Marine Harriers flew thousands of close-air support sorties over Iraq, a pattern repeated in 2003. RAF Harriers were heavily involved in day and night sorties in the later conflict. No Harrier fighter combat has taken place since 1982, but the AV-8/Harrier continues to defend the fleets of five nations.

Panavia Tornado Air Defense variants

Developed from a bomber design for the Royal Air Force, the Tornado ADV offered a quantum leap in combat effectiveness compared to its predecessor, the Lightning. A compromise, the ADV has not been an unqualified success.

PANAVIA TORNADO F.MK 3

Crew: two

Powerplant: two Turbo-Union RB.199-34R Mk 104 turbofans rated at 16,520lb of thrust (73.48kN) in afterburner

Maximum speed: 1,453mph (2,338km/h)

Combat radius: more than 1,151 miles (1,852km)

Service ceiling: about 40,000ft (12,192m)

Weight: 61,700lb (27,986kg) loaded

Armament: one internal 1.06-in (27-mm) Mauser cannon, plus four semirecessed Sky Flash/AMRAAM and four AIM-9L/M or ASRAAM air-to-air missiles

Dimensions: span (spread) 45ft 7.5in (13.91m); length 61ft 3.5in (18.68m); height 19ft 6.25in (5.95m)

Far right: *An unarmed Tornado F.3 of No. 229 OCU gets airborne using full reheat. Lightly loaded, the F.3 is an impressive display performer.*

Since the late 1980s, the Tornado F.3 has been the United Kingdom's main air defense asset. It is one of the last aircraft designed with bomber interception as its primary role, and as such it has certain limitations in the post–Cold War world. Upgrades and new weapons have kept it an effective warplane into the twenty-first century while its replacement has slowly approached service.

The original Royal Air Force (RAF) requirement for the MRCA (multirole combat aircraft), which eventually became the Panavia Tornado IDS (Interdictor Strike) aircraft, was issued in 1968. Even then a separate fighter version was considered, optimized for patrolling the North Sea and engaging multiple (Soviet bomber) targets beyond visual range with a battery of missiles. The fighter requirement was formalized in 1971, before the first flight of the IDS prototype in August 1974.

The RAF considered the F-14 for its fighter requirement, but it was deemed too expensive if supplied complete with its AWG-9 weapons

Right: *The original Tornado F.2 was not combat capable and used only for testing and initial pilot training.*

PILOTING THE TORNADO

Above: Saudi Arabia has been the only non-British nation to purchase the ADV, though Italy has leased two squadrons worth of ex-RAF F.3s.

Tornado F.3 (and former Lightning) pilot Ian Black compared the experience of flying the two in *JETS* magazine. "Pre takeoff checks [in the F.3] are lengthier than in the Lightning, but then again the aircraft is a considerably more complex machine. Ensuring the wings are swept forward and the flaps are down, the pilot spools up the two RB.199 turbofans. Reheat is engaged with the brakes on and the Tornado nose nods down. Brakes off, the aircraft accelerates quickly (when clean) or gathers pace slowly (fully laden). Once airborne the gear is retracted and reheat left in until 300 knots, which is the best single-engine speed should a failure occur. As the HUD indicates 350 knots the nose is raised and a sedate climb ensues, maintaining 350 knots or Mach 0.73.

"Unlike the Lightning, the F.3 performs best at around 15,000ft and below. Heading for its CAP point, the F.3 will normally contact an AWACS for his instructions. No worries now about fuel as the massive underwing tanks will still be partially full.

"Unlike the Lightning's weapons system the F.3's suite is comprehensive. After many initial problems, the Foxhunter radar is finally producing the goods, and coupled with JTIDS it allows great situational awareness. With the front-seater flying the aircraft and the back-seater taking the role of battle manager, the two-man crew concept is a positive bonus in a high workload environment.

"As a pure interceptor, the F.3 performs well against medium- and low-level nonagile threats. Where the aircraft falls down is against high-flying targets or agile fighters. Having said that, even in combat, the aircraft is very forgiving. With its fly-by-wire controls and SPILS (spin incidence limitation system) this heavy fighter (which, fully loaded, weighs as much as a World War II Sunderland flying-boat) is surprisingly agile. As a pilot it's very reassuring that to know that the aircraft will look after you. Even at low speed the Tornado is very predictable and docile. Aircraft like the Lightning and Phantom did have a tendency to depart controlled flight in combat if you were too aggressive at low speeds and high angles of attack.

Below: The Tornado F.3 is really a two-crew aircraft, requiring a backseater to control the sophisticated radar, weapons, and defensive systems.

"Another major plus over the Lightning is the F.3's handling on landing. It's a very straightforward aircraft to fly in the circuit and landing is a piece of cake using the HUD. Displayed in front of you is a symbol for your flight path vector, and all you have to do is place this over the runway and point the aircraft. Perfect landings every time!"

Another (anonymous) pilot had this to say about the F.3's top speed: "The F.3's straight line top speed is theoretically limited to 915 mph (or 800 knots) indicated air speed (IAS) due to structural considerations. This is not an absolute limit, as one pilot notes: 'Some years ago, before I knew any better, I saw 850 [knots] IAS at sea level (yes, the ground was below sea level) and the jet was still accelerating. We went past an F/A-18, which was in full blower and doing his best, with about 100 kts of overtake. It was a pretty sight. At high level I've seen Mach 2, but the fuel gauge was saying, 'Go home.'"

***Left:** The Tornado was originally designed as a low-level strike fighter, and as such it is one of the fastest aircraft in the world.*

system—and not much use without it. The F-15 was seen as suited better to fighter-versus-fighter combat, and its radar capability was regarded as somewhat limited. The RAF also wanted a two-seater with a dedicated weapons systems operator. Eventually, Britain launched an Air Defense Variant (ADV) of the Tornado in March 1976, adjusting its orders so that 165 of the 385 of the RAF's Tornadoes would be of the new variant. A more general reorganization of UK air defense at the time saw greater concentration on tanker support and AWACS control, and an eventual retirement of the Bloodhound surface-to-air missile.

Like the IDS, the ADV was constructed by the three partner nations, with MBB in Germany building the center fuselage section and Aeritalia in Italy the wings. Front and rear fuselage construction and final assembly was the United Kingdom's responsibility. The first of three ADV prototypes flew from Warton on October 27, 1979 with Dave Eagles as pilot and Roy Kenward as flight test observer. It was followed by 18 Tornado F.Mk 2s, which were issued to No. 229 Operational Conversion Unit (OCU) from November 1984.

Delays with the Foxhunter radar saw most of the F.2s delivered with ballast fitted in the nose. This led to jibes about the "Blue Circle" radar, a reference to the color-coded designations of some UK avionics equipment and to a well-known cement company. In many other ways the F.2s were very limited, and they were withdrawn by August 1986.

The ADV was designed around the Marconi AI.Mk 24 Foxhunter radar. The main armament is a quartet of BAe Dynamics Sky Flash semiactive radar-homing air-to-air missiles. This is an improved version of the AIM-7E Sparrow with an improved seeker and fuse. In order to carry these missiles without recourse to pylon-mounted launchers, the fuselage was stretched by 4ft 5.5in (1.36m) compared to the IDS Tornado to allow four Sky Flashes to be carried semirecessed in the underside of the fuselage. The stretch also made room for an extra 165-Imperial-gallon (750-liter) fuel tank and some extra avionics. To ensure clean separation of the missiles, they are swung into the airflow by launchers made by Frazer Nash, historically a maker of bomber gun turrets.

Four Sidewinders could be carried on the inboard pylons, which can also carry fuel tanks of up to 495 gallons (2,250 liters). These enormous tanks are sometimes called "Hindenburgers" after their Zeppelin-like proportions. The inner pylons can also carry Phimat or BOL chaff-dispensing pods. More recently, outer pylons as on the IDS

***Below:** For low-level and low-speed flight, the Tornado's wings are swept forward. Here the leading-edge flaps are also deployed.*

Above: *The Tornado ADV has a pair of large airbrakes mounted on the rear fuselage for a short landing run.*

Below: *Working in concert with the E-3D Sentry, the Tornado F.3 is the first line of the UK's air defenses.*

have been added to carry such things as the TRD towed radar decoy.

The port-side 1.06-in (27-mm) Mauser cannon was removed to allow room for more avionics and a fully retractable refueling probe, unlike the bolt-on unit of the IDS. Although the controls have conventional mechanical linkages, the ADV has a triple-redundant fly-by-wire stability augmentation system that gives increased roll-rate and reduces stick force needed for most maneuvers. The wings sweep up to 67 degrees as on the Tornado IDS, and the pylons swivel automatically to remain parallel with the airflow.

The main production version was the Tornado F.3, which progressively replaced the Lightning and the Phantom after it entered RAF service with No. 29 Squadron at Coningsby in early 1987. Five further operational squadrons were to be equipped, with one (No. 11) adopting the specialized maritime air defense role.

The F.3 has Rolls-Royce RB 199 Mk 104 turbofan engines rated at 16,520lb of thrust (73.48kN) each in afterburner, rather than the lower powered Mk 103s inherited from the Tornado IDS. It also had radar of various improving standards over the course of its service.

F.3s were rushed to Dhahran, Saudi Arabia, in August 1990 to counter the threat from Iraq after the invasion of Kuwait. Before the end of the month, they had been swapped for aircraft with "war mods" that included twin chaff/flare dispensers under the fuselage and radar-absorbent material (RAM) on the leading edges of the wings and tailplanes. They were largely tasked with defense of parts of Saudi airspace and did not have the opportunity to fire on Iraqi aircraft during Operation Granby, the British code name for their part in Desert Storm.

Since the mid-1990s, a detachment of F.Mk 3s has been based at Mount Pleasant Airport to provide air defense for the Falkland Islands. In memory of the Sea Gladiators that defended Malta in 1940, the four aircraft wear the codes "F," "H," "C," and "D," standing for *Faith, Hope, Charity,* and *Desperation.* Tornado F.3s participated in Operation Deny Flight over Bosnia, Operation Southern Watch over Iraq, and in Operation Telic, the UK contribution to the 2003 Iraq war. In none of these operations has an F.3 actively engaged a hostile aircraft.

The greater "area rule" effect of the longer fuselage helped give better acceleration and low-level speed than the IDS. The F.3 is probably the fastest accelerating aircraft in the world at low level. Yet is was always a compromise design based on a bomber that was designed for high speed at low level, not endurance or agility. At higher levels, the F.3 suffers from a lack of speed and acceleration.

When the ADV was conceived, there was no threat from long-range fighters escorting Soviet bombers; however, by the time it entered service, the Sukhoi Su-27 and MiG-31 had been fielded by the Soviet Union (although no one would call the "Foxhound" agile), requiring more concentration on fighter-versus-fighter combat training. Good tactics, the situational awareness provided by the two-man crew, and employment of AWACS and JTIDs have overcome some of the shortcomings of the F.3.

The Tornado ADV has not, however, had a great deal of export success. Under the huge Al-Yamamah arms deal in 1985, Saudi Arabia ordered 24 Tornado ADVs, which equipped two squadrons from 1989. A later order was changed to one for more IDS Tornadoes. An order for eight aircraft from Oman was put back, then replaced by one for Hawk 200s. In order to bridge the technology gap between the F-104 Starfighter and the Eurofighter 2000, Italy leased 24 F.3s from Britain from 1995. These aircraft are being returned as Italy has since leased F-16s in preparation for receiving the Eurofighter Typhoon.

Above: *A Tornado F.3 of No. 56 "Firebirds" Squadron comes out of its hardened aircraft shelter (HAS).*

As the Typhoon made its slow progress toward RAF service, the F.3 was progressively upgraded with improved radar, ECM, the JTIDS datalink, and more recently, the ASRAAM (Advanced Short Range Air-to-Air Missile), the United Kingdom's choice as an AIM-9 replacement.

In 2003, it was revealed that the RAF's F.3s had added an important secondary capability with the addition of the BAE Systems ALARM (air-launched antiradiation missile). Like the F-14, which developed a precision-attack capability late in its career, the F.3's "Wild Weasel" role may prolong its service career beyond its expected out-of-service date. Another possibility is that the F.3 will be integrated with the MBDA Storm Shadow cruise missile as fielded on RAF Tornado GR.4s during the 2003 Iraq war, turning this interceptor into a potent strike aircraft.

Below: *With wings swept fully back, a Tornado F.3 of No. 29 Squadron taxies into its parking place during a deployment to the US.*

Sukhoi Su-27 and Su-30 Flanker

Sukhoi's phenomenal Su-27 and Su-30 fighters combine speed, maneuverability, and range with heavy armament. The basic airframe retains much potential, but most developments are being driven (and paid for) by export customers.

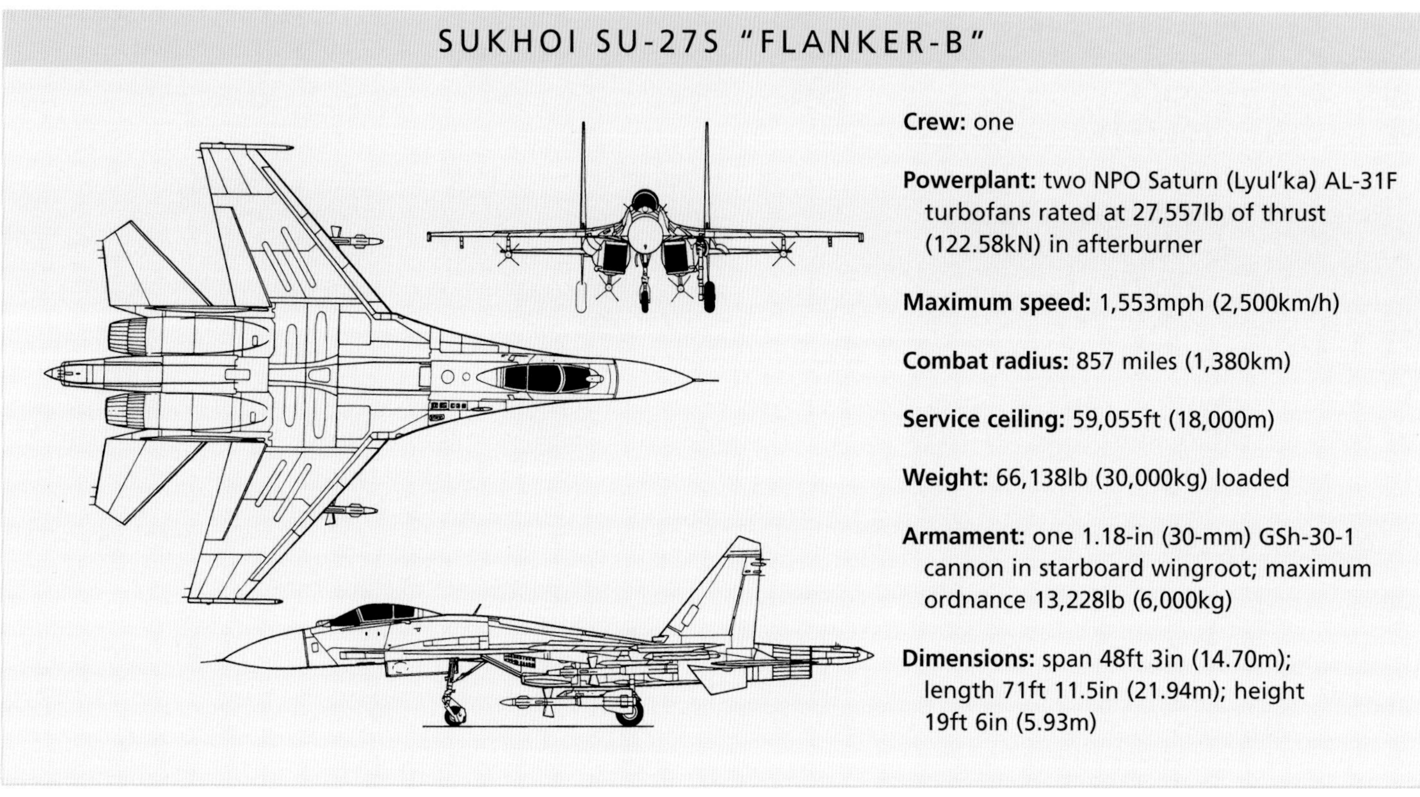

SUKHOI SU-27S "FLANKER-B"

Crew: one

Powerplant: two NPO Saturn (Lyul'ka) AL-31F turbofans rated at 27,557lb of thrust (122.58kN) in afterburner

Maximum speed: 1,553mph (2,500km/h)

Combat radius: 857 miles (1,380km)

Service ceiling: 59,055ft (18,000m)

Weight: 66,138lb (30,000kg) loaded

Armament: one 1.18-in (30-mm) GSh-30-1 cannon in starboard wingroot; maximum ordnance 13,228lb (6,000kg)

Dimensions: span 48ft 3in (14.70m); length 71ft 11.5in (21.94m); height 19ft 6in (5.93m)

Far right: *The "Russian Knights" fly the largest, most powerful aircraft of any aerobatic team. When not on the road they are based in Kubinka, near Moscow.*

Right: *With its unusual marking down the left fuselage side, this Su-27 "Flanker A" was known as the "Lipetsk Shark" after its base in Western Russia.*

The Su-27 was once regarded as the "Soviet superfighter" able to take on and defeat any NATO fighter or strike aircraft. Not long after its service debut, the Soviet threat itself disappeared, but the proliferation of increasingly sophisticated versions, particularly in Southeast Asia, is giving Western defense planners considerable cause for concern.

Pavel O. Sukhoi's design bureau began studies into advanced fighters in 1969. In the same time period, the Soviet military leadership decided that no single aircraft could undertake all the roles demanded of modern fighter-type aircraft and laid down the parameters for a mass-produced light fighter and an advanced heavy tactical fighter. These concepts paralleled the US LWF and ATF programs, which produced the F-16 and F-15, respectively. Soviet doctrine emphasized different performance characteristics, however, particularly as regarded the input of the pilot to the conduct of a combat mission.

A request in 1971 for proposals for the two requirements attracted responses from MiG, Yakovlev, and Sukhoi. The latter bureau offered two twin-tailed designs, one of them a

Above: The Su-27 made its Western debut at the 1989 Paris Air Show in June 1989. At that time it was still more than a year away from entering service.

rather radical lifting-body design with large leading-edge root extensions (LERXs) and a noticeably drooped nose. This design, which was unlike any previous Soviet fighter, was chosen for development as the T10. Mikoyan's light fighter proposal was to become the MiG-29.

The T10 was refined through many wind-tunnel tests of variations of the basic layout until the design was frozen in 1975. Chief designer Mikhail Simonov completed the detail design after Pavel Sukhoi's death in 1975, and the T10-1 prototype, powered by two 24,691-lb thrust (110-kN) Lyul'ka AL-21F-3 turbofans flew on May 20, 1977 with Vladimir Ilyushin at the controls. Blurry video of this event was to give Western observers without high-security clearance the first look at the new Sukhoi in the mid-1980s, by which time the much revised production Su-27 was in service.

Although the T10-1 flew before the MiG-29 prototype, it took somewhat more effort to produce a service-ready fighter from the Sukhoi. Like the MiG, the Sukhoi needed its nose gear moved aft, but other modifications required after the structural failure of the second T10 prototype and a change of engines to the smaller AL-31Fs delayed the program, as did the failure to meet specification targets. The design had to be completely redesigned to lower weight, increase useful load and remain maneuverable at low speeds.

The resulting T10-S, which flew on April 20, 1981, became the true basis of the Su-27, which NATO and its allies called the "Flanker." A new wing with straight-edged tips and missile rails was fitted. Control was effected with flaperons and leading-edge slats, acting on inputs from the fly-by-wire system, the first in a Soviet fighter. There were hardpoints on the wings and nacelles for 10

PILOTING THE SU-27 FLANKER

Above: The "Test Pilots" team of two Su-27Ps were regular visitors to airshows in the UK and western Europe in the 1990s.

One of the most unusual air combats of modern times took place on February 26, 1999. An Ethiopian Air Force Su-27SK was escorting a flight of MiG-21s on a strike mission in the Badme region, when the female pilot of the Sukhoi, Captain Aster Tolossa, detected a quickly approaching contact on her radar. She turned to intercept the unknown aircraft, which turned out to be an Eritrean MiG-29UB. After some maneuvering between the two aircraft, the Fulcrum, which was apparently unarmed, wound up above and behind the Flanker. Tolossa was able to contact the MiG pilot on the radio and discovered to her astonishment that he was her former instructor from flight school in Russia! She warned him that she was in a position to destroy his aircraft and he would be shot down if he did not obey her instructions and land at Debre Zeit. The Russian pilot refused and Tolossa fired a missile, probably an R-73, at the MiG, which successfully evaded it, as it did a second missile. The faster Sukhoi then chased down the MiG and destroyed it with 1.18-in (30-mm) cannon fire. Tolossa returned to a hero's welcome.

fuel tanks or weapons racks. Missile armament included the R-27 (AA-10 "Alamo"), R-73 (AA-11 "Archer") and R-77 (AA-12 "Adder") air-to-air missiles. Fixed armament is one Gsh-301 single-barrel 1.18-in (30-mm) cannon fitted on the right side of the forward fuselage.

The drooping nose and bubble canopy gave exceptional vision. As on the MiG-29, there were intake doors and auxiliary louvers. The huge vertical fins were supplemented by ventral fins at the tailplane roots. In all the Su-27 was huge, even larger than the F-15, which itself was bigger and heavier than a World War II medium bomber such as the B-25.

Production started in 1982 and service entry began in 1984. Before long, NATO fighters and patrol aircraft intercepted Flankers over the Baltic. On one occasion, a Norwegian P-3 had a minor collision with a fully armed Su-27. The first Flankers appeared in the West at the 1989 Paris Air Show and demonstrated their exceptional maneuverability (when lightly loaded) in the daily flying display. One maneuver developed by Sukhoi test pilot Viktor Pugachev was the "Cobra," consisting of a rapid pull-up to almost zero forward airspeed followed by a pushover back into forward flight. The combat utility of such a move (as with the tailslides performed by the MiG-29 and Su-27) has been questioned, but it is said to break the lock of Doppler-based radars, as well as forcing a nearby enemy to "fly-through" and present a rear-aspect target to the Sukhoi.

The standard SU-27S "Flanker-A" single-seater was partnered by the Su-27UB "Flanker-B" two-seater, which is also equipped with N001 radar and standard weapons. The Su-30 emerged as a fully capable missionized two-seater for long-range interception and strike missions. Extra fuel capacity gives double the range of the Su-27UB.

Sukhoi displayed various demonstrators during the 1990s. One of the most interesting was the single-seat Su-37, which astounded the West with its incredible back flips and other maneuvers, made possible by its thrust-vectoring control (TVC) AL-37FU turbofans and canard foreplanes. The Su-37 has led to the Su-30MK series of two-seaters using TVC versions of the AL-31F.

The Su-27K (or Su-33) equips Russia's sole conventional aircraft carrier, the Admiral *Kuznetsov*. This is a canard-equipped single-seater with wing folding and an arrester hook. Catapult provisions are not required, as the Su-33 uses a "ski-jump" system and the huge power of its engines to get airborne without assistance.

The Su-27 was not exported or supplied to Warsaw Pact member nations by the Soviet Union, as was the MiG-29. With the breakup of the Soviet Union in 1990–92, large numbers of Su-27s came under the control of the newly independent republics, such as Ukraine, Belarus, and Kazakhstan. Surplus Su-27s that former Soviet republics or Russia itself do not want have turned up in the hands of a number of nations—usually those who do not want to discuss the details, either with outsiders or their own people—including Syria and possibly Angola. Vietnam moved up a league in defensive capabilities with the acquisition of a squadron of Su-27SKs from 1995. Indonesia has become the latest user with the acquisition of two Su-27SKs and two Su-30MKs in 2003. It also seems quite likely that the US Air Force's "Red Hats" threat assessment

Below: *China has become the biggest operator of the "Flanker" outside Russia. This is one of the 74 Russian-assembled aircraft delivered from 1992.*

Above: *The Su-30MK was the prototype version for export. Aspects of this model and the Su-37 demonstrator were combined to create the Su-30MKI for India.*

Above: A large HUD dominates the pale blue cockpit of the Su-27. The effectiveness of the K-36 ejection seat has been publicly proved on several occasions.

unit has secretly operated up to four Su-27s for a number of years, as the cliché has it, "from secret bases in the Nevada desert," although this has never been officially acknowledged.

The Su-27 has been involved in few air combats to date. Ethiopia and Eritrea both rearmed with modern combat aircraft during 1999 following a period of air combat involving Ethiopian MiG-21s and MiG-23s, and Eritrean Aermacchi trainers. Former Russian Air Force pilots and groundcrew were active on both sides of the conflict. There had been little time to train or convert many local pilots to fly the sophisticated new fighters, although about 20 aircrew were locals. The Ethiopian Air Force (EtAf) soon had about 38 fixed-wing aircraft, mostly secondhand from Russia. Eight of these were Su-27SKs delivered in December 1998.

During two periods of air combat, in February/March 1999 and May 2000, Ethiopian Su-27s destroyed six Eritrean MiG-29s; at least three of these kills were made by local pilots. An unfortunate civilian Lear jet that strayed into the war zone on a delivery flight was also brought down in 1999 by an EtAf Flanker. Ethiopia bought seven more Su-27SKs in 2002, and it was reported in 2003 that Eritrea had acquired four ex-Ukrainian Su-27s of its own.

Although the Chinese have long been working on various indigenous fighter projects, since 1992 they have bought 74 Su-27s and 80 Su-30MKKs, and have undertaken license production of the Su-27 as the Shenyang J-11. Early Chinese-built aircraft were reportedly poorly assembled, but in 2002 a top Sukhoi official was embarrassed to admit that construction quality and finish had become better than on Russian-built aircraft. At least 75 J-11s are thought to have been built locally to date, and kits for modification of up to 100 to the equivalent of Su-27SM standard have been supplied from Russia. This midlife upgrade includes LCD display screens, compatibility with AA-12 (R-77) air-to-air missiles, an electro-optical targeting pod, and a new electronic warfare (EW) system. Only a handful of Russia's own Flankers had been upgraded to Su-27SM standard by the end of 2003.

India is building up its Flanker fleet by stages, starting with an initial batch of baseline Su-30s to train pilots, and moving up through various avionics standards to the Su-30MKI, which will be the first thrust-vectoring fighter to be fielded operationally by any air arm. The MKI will be more sophisticated than any Flankers in the Russian military, with its canards, N011M Bars

Right: The side-by-side cockpit Su-32 has entered production at a low rate and will replace the Su-24 "Fencer" and some Tu-22M "Backfires" with the Russian Air Force.

phased-array radar (which can simultaneously track 15 targets and engage four at ranges of up to 93 miles/150km) and wide weapons options. Unlike China's aircraft, the Indian aircraft will have extensive ground-attack capabilities, including the nuclear strike role.

A separate line of development has seen the Su-34 (originally the Su-27IB, then Su-32FN) fighter-bomber with side-by-side seating and "duck-bill" nose containing V004 phase-array radar. The extended tailboom contains rear-facing radar. The "Sea Snake" avionics complex can detect air or surface targets (including submarine periscopes) at ranges up to 155 miles (250km). Entry to the armored cockpit (which contains a foldaway galley, a bunk, and a toilet between the seats) is through the nosewheel bay. Range and weapons capacity exceeds that of the F-15E Strike Eagle. The Su-34 is likely to eventually replace the Su-24 "Fencer" in Russian service, but may not be offered for export.

The Su-27KUB carrier-capable trainer shares the side-by-side cockpit layout with the Su-34, but has a standard "round" nose. An attack version based on the KUB is being offered for land-based Russian Navy units.

About 450 Flankers were in Russian service by the mid-1990s. Only one unit has been equipped with the Su-30 due to cuts in the budget for new aircraft procurement. The production of new Su-30s for domestic use and the upgrade of Su-27s in Russian service are proceeding at a very slow rate. For the time being, Sukhoi will have to fund future Su-27 developments and any planned new aircraft (such as the forward-swept wing Su-47 *Berkut*) on income from export sales.

***Above:** Russia's single operational carrier is equipped with a squadron of Su-33s. Folding wings and canard foreplanes distinguish this version.*

***Left:** About 700 Su-27s entered service with the USSR's aviation forces. Fewer than 350 remain operational with the unified Russian Air Force today.*

Dassault Rafale

Dassault's Rafale has beaten the Eurofighter and F/A-22 into squadron service and has flown operational missions in the Afghan war. It offers stealth, high performance, and maneuverability, as well as sophisticated new weapons.

Far right: *The Rafale A was the demonstrator for France's original ACX program, first flying in 1986.*

Below: *The first navalized version of the Rafale was the Rafale M (Marine) prototype, which first flew in December 1991.*

The Dassault Rafale is that rarity among major combat aircraft today, being a national program rather than a collaborative venture. Unlike the Eurofighter Typhoon and the Gripen, the Rafale's airframe, engines, and most of the avionics are all made in the same country. Although not free from political interference and budgetary problems, the Rafale program has outpaced the multinational Typhoon in getting aircraft into (limited) service, despite a later start.

Studies for a successor to the Mirage 2000 dubbed the ACX (Avion de Combat Experimental) began in 1980–81. West Germany and Great Britain were at the same time formulating what would become of the Eurofighter (EFA), later the Typhoon. As related in the entry on that aircraft, France joined the Eurofighter program along with Italy and Spain, but soon demanded the lion's share of the work, the testing and leadership of the organization. Meanwhile, it continued to work on its own ACX project, while the other nations were working toward a fighter based largely on the British Aerospace (BAe) EAP.

Authority for two ACX demonstrators, later

DASSAULT RAFALE C

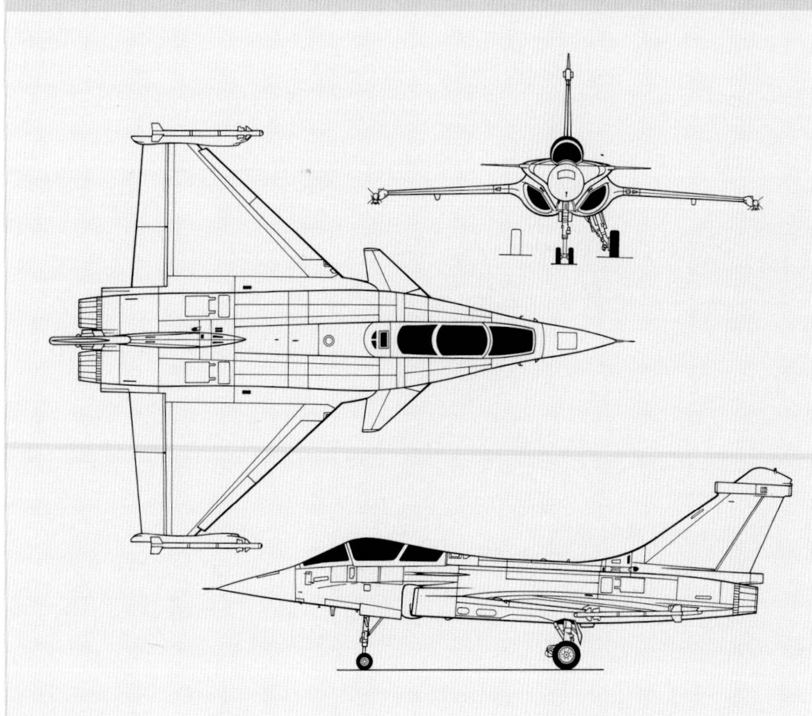

Crew: one

Powerplant: two SNECMA M88-2 turbofans rated at 19,555lb of thrust (86.98kN) in afterburner

Maximum speed: 1,321mph (2,125km/h)

Combat radius: 655 miles (1,055km)

Service ceiling: 50,000ft (15,240m)

Weight: 19,973lb (9,060kg) loaded

Armament: one 1.18-in (30-mm) GIAT DEFA 791B cannon, 14 stores stations for a maximum of 17,637lb (8,000kg) of ordnance

Dimensions: span (over wingtip missiles) 35ft 9.25in (10.9m); length 50ft 2.5in (15.3m); height 17ft 6.75in (5.34m)

reduced to just one, was given to Dassault in April 1983. At the same time, enginemaker SNECMA was contracted to develop the M88 turbofan. The niche for the ACX soon expanded from a Mirage 2000 replacement to encompass that of the Jaguar bomber and the *Aéronavale*'s Crusader and Super Etendard as well. To meet this naval requirement, France wanted a smaller and lighter aircraft than the Eurofighter was becoming.

In April 1985, the ACX was renamed Rafale, or "squall," in line with Dassault's previous meteorologically themed aircraft, the Ouragan ("hurricane") and Mirage. Three months later France left the Eurofighter program altogether and accelerated work on its demonstrator, the Rafale A. Like all Mirages except the F1, the Rafale A was a tailless delta, albeit with squared-off wingtips mounting missile rails. As with some Mirage III and V derivatives, canard foreplanes were fitted. The forward fuselage sides curved inward toward the intake mouths, contributing to a lower frontal cross-section.

Below: *Five Rafale prototypes are seen together in January 1986. From the bottom, the Rafale M No. 2, Rafale B, Rafale M No. 1, Rafale C, and Rafale A.*

Piloted by Guy Mitaux-Maurouard, the Rafale A first flew on July 4, 1986 with General Electric F404 engines as an interim measure. In 1990 and after 460 test flights, one test was an F404 replaced by a development SNECMA M88-2, and a second round of test flights expanded the envelope to Mach 1.4 and 40,000ft (12,192m). The Rafale A was retired after 865 test flights in January 1994, having established and proved the basic design, configuration, and performance of the definitive Rafale, or ACT (*Avion de Combat Tactique*), as well as its fly-by-wire control system and mainly composite structure.

Unusually, with a span of 36ft 9in (11.20m) and a length of 51ft 10in (15.80m), the Rafale A was larger than the development and production aircraft that followed. Although extremely similar in appearance, subsequent aircraft had a reprofiled fin junction, more rounded wingroot fairings, and a gold-coated canopy. These features all serve to reduce the radar cross-section, as does special paint with radar-absorbent material. More than 50 percent of the structure is composed of

Right: *Before embarking on a carrier, the Rafale Ms were tested on the land-based catapult and arresting system in New Jersey and Maryland.*

PILOTING THE DASSAULT RAFALE

Like the other agile "superfighters" of the 1990s, the closest the Rafale has so far come to combat is the competitive world of the international air show. At Paris in 2003, the Rafale B display pilot was the very experienced, cigar-loving Eric Gérard, who had been the first to land a Rafale aboard the carrier *Charles de Gaulle,* among other firsts. In 1991, he joined Dassault Aviation as an experimental test pilot. In an interview for the show organization, he described some of the best points of the Rafale as a display aircraft. "Most of the time the demonstrations are flown in a tight airspace," he explains. "Thanks to the power available from the M88 engines, I can easily recover speed and energy after each tight turn. The M88 response is also excellent: stress is high on the engines when you apply the power from idle to full afterburner several times in a row. With the M88, it takes only five seconds to go from idle to afterburner, which is really exceptional.

"In less than seven minutes, the Rafale B has to show all its strength and agility. Without forgetting the exceptional performance of the braking system, which adds a final touch to a brilliant display: thanks to its carbon brakes, the Rafale decelerates in less than ten seconds in front of the spectators, whereas the competition still uses the old-fashioned and cumbersome braking parachute system.

"My presentation will be classical for the Rafale but very dynamic," summed up Eric Gérard, who practiced his program six times in Istres in southern France before landing the Rafale at Le Bourget for the Air Show.

Above: *The Rafale (this is a C) has impressed crowds and potential customers worldwide with its astonishing aerobatic displays.*

composite and new materials. The French air force refers to its aircraft generically as the Rafale D (for *discret*, or "stealth").

The Rafale C was the prototype single-seater for the *Armée de l'Air*, first flying on May 19, 1991, followed by the two-seat Rafale B in April 1993. Initially envisaged as the conversion trainer, the Rafale B is now to be the main *Armée de l'Air* operational version, with 139 two-seaters and 95 single-seaters on order. French experience with single-seat aircraft such as the Jaguar and two-seaters such as the Mirage 2000N has shown the value of a second crew member in "burden-sharing" during complex attack missions.

The fall of the Berlin Wall saw changes in defense priorities throughout Europe. By 1992, the Rafale program was well ahead of the rival Eurofighter, but the French government chose to delay development as a cost-saving measure, and it canceled a second AdlA single-seat prototype. This lower pace saw Dassault lose some of its lead to its competitors.

Budget cuts limited the *Aéronavale*'s purchase to

Above: *The development aircraft, the two-seater Rafale B, is seen here armed with Apache cruise missiles.*

60 aircraft. A two-seat Rafale N version was added to the plan quite late in the day, with a decision to split the order into 25 single- and 35 two-seaters announced in December 2002. The N will carry slightly less fuel than the M and have no cannon, and is expected to enter service after 2007. France would like to build a second aircraft carrier, but the design remains undecided and funding has not been allocated. The *Armée de l'Air* has also chosen to order a higher proportion of two-seat Rafale Bs. Its planned buy of 234 aircraft now consists of 139 Bs and 95 Cs.

The single-seat Rafale has an internal fuel capacity of 1,519 gallons (5,750 liters), and five of the pylons are plumbed for drop tanks, each able to carry a 330-gallon (1,250-liter) drop tank, although the centerline station can carry a 528-gallon (2000-liter) tank. For export customers wanting even more fuel, and who may not have an indigenous air-refueling capability, Dassault has developed shapely conformal fuel tanks, which add a further 608 gallons (2,300 liters).

The main instrument panel is unusual even by modern standards. It is dominated by a central "head-level display" flanked by two touch-sensitive MFDs and topped by a huge wide-angle HUD. There are no backup conventional instruments. The throttle and side-stick controller control many additional functions, as does the sophisticated direct voice input (DVI) system. This has a vocabulary of up to 300 words and, combined with the upcoming helmet-mounted sight, will allow the future Rafale pilot to engage and destroy an enemy "over the shoulder" with such weapons as the Matra Mica, with its "lock after launch" capability. The Mica will appear in both infrared and radar-homing versions, initially as a replacement for the short-range Magic 2, and later in a long-range version.

The single-seat Rafales have a new 1.18-in (30-mm) GIAT M 791 single-barreled cannon. To reduce maintenance, the easily removable cannon pack will not be installed except on combat missions or in training involving actual firing. More important in self-defense is the sophisticated MBDA/Thales Spectra EW system, which incorporates a precise threat-location capability for use against airborne and ground-based threats. Using "sensor fusion" of Spectra, radar and IRST, the Rafale pilot can quickly establish the "air picture" of targets, threats, and allied units. Spectra also incorporates an ECM suite to protect against a variety of threats.

The *Aéronavale*'s more pressing requirement has seen that service be the first to induct the Rafale. The air force and naval versions are said to have 80 percent airframe and systems commonality, but the Rafale M has a tailhook and a strengthened undercarriage for carrier operations. The nosewheel incorporates a unique "jump strut," which holds tension until the end of

***Below:** Though unequipped with all the avionics and weapons systems of the production aircraft, the Rafale A was slightly larger than the later versions.*

***Right:** The Rafale's cockpit is dominated by massive multifunction displays and has no conventional electromechanical instruments.*

the catapult track, and then springs the nose upward to the optimum takeoff angle. This obviates the need for a ski-jump ramp and allows a reduced-length carrier deck.

The Rafale M joined the reformed *Flotille 12* (12F) in May 2001, and seven aircraft were deployed aboard the carrier *Charles de Gaulle* in December 2001 on a semitrial basis alongside Super Etendards and E-2C Hawkeyes. During this period, the Rafales flew operational patrols over Afghanistan, but saw no combat. The chance to fly practice dogfights with US Navy fighters was eagerly taken up, but it has been reported that the F/A-18 Hornet squadrons declined to compare the two types in beyond-visual-range engagements, a tacit admission of the much more modern Rafale's superiority in this regard.

Initial operational capability of 12F was declared in October 2002. Future software upgrades will see the Rafale M fully take on the air-to-surface mission and replace the Super Etendard by 2010. Currently the only weapons options are the cannon, and Magic 2 and Mica AAMs. One of the first air-to-surface weapons will be the SCALP-EG cruise missile, a French version of the Storm Shadow, already deployed by the Royal Air Force and used in Iraq. The ASMP-A nuclear missile is likely to follow, as is the AM.39 Exocet.

Only five Rafale B and C models have so far been delivered to the *Armée de l'Air*, which is waiting on the availability of the new multirole software standard before fielding a full squadron from about 2006.

French Rafales are expected to remain in French service up to 2040, the largely composite airframe contributing to a long individual aircraft life. The Rafale has a reasonable export potential with some of the richer Asian and Middle Eastern nations. The Rafale lost out in the South Korean FX fighter competition to the Boeing F-15K in April 2002, but is still on offer for requirements by the United Arab Emirates, Singapore, India, and other nations. One-time Mirage operator Australia was a hoped-for customer, but seems to have thrown its lot in with the Joint Strike Fighter (JSF) program.

Above: *The Rafale first entered operational service with 12* Flotille, *whose at-sea home is the nuclear-powered carrier* Charles de Gaulle.

Below: *With the Apache cruise missile, the* Armée de l'Air's *two-seat Rafale will be a potent long-range strike platform.*

SAAB JAS 39 Gripen

The JAS 39 Gripen (griffon) is the latest advanced combat aircraft designed by Saab for the Swedish Air Force. It has considerable export potential, especially with nations unable or unwilling to acquire the latest models of F-16.

***Far right:** The near aircraft has Maverick and Rbs15 air-to-surface missiles on the wing pylons. The other has AIM-120 AMRAAMs.*

With the Saab Gripen, Sweden has continued to innovate in combat aircraft design, producing an aircraft the equal of any lightweight fighter anywhere. The Gripen will serve the Swedish air force (*Flygvapnet*) for many years, but will also be the first Swedish fighter to see service outside Scandinavia, as several nations have or are likely to select it as their next-generation fighter.

To meet a somewhat vague 1970s requirement for an aircraft to eventually replace various versions of the Viggen, Saab considered several options. One was a "Super Viggen," studied under the designation A20. This would have appeared in several different versions for different roles, as had the Viggen itself. Another was a new light ground-attack/trainer design called the B3LA. Versions would have appeared as the A 38 attacker and the Sk 38 trainer.

Progress was made on the B3LA, but in 1978 the Swedish government canceled the project. Facing disbandment, Saab's design team refocused its efforts toward a smaller, lighter, new technology aircraft to replace the attack Viggen. The government approved

***Right:** Sweden's Gripens are devoid of colorful unit markings. Some wear the wing number or letter on the nose or the fin tip.*

SAAB JAS 39C GRIPEN

Crew: one

Powerplant: one Volvo RM-12 turbofan rated at 18,100lb of thrust (80.5kN) in afterburner

Maximum speed: 1,321mph (2,126km/h)

Combat radius 497 miles (800km)

Service ceiling: not available

Weight: 30,800lb (13,989kg) loaded

Armament: one internal 1.06-in (27-mm) Mauser cannon, weapons load includes AIM-9L (Rb 74) and AIM-120 (Rb 99) air-to-air missiles

Dimensions: span 27ft 6in (8.4m); length 46ft 3in (14.1m); height 14ft 9in (4.5m)

PILOTING THE GRIPEN

The Gripen has impressed audiences with its precise air display routine from South Africa to South America, and at the biennial Farnborough Air Show. Writer Robert Hewson described the 2002 display routine for readers of the daily *Show News* paper: "The Farnborough crowd will be the first people to see the new Gripen display for '02, flown by Saab test pilot Fredrik Müchler. Fredrik has been flying the Gripen since 1997—the year it entered operational service with the Swedish air force—and now has about 600 hours on type. Fredrik flew his first Gripen display in 1998, but this year's display is more dynamic than ever. 'It's a tight and precise routine,' he says, 'showing that the aircraft has very clear-cut and repeatable handling characteristics. For a pilot, it's nice to be able to say that maneuvers are repeatable and always controlled, but the Gripen is also very sharp.'

"This is the first year that the Gripen display aircraft has flown with the latest version of the aircraft's flight control system (FCS), version R12.5—standard on air force aircraft since 2001. R12.5 delivers better turning performance, a lower cornering speed, a higher angle-of-attack limit, and a reduced minimum speed (down to 112mph from 143mph). It has taken a little time to qualify a display with the R12.5 FCS because of the need to integrate the aircraft's 'Smokewinders' into the system—'Integrating Smokewinders with the latest FCS software hasn't exactly been an air force priority,' noted Fredrik.

Above: The first two-seat JAS 39B first flew in March 1996. Pilot training was (and still is) conducted with simulators and single-seat Gripens.

"Fredrik has had to adjust his routine to fit in with the new display parameters at Farnborough. The minimum height for displays is now 200 meters and Fredrik noted, 'We're all used to thinking at 100 meters. That's a good height to give you good reference with the ground and good visual contact all round. Sometimes going higher can be a bit tricky for all those reasons, and the new "climb on turn" regulation is another complication. But it's our job, it's what we do—so we go and do it.'

"The display routine begins with the Gripen blasting off into a steep right turn climbing away from the crowd, in line with the new regulations. The aircraft performs a split-S to come back to display center followed by a 7-*g* pull-up to the vertical, and then a roll through 130 degrees before going nose down to make a spiraling descent back along the display line. Fredrik performs a slow, straight roll followed by a right/left yo-yo to return to the display line once more. The rapid reversal of the yo-yo maneuver brings the Gripen back for a high-speed pass, at around Mach 0.75. At the end of the pass, Fredrik makes a snap roll and from that, pulls straight into a maximum rate 9*g*, 360-degree left-hand turn, then back to the display line, wings level, to loop up to 1,000 meters.

"Fredrik exits the loop with a 90-degree turn out from the display line, before making a left-hand turn into a right-hand barrel roll. This ends with a left-hand turn back to 90 degrees to the display line and then a Derry turn to fly out along the display line—but in the opposite direction to the loop. Fredrik makes a roll over the top—tight, only up to 700 meters at the top—before going 60 degrees nose-down into a left-hand turn to continue about 45 degrees off the display line into another Derry turn and then slowing right down to minimum speed for a slow pass at 26 degrees Alpha [angle of attack].

"At the end of this pass the burners go on and the Gripen launches into a right-hand 360-degree turn—accelerating all the time while at maximum turn rate—to return along the display line. Fredrik climbs vertically to about 600 meters rolling over into a split-S from 900 meters, then makes another barrel roll to the right before popping the Gripen's gear down straight away to make a trademark ultra-short landing, within a breathtaking 400 meters. Job done."

the basic concept as the System 39 in 1980, but insisted that it also replace the latest fighter Viggen, the JA 37.

All previous Saab jet fighters had been built in multiple versions for specific tasks. The concept behind System 39 was to incorporate three main roles, fighter (*jakt*), attack (*attack*), and reconnaissance (*spaning*), in one aircraft, hence the JAS 39 designation. A Saab design was not the only option, and purchase or license production of a foreign design such as the General Dynamics F-16, Northrop F-20, or McDonnell Douglas F/A-18 was considered. A collaborative program with one or more other countries was also suggested, and Saab considered joining the Eurofighter consortium until it became apparent that this project would not bear fruit in time to meet *Flygvapnet*'s needs. The point in 1980 at which it was decided to proceed with a Saab-designed, single-engined canard delta configuration fighter was a long time in coming. The fact that the Gripen bears a broad similarity to the Viggen it is replacing masks many wrong turns and much political debate, often over the fundamental need for such a highly expensive project at all.

The main players in Swedish high-tech industry set up a consortium to coordinate sourcing and production of the many systems and components in the JAS system. This IG JAS (Industrial Group JAS) includes Saab-Scania, Volvo, and Ericsson, among others, as well as the *Flygvapnet*'s procurement organization, the FFV.

The JAS 39's designers saw no reason why the new fighter had to be in the same weight and size class as the Viggen or the other fighters under development elsewhere. Improvements in engine design, the development of composite materials and the miniaturization of electronics allowed a superior combat aircraft to be built that was about 60 percent the size of its predecessor. Airframe size was partly defined by the size of the chosen powerplant, the Volvo RM12 turbofan, which was an improved license-built version of the General Electric F404 as used in the F/A-18. This smaller diameter engine allowed a slimmer fuselage. The fly-by-wire flight control system (FCS) reduced the weight further compared to a conventional mechanical system. Thrust reverse was dispensed with, as the lighter weight combined with more efficient brakes and deflection of the canards on touchdown contributed to a landing roll of 1,640ft (500m).

Approval for prototypes and an initial batch of 30 production aircraft came in June 1982, and the

Above: *Sweden has a large amount of airspace to defend, but also a lot of lightly inhabited terrain over which to conduct realistic training.*

Below: *The first Gripen had a short career before it was wrecked in a landing accident two months after its first flight.*

Above: F7, in Såtenäs, in central southern Sweden, was the first wing to receive Gripen, in 1996.

Below: The first batch of production Gripens featured black radomes, and full-color national insignia, but these were soon toned down.

first of five JAS 39A prototypes flew on December 9, 1988 in the hands of Stig Holmström. This first aircraft had a short career, being lost in a landing accident in February 1989 caused by an FCS problem. The prototype went out of control and cartwheeled as it touched down at Linköping at the end of its sixth flight. Despite the prototype's accident, and the loss of the first production Gripen during an aerobatic display in August 1993 (also due to an FCS problem), the Gripen has had a remarkably good safety record. In six years service to date, one aircraft has crashed into a lake (the pilot ejected safely) and another was written off when overpressurized during refueling.

The Gripen program was always planned to develop in stages. The first 108 JAS 39A models represent the baseline single-seat version for the *Flygvapnet.* Subsequent single-seaters are being delivered as the JAS 39C, which will have many improvements, not least to its interoperability with Nato forces. The C has a retractable in-flight refueling probe, Nato-standard IFF equipment, onboard oxygen generation, and cockpit displays, which can be switched from Swedish to English and metric to imperial with the touch of a button. The displays themselves are compatible with night-vision goggles. The baseline JAS 39A cockpit is dominated by three large multifunction displays (MFDs) and a wide-angle head-up display (HUD). The instrument panel on late As and subsequent aircraft will have even larger MFDs, giving the largest area of active cockpit displays of any fighter. The displays consist of three elements. There is a flight data display with essential flight instrumentation, plus weapons status and warning information. Secondly, there is a horizontal situation display which provides the "big picture" of the aicraft's position, as well as that of all other aircraft, missile, and sensor ranges and so on. Finally, there is a multisensor display, which presents the information from the Ericsson pulse-Doppler radar. To fit all this in, the last electro-mechanical cockpit instruments have been deleted from the Gripen cockpit.

Not immediately apparent to the casual viewer is the integration of the Gripen into Sweden's sophisticated integrated defense system and the essential part that the "fighter link" datalink system plays in operations. The Gripen is able to "talk" with other Swedish fighters, ground stations, ships, and the Erieye radar in the Argus AWACS aircraft and to share the battle picture without radio voice communication or use of the Gripen's own radar. Although the Gripen is not configured as a stealth aircraft as such, its small size and ability to reach attack position using largely passive means confer upon it extremely good low-observability characteristics.

The attack part of the Gripen's capability was the first to be integrated, largely supplied by the AGM-65 (Rb 75) Maverick antitank missile, the Rbs 15F antiship missile, and the DWS 39 submunitions dispenser. Rocket pods and bombs can be carried, but are rarely seen. Air-to-air

weapons initially comprised only the AIM-9L (Rb 74) Sidewinder, but integration of the AIM-120B (Rb 99) AMRAAM was achieved as the Gripen entered service.

The Gripen was formally inducted into *Flygvapnet* service in June 1996. The first Gripen wing was F7 in Såtenäs, which is also the home of the high-tech *Gripencentrum*, or Gripen training center. Uniquely for a modern fighter, the Gripen has reached initial operational capability and beyond without the use of a two-seat variant. All of the first generation of Gripen pilots and instructors were highly experienced on the Draken or Viggen. Conversion to the JAS 39 was achieved by use of linked dome simulators at the *Gripencentrum* and actual flights in the single-seat JAS 39A. An experienced pilot can be converted in about six months, whereas a new pilot coming from the relatively low-performance Sk 60 trainer requires about a year to become operational.

A two-seat Gripen, the JAS 39B, has indeed been developed, and 28 of the 204 aircraft on order for *Flygvapnet* will be dual-cockpit models. The 14 JAS 39Bs have the same capabilities as the A model, except that the internal gun is not fitted. The second batch of two-seaters, the JAS 39D, will be a very different aircraft. As part of the Swedish military's push to embrace "network-centric warfare," the back-seater of the D will have a fully independent cockpit, albeit with access to the flight controls and mission sensors as needed. He or she (although there are no female Swedish combat aircrew as yet) will be able to act as an on-scene mission commander for a whole package of Swedish or coalition combat aircraft. The D crewman will even be able to command and control unmanned aerial vehicles (UAVs) and unmanned combat aerial vehicles (UCAVs). Other potential roles for the evolved two-seater include suppression of enemy air defenses and electronic warfare.

Although any Gripen is capable of the fighter, attack, and (with the addition of a pod) reconnaissance roles, it is likely that individual units will adopt dedicated roles in future, as the workload required to train for and master each role is probably too great for most pilots.

Despite several false starts, the Gripen seems likely to become the most successful Saab fighter on the export market. Saab offers full industrial cooperation for Gripen customer nations rather than simple offset trade deals. This has, for example, included such things as the construction of domestic appliance factories. In 1998, South Africa ordered 28 Gripens for delivery beginning in 2007. These will be integrated with local weapons such as the Kukri and Derby air-to-air missiles, and will be fitted with retractable refueling probes. Hungary is to lease 14 Gripens from Sweden, but competitions to supply Poland, Austria, and Chile have been unsuccessful. Saab is concentrating its sales efforts on the long delayed and several times postponed Czech Republic fighter decision, and further afield, in places such as Brazil, India, and Thailand.

Future Gripen upgrade options include a re-engining plan and conformal fuel tanks to extend range. With the anticipated lengthy career of the Gripen, it is unclear whether Saab and Sweden will be able to maintain the combat aircraft design and manufacturing capacity until the time comes to replace it. It is quite possible that the Gripen will be Saab's last fighter. If so, it will be a fitting swan song to a tradition of effective and innovative warplanes reaching back to the 1940s.

Left: *Two-seat Gripens will have a significant war role as battle coordinators. The initial JAS 39B seen here can employ the same external weapons as the single-seat A model.*

Below: *Gripens have mostly been painted in tactical gray tones. The trim in national colors on the first prototypes is about as much color as any Gripen has yet shown.*

Eurofighter Typhoon

Built in Europe, the Eurofighter 2000 has overcome many hurdles to enter service the superior to any likely adversary. Its most serious competition is in the export arena, mainly from older but combat-proven American fighters.

EUROFIGHTER TYPHOON F.2

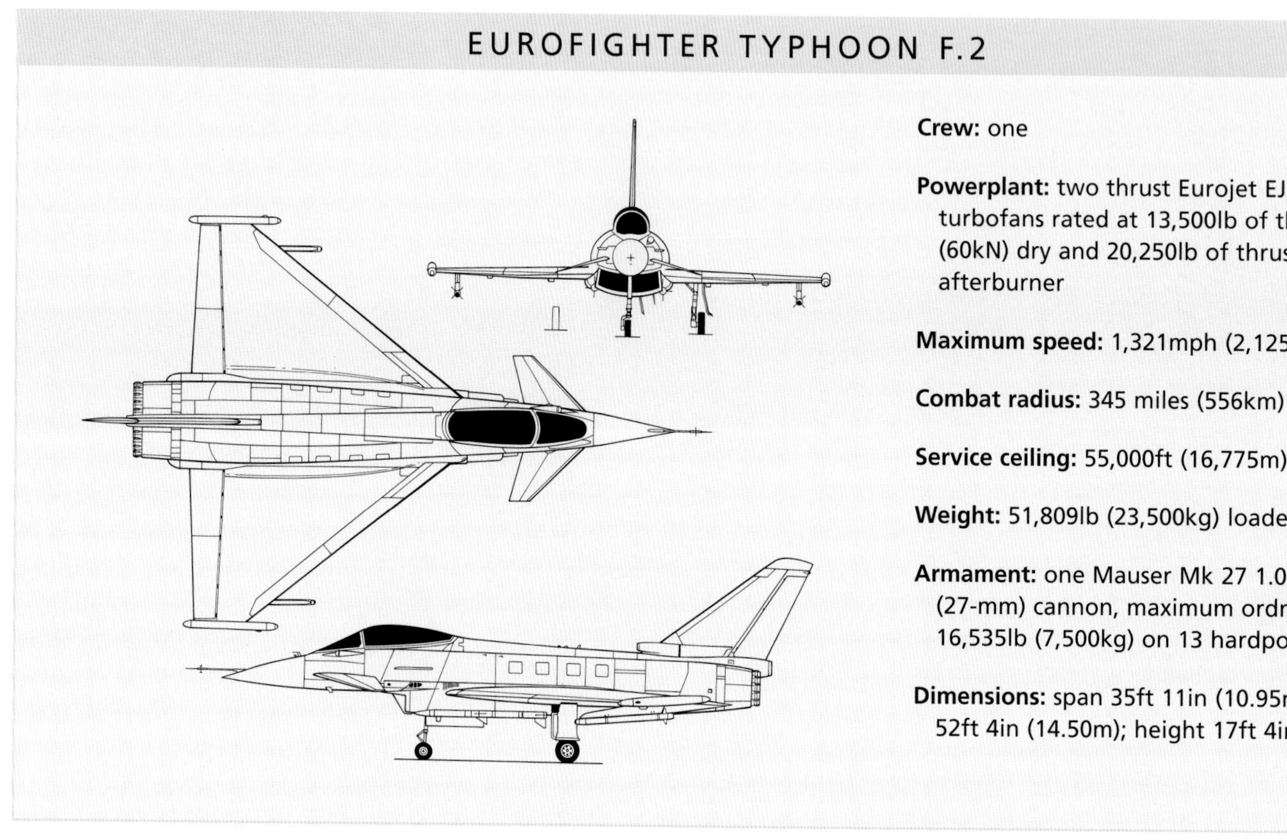

Crew: one

Powerplant: two thrust Eurojet EJ200 turbofans rated at 13,500lb of thrust (60kN) dry and 20,250lb of thrust (90kN) in afterburner

Maximum speed: 1,321mph (2,125km/h)

Combat radius: 345 miles (556km)

Service ceiling: 55,000ft (16,775m)

Weight: 51,809lb (23,500kg) loaded

Armament: one Mauser Mk 27 1.06-in (27-mm) cannon, maximum ordnance 16,535lb (7,500kg) on 13 hardpoints

Dimensions: span 35ft 11in (10.95m); length 52ft 4in (14.50m); height 17ft 4in (5.28m)

Far right: *The Typhoon will give the RAF its first modern agile air combat fighter. Eurofighter is in a league of its own.*

Right: *This early artist's impression of the EF 2000 has a closer resemblance to the EAP demonstrator than the production aircraft.*

Long in the gestation and plagued with political and budgetary difficulties among the four partner nations, the Eurofighter Typhoon is now entering service, 10 years after originally planned. As it does so, it will give four air forces a fighter of unprecedented maneuverability and a beyond-visual-range combat capability superior to any likely to be encountered for the foreseeable future.

In the early 1980s, both Germany and the United Kingdom were looking toward an eventual replacement for the F-4 Phantom in the fighter, strike, and reconnaissance roles. The United Kingdom also needed to replace the Jaguar and Harrier in the long term. Both nations drew up configurations for a new fighter-bomber. The German designs, in particular, bore a strong resemblance to the Eurofighter that was to fly a decade later and enter service a decade after that.

Facing a distinct lack of government support, the industrial partners behind the Panavia Tornado—British Aerospace (BAe, now BAE Systems), Messerschmitt Bolkow Blohm (MBB, later DASA, now

EADS), and Aeritalia of Italy (now Alenia)—used their own funds to develop a common project, the Agile Combat Aircraft (ACA), optimized for air-to-air fighting. Spain's CASA later joined the group, and France came aboard, offering the expertise of Dassault in making delta-winged supersonic fighters.

The ACA was intended to have an in-service date in the early mid-1990s, even as early as 1992, with upgrades over the next decade. This was to prove wildly optimistic, more due to politics rather than technical problems. The main sticking point was France, which needed air-to-surface capability first and air-to-air second, unlike the other nations the priority of which was air defense. By mid-1985, it was clear that a "quintelateral" base for the program would not work. The French insisted on leadership of most

PILOTING THE EUROFIGHTER 2000 TYPHOON

***Above:** The first British Eurofighter flies near the British Aerospace (later BAE Systems) factory at Warton.*

The Typhoon has made regular appearances at the world's major air shows as part of its sales and public relations efforts. A part of this has been an impressive air display routine, described here in somewhat breathless prose by the Eurofighter PR department:

"The Eurofighter Typhoon, during it's 2003 Air Displays, has consistently demonstrated its superb manoeuvrability in a display volume so small, always close and in front of the public, that it has been unmatched by any other aircraft.

"The display starts with a performance take off (less than 300 metres take-off distance) and climb directly for a loop that demonstrates the impressive excess power of the aircraft.

"Coming out of the loop, the pilot performs a high alpha roll, a turn to the right and another high alpha roll in front of the public in order to show the aircraft's capability in manoeuvring around the three axis.

"The display continues with a half Cuban eight, then a break turn, followed by a tight turn to position the aircraft for a loop in front of the public. Coming out of the loop the pilot performs a break turn and a horizontal eight.

***Right:** Eurofighters are being assembled at identical factories in Britain, Spain, Italy, and Germany.*

"Turning in front of the public, the pilot manoeuvres for a defensive barrel roll in order to demonstrate the spectacular ability of the aircraft to rotate around the three axes and to slow down from combat speed to minimum speed in a very short amount of time. At this point, you will see the Eurofighter Typhoon almost still in the air, flying at very low speed (more than 30 degrees nose up) and then accelerate while turning very tightly.

"At the end of the spiral climb, the pilot will turn the aircraft for a split S, followed by a break turn and a loop. Coming out of the loop, the pilot pulls the aircraft into a steep climb, performs two high alpha rolls and, at the end, closes the manoeuvre with a split S directly for landing, demonstrating again the unique capability of the Eurofighter to manoeuvre and slow down in very small spaces."

of the key posts within the organization and 50 percent of the work share, and also wanted to build and test all the prototypes in France.

The French really wanted to proceed with their own design, based on the ACX, a demonstrator for which (later named Rafale A) was already under construction. France pulled out, but the remaining countries decided to proceed with what was now called the European Fighter Aircraft (EFA), of which 765 were to be built (250 each for the Royal Air Force (RAF) and the *Luftwaffe*, 165 for the *Aeronautica Militare Italiana* (AMI), and 100 for Spain's *Ejercito del Aire*). Delivery to the participating air forces was to begin from 1998 at a total program cost of £20 billion. The first prototypes were to fly in 1991.

After a rapid development, in 1986 BAe flew a technology demonstrator aircraft called the EAP (Experimental Aircraft Prototype). Although superficially similar to the Eurofighter that was to follow, the EAP was constructed mainly of heavy alloys and used many Tornado components, including the fin and engines. It has been pointed out that the EAP was the only aircraft to be entirely designed and built under the BAe banner and not a collaboration or inherited from another manufacturer when BAe was created. The EAP was retired in 1991, but provided much useful data on the general configuration and the flight control system (FCS) for the EFA.

Unfortunately, other factors then came into play. The fall of the Berlin Wall saw the German government forced to spend billions on reunification and reconstruction of the former East Germany. In 1992, it threatened to pull out, but hoped the technology so far demonstrated could be used in a lighter European aircraft. Italy threatened to follow suit, but was persuaded to stay in. The Germans themselves had devised a punitive penalty system that was written into the contracts, and by this time it was too expensive to go back to square one. Various less capable "New EFA" configurations were studied before Germany decided to procure a smaller number of standard aircraft, stripped of their advanced defensive aids subsystem (DASS). By 1993, the schedule had slipped so that production was delayed until 1995 with deliveries from 2000. The program cost had risen to about £41 billion.

Complex renegotiations saw the four nations diverge in the equipment fit. Germany eventually decided to procure 40 of its aircraft optimized for

Left: *Unlike the Rafale, the EF 2000 has a conventional center-mounted control stick.*

Below: *One of the British Eurofighter development aircraft refuels from an RAF VC 10 tanker.*

Left: *Norway is one of several possible export customers for the Typhoon. This German development aircraft was evaluated by a Norwegian pilot.*

Left: *Germany was the first partner nation to fly an EF 2000, in March 1994. Service entry began nearly a decade later.*

Below: The first British Eurofighter was painted black during spinning trials in 2000.

ground attack to replace Tornado bombers. Construction was divided among the four partner nations, each with its own final assembly line. Britain was to build the cockpit, nose, tail, and part of the rear fuselage; Italy was to build the rest of the rear fuselage and the left wing, as well as the armament control systems; Spain had the right wing and communication systems. Germany's responsibility was the flight control system, radar,

Above: This development Eurofighter only carries a pair of dummy missiles. The production aircraft will be armed with a wide range of mostly European weapons.

and identification systems. Modern computer-controlled design and manufacturing processes allow the airframe components to come together with precision despite being manufactured in diverse locations. The first aircraft—German—made its long-awaited first flight on March 27, 1994 from Manching, Germany, and began what was to be a successful flight test program. It was followed by six others, three of them two-seaters.

The Typhoon has a delta wing and canard foreplanes. The aircraft is naturally unstable in pitch and is kept in trim by the FBW control system acting on the foreplanes. The structure is 70 percent carbon-fiber composites (CFC) by surface area, 12 percent glass reinforced plastics (GRP), and only 15 percent metal, mainly aluminum and titanium alloys.

Although the first prototypes used some conventional dial instruments, the cockpit of the production aircraft is dominated by three multifunction displays (MFDs). Each has a three-color CRT display. The HUD is a wide-angle GEC Marconi unit, which is able to display imagery from the infrared search-and-track system, as well as conventional flight and weapons aiming information. The cockpit is "completely marvelous," says test pilot Chris Worning. "Information is there when you need it. Not too much and not too little."

Most radical is the British Aerospace direct voice input (DVI) system. This allows many functions, such as slewing the radar, selecting (but *not* firing) missiles, changing cockpit displays, and checking fuel status to be activated by the pilot's spoken keyword. The sophisticated helmet sight system will allow HUD and other symbology to be projected on the visor and weapons to be aimed up to 180 degrees off boresight.

The new ECR-90 multimode pulse-Doppler look-up/look-down radar was selected for development in May 1990, building on the proven and highly regarded Blue Vixen used by the Sea Harrier. While optimized for AMRAAM use, ECR-90 also provides continuous-wave (CW) illumination for semiactive radar homing air-to-air missiles. An infrared search and track (IRST) sensor supplements the radar. Integrated defensive aids comprise missile approach, laser, and radar warning systems, wingtip ESM/ECM pods, chaff/flare dispensers, and a towed radar decoy.

The EFA was renamed the Eurofighter 2000 in 1994, and in 1998 the Eurofighter Typhoon. At the time it was said that the German, Italian, and Spanish equivalents (Taifun, Tifone, and Tifón, respectively) would be used by the different air forces, but that idea appears to have quietly died.

Soon after the test program began, there was

pressure in Germany to halve its order but keep the same share of the work. Another renegotiation saw all the nations reduce their orders. The new total of 620 comprised 232 for the United Kingdom, 180 for Germany, 121 for Italy, and 87 for Spain. Britain's work share was increased. The overall program cost was slightly reduced, due to the smaller order, to £39 billion.

The Typhoon has had some export success and remains a contender in several other nations' requirements. In 1998, Greece became the first nonpartner nation to order the Typhoon, agreeing to purchase 60, with options for 30 more. A final contract signature was delayed due to the cost of staging the 2004 Olympic Games. Austria has ordered 24 Typhoons to replace its elderly Saab Drakens from 2007. Singapore remains a possible customer, and Norway has shown a strong interest in the type.

On November 21, 2002, the Eurofighter program suffered its first accident. The Spanish two-seat prototype was conducting single-engine flight tests when the other engine failed and neither could be relit. The cause was traced to a fault in an early version of the EJ200 engine, since superseded.

The Typhoon has a fixed armament of one 1.06-in (27-mm) Mauser cannon on the starboard side of the fuselage. Controversially, the RAF proposes to delete the gun from its second batch of aircraft. The gun will actually be retained for balance reasons, but not connected or supplied with ammunition. The reasoning is financial, eliminating the maintenance and support costs of the gun over the aircraft lifetime. As well as AMRAAM and ASRAAM missiles, already in service, the Typhoon will be integrated with the MBDA Meteor beyond visual range air-to-air missile (BVRAAM) and the Iris-T short-range infrared air-to-air missile. Of the 13 hardpoints, 12 can carry air-to-air missiles.

Air-to-ground weapons proposed but not yet cleared for the Typhoon include the Storm Shadow cruise missile, Brimstone antiarmor missile, ALARM antiradar missile, Harpoon antiship missile, and the full range of Nato laser-guided, satellite-guided, and free-fall bombs.

By June 30, 2003, the first production aircraft was ready for handover at a ceremony at Manching. The total program cost was now more than £50 billion. A few weeks later, the Typhoon finally began to enter service, at least with operational test units. Most of the first aircraft will be two-seaters, such as the 13 Typhoon T.1s delivered to the RAF's Typhoon Operational Evaluation Unit (OEU), also known as No. 17 Squadron. The RAF single-seaters are designated Typhoon F.2.

Full squadron service is expected in 2006, and the Typhoon will remain in use till 2050. Future upgrades may include a thrust-vectoring version of the EJ200 engine.

Above: *A Typhoon's wingtip pods contain radar warning equipment on the left wing and the defensive aids sub system (DASS) on the right.*

Below: *The second German Eurofighter was the fifth to fly. It had the Eurojet EJ 200 engine unlike the first two aircraft, which had RB.199s as in the Tornado.*

Lockheed Martin F/A-22 Raptor

The hugely expensive F/A-22 will offer the USAF its first real stealth fighter and introduce thrust vectoring and "supercruise." Beset by budget difficulties and a changing world, many question the need for it in the twenty-first century.

LOCKHEED MARTIN F/A-22A RAPTOR

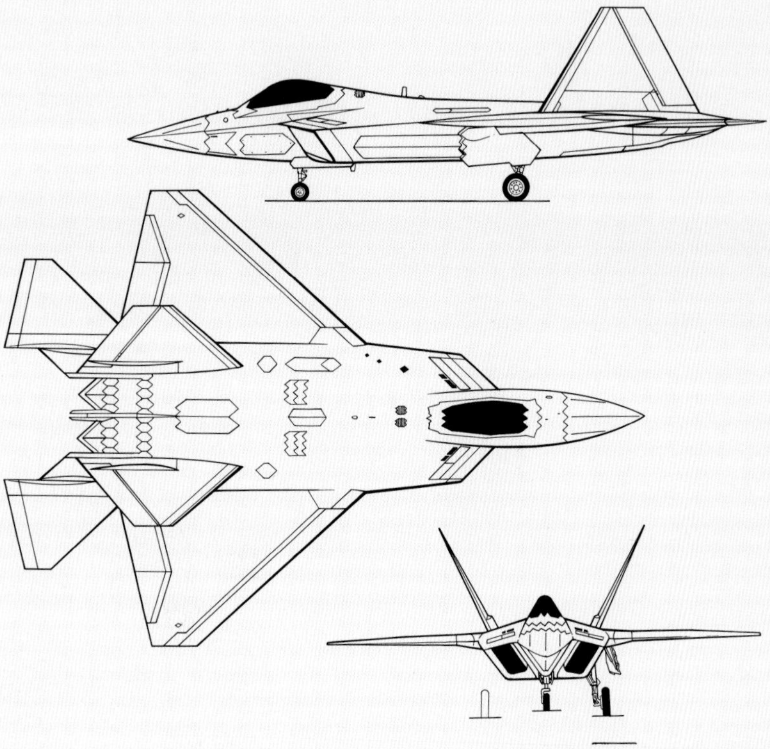

Crew: one

Powerplant: two Pratt & Whitney F119-PW-100 turbofans with thrust vectoring rated at 38,000lb of thrust (169kN) with afterburner

Maximum speed: more than 1,320mph (2,130km/h)

Combat radius: classified, but ATF specification for 808 miles (1,300km)

Service ceiling: more than 60,000ft (18,288m)

Weight: 65,337lb (29,637kg) loaded

Armament: one M61A2 Vulcan 0.79-in (20-mm) cannon, three internal weapons bays containing up to six AIM-120C AMRAAMs and two AIM-9X Sidewinders

Dimensions: span 44ft 6in (13.56m); length 62ft 1in (18.9m); height 16ft 7in (5.05m)

***Far right:** The YF-22s were painted in the gray colors seen on USAF F-16s. This is N22YF, the first aircraft.*

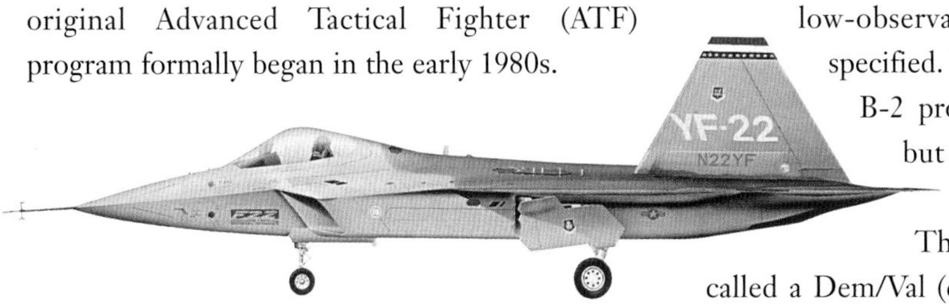

***Right:** The F-22A Raptor was preceded by two YF-22s, which differed in many respects, only some visibly.*

Designed as an "Air Dominance Fighter," the Lockheed Martin F/A-22 Raptor has been long in gestation, but promises to offer the US Air Force (USAF) a virtually unbeatable fighter for the twenty-first century. Its huge cost and doubts over its utility in a world post–Cold War may see far fewer Raptors serving than was planned when the original Advanced Tactical Fighter (ATF) program formally began in the early 1980s.

The major US military aircraft manufacturers had all done work on an abortive ATF requirement in the 1970s, so were well placed when the USAF invited industry to share ideas for a new fighter in 1981. More detailed requirements were issued in 1983 and emphasized speed and range. For the first time in an official requirement, low-observability or "stealth" was specified. In this period, the F-117 and B-2 programs were well under way, but remained in the "black" world, shrouded in secrecy.

The USAF conducted what they called a Dem/Val (demonstration and validation)

Right: Details of the YF-22 were kept secret until after the first prototype was completed. The first aircraft was unveiled to the media and invited guests in 1990.

program, rather than a "fly-off" as with the YF-16 and YF-17. This began with analysis of "paper" proposals from Boeing, General Dynamics, Grumman, Northrop, and Lockheed. In 1986, the two prime contractors were chosen, and they selected program partners to help develop their highly sophisticated designs into production aircraft. Lockheed, with Boeing and General Dynamics, was contracted to build two YF-22 prototypes, while Northrop, partnered with McDonnell Douglas, was to build two YF-23s. One of each was to have General Electric YF-120 engines and the other Pratt & Whitney YF-119s.

PILOTING THE LOCKHEED MARTIN F/A-22 RAPTOR

Above: The F-22 is the first fighter designed from the start with thrust-vectoring engines. The F119's nozzles operate through a 40 degree arc.

As well as its high-speed capabilities, the F/A-22 has incredible low speed maneuverability, as test pilot Jon Beesley also wrote in *Code One.* "Just as the Raptor will change the nature of air combat at supersonic speeds, it will also enhance the capabilities of engagements at low speeds. These enhanced capabilities, only dreamed about in the past, are emerging from the high angle-of-attack, or AOA, test program.

"Many aircraft define the beginning of high AOA flight at about 30 degrees. On the F-22, stable flight test points are routinely held stable at a positive 60 degrees AOA and a negative 40 degrees AOA. Before the Raptor, only experimental or specialized aircraft, such as the thrust-vectoring X-31 or F-16MATV, could claim 60 degrees AOA.

"As we began the flight test program, we were keenly aware that lateral directional stability of most fighter aircraft drops off sharply between 25 and 30 degrees AOA. Our initial tests of the F-22 showed sideslip excursions around 30 degrees AOA, which were greater than we desired and which indicated a lower stability than predicted. Although this instability was not great enough to stop the testing, we addressed it in the first software update. Through the magic of software and all the smart folks who know how to use it, the airplane now passes through this AOA range with no apparent change in handling qualities.

"The magic of the flight control system and the wizardry of the thrust vectoring supply ample pitch control in the Raptor. Pitch control is never in question when we move the nose around at high AOA. We have demonstrated pitch rates of greater than forty degrees per second and abrupt pull-ups at 35,000 feet. These 'Cobra-like' manoeuvres will be even more impressive at lower altitudes where we will have higher thrust available for thrust vectoring."

Right: "Raptor 01" was the first F-22A development aircraft and is seen here at Edwards Air Force Base during the test program in 1997-98.

Dave Ferguson flew the first Lockheed YF-22, with the GE engines, from the factory at Palmdale to Edwards AFB on September 29, 1990. The second aircraft followed a month later. The YF-22, unofficially named Lightning II, had an unusual triangular cross-section nose section, large tailfins, and smaller tailplanes. The square-section engine nozzles rotated up and down to vector the thrust for exceptional maneuverability.

The Northrop/McDonnell Douglas YF-23 was faster, lighter, and probably stealthier than the YF-22, but lacked thrust vectoring. The very shallow angle of its all-moving vertical tails allowed control in roll, pitch, and yaw, supplemented by large two-section flaperons on the diamond-shaped wing.

In April 1991, the F-22 with the F119 was chosen as the winning combination. Lockheed had convinced the USAF it could better manage the whole project and had demonstrated a wider flight envelope than Northrop. The YF-22 was substantially revised before Paul Metz flew the first engineering and manufacturing development (EMD) F-22 on September 7, 1997. The tailfins were reduced in area, the wing and tailplane planform changed, and the nose reshaped, and APG-77 active array radar was fitted.

Many fundamental aspects of the F-22's design, such as its same-plane wing and tailplane, the alignment of fins and intake sides, and use of internal weapons bays, are intended to minimize its radar cross-section and make it "stealthy." Advances in low-observable (LO) technology since the 1970s-designed F-117 Nighthawk mean that a "faceted" shape is no longer essential and curved surfaces can be used in a stealth design. Radar-absorbent materials are used throughout the F-22, and all antennas are embedded within the surfaces and leading edges. The lower weapons bay can carry up to six AIM-120C AMRAAMs, with two AIM-9X Sidewinders in the side bays. The M61A2 cannon is concealed behind a quick-opening door in the starboard wing root.

One of the main selling points of the F-22 is "supercruise," or the ability to fly at high supersonic speeds without afterburner. Afterburner is used to boost the aircraft to the point and then turned off to cruise supersonically. Supercruise was actually possible with some earlier aircraft, such as the B-58 Hustler, EE Lightning, and Su-15 "Flagon," but the Raptor is the first aircraft to have been designed with it from the outset. As test pilot Paul Metz explained in Lockheed Martin's in-house magazine *Code One*, supercruise gives both offensive and defensive advantages. "The ability to move against an adversary at high speeds gives fighter pilots advantages they call 'first look, first shot, first kill.' The first pilot to see an adversary is more likely to get off a successful shot and survive the encounter. The kinematic range of an AIM-120 AMRAAM, for example, increases by 50 percent as aircraft speed increases from 0.9 to 1.5 Mach (this assumes an altitude advantage for the shooter). That is, the missile can reach targets 50 percent farther away

***Above:** The second F-22A is seen on an early flight from the factory in Marietta, Georgia. The Raptor promises "air dominance" over any battlefield.*

***Left:** Raptor's stealth is due to careful alignment and the blending of surfaces. Access panels are kept to a minimum to preserve surface smoothness.*

because its initial speed coming off an F-22 flying 1.5 Mach is much faster. The Raptor easily supercruises in this speed regime. This missile range advantage intensifies the F-22's sensor advantage—the radar on a Raptor can see a bandit long before a bandit's radar detects a Raptor."

"In a defensive situation, supercruise increases stealth," says Metz. "Although not yet a 'cloaking device,' stealth does delay the enemy's shot opportunity until late in the engagement. Against a ground-to-air threat, high speed equates to reduced reaction times from detection to launch and reduced kinematic ranges for surface-to-air missiles or antiaircraft artillery."

The Raptor can be fitted with four underwing stores pylons for carriage of weapons or external fuel tanks, although this would greatly compromise the stealth performance. In combat, external weapons would not be carried until after the first days of a war, when the enemy's radar-based air defenses will have been largely neutralized. The USAF Global Strike Task Force (GSTF) concept envisages using the F/A-22 and the B-2A Spirit as a "kick-down-the-door force" destroying the enemy's command and control system and achieving air dominance by sweeping opposing fighters from the skies.

In September 2002, the head of Air Combat Command and the Secretary of the Air Force announced the redesignation of the Raptor as the F/A-22—the extra letter signifying attack: "to emphasize the multiple roles and many dimensions of the Raptor." It should be noted that

Above: *Chief F-22 test pilot Paul Metz boards the first Raptor for a test flight. Metz flew the YF-23 for Northrop before joining Lockheed in 1991.*

Right: *Viewed head on, the intakes and fins are aligned and the tailplane is mounted behind the wing to reduce the edges and corners the radar can lock on to.*

to date no testing or even carriage of air-to-ground weapons has occurred, mainly to keep the flight test program within the allotted budget.

Plans originally called for up to 750 F-22s, including a two-seat F-22B variant, but this was canceled in 1996 due to a lack of funding. A dual-control version may appear in the future. The Pentagon later reduced the planned fleet from 648 to 442 and, finally, 339 Raptors and delayed the operational service date from 2001 to 2005. Each of these changes increased the program and unit costs.

Some advocates are calling for F/A-22 numbers to be raised again to 700 aircraft to meet USAF plans for seven wings and to equip each of 10 Air Expeditionary Forces (AEF) with two squadrons each. This would also bring the unit flyaway price down to around $75 million, close to that of the F-15. Currently a Raptor is valued at $83 million, excluding research and development costs.

The first F/A-22 to be delivered to the USAF arrived at Nellis AFB, Nevada, in January 2003. The first F/A-22 to be used for training new pilots was delivered to the 43rd Fighter Squadron at Tyndall AFB, Florida, in September 2003, and initial operational capability (IOC) with the 1st Fighter Wing at Langley AFB, Virginia, is slated for 2005. Deliveries are expected to continue until 2013 to meet the USAF orders. Export potential is limited by government restrictions on technology transfer, but future customers may include F-15 users Japan, Israel, and Saudi Arabia.

Above: *It will have been nearly 20 years since the first YF-22 flew before a Raptor squadron is declared fully operational.*

Left: *Radar-absorbent materials and coatings reduce the visual and infrared signature of the F-22A. The first USAF aircraft wear more traditional colors.*

Lockheed Martin X-35 JSF

The X-35, Lockheed Martin's winning contender in the Joint Strike Fighter contest, is in some ways deceptively conventional. In fact, it embodies a range of capabilities that will fulfill requirements well into the twenty-first century.

***Right:** The X-35B was rebuilt from the X-35A and in July 2001 demonstrated its ability to make a short takeoff, a supersonic dash, and a vertical landing.*

The Joint Strike Fighter (JSF), the biggest military aircraft procurement program in history, will replace Harriers and Hornets, F-16s, and A-10s within the US services and will likely equal the F-16 for export sales. More than 3,000 are to be built for the US and UK alone, but this may eventually reach more than 6,000 examples, with many nations almost certain to select it as their next fighter.

In the early 1990s, the US armed forces were facing a "tactical aviation train wreck." The US Air Force (USAF) was facing block obsolescence of the F-15 and F-16, the US Marine Corps (USMC) needed a Harrier replacement, and the A-12 Avenger attack aircraft of the US Navy (USN) had just been canceled due to massive cost overruns.

A post-Cold War "bottom-up" defense review led to a project called JAST (Joint Advanced Strike Technology). It studied how civilian methods, including "lean manufacturing," could be used to lower procurement costs. The "joint" part of JAST (and JSF) was cooperation between the three services (and the British, who also sought a Harrier replacement) to devise a family of related airframes that could meet each service's needs, yet be similar enough to achieve significant production economies.

Getting tri-service agreement to essentially build the same aircraft was hard. The USAF valued speed, sophisticated avionics, and stealth, the USN wanted

X-35C JOINT STRIKE FIGHTER DEMONSTRATOR

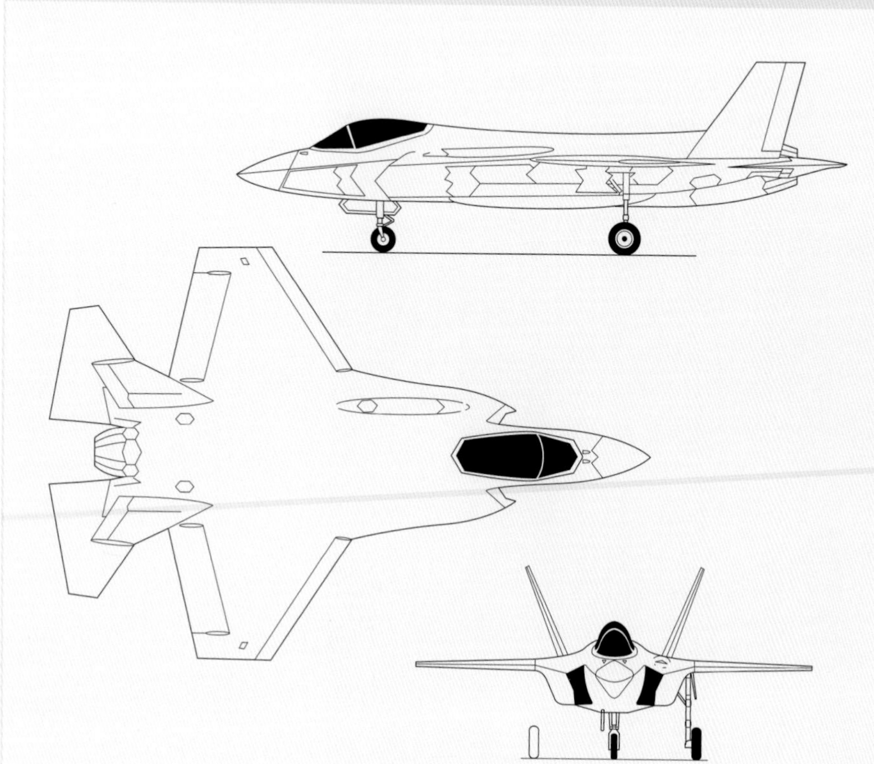

Crew: one

Powerplant: One Pratt & Whitney F119-PW-611C turbofan derivative, rated at 42,000lb of thrust (187kN) with afterburning

Maximum speed: Mach 1.5

Combat radius: 691 miles (1,112km)

Service ceiling: more than 50,000ft (15,240m)

Weight: 50,000lb (22,680kg) loaded

Armament: Six AIM-120C AMRAAM or two AIM-120C AMRAAM and two 2,000-lb (907-kg) JDAM in internal fuselage bay; provision for one 0.79-in (20-mm) M61A2 rotary cannon with 400 rounds in starboard wingroot (USAF CTOL variant); provision for four underwing pylons with 5,000lb (2,268kg) capacity each

Dimensions: span 43ft (13.12m); length 50ft 11in (15.52m); height 13ft 4in (4.07m)

X-35B
STOVL

***Above:** One of the specific features of the X-35C is a stronger undercarriage able to take the added stresses of catapult takeoffs and arrested landings.*

two engines and two seats, and the USMC wanted vertical or short takeoff capability. The USN was eventually convinced that a single modern engine could be made to be more than twice as reliable as the previous generation of fighter powerplants. It was also assured that a single-crew airplane would be as effective as a two-seater. A goal of 80 percent commonality between the three services' aircraft was set and sticking to target costs was awarded as much priority as meeting performance figures.

In 1994, grants of $30 million apiece were given to Boeing, Lockheed Martin, Northrop Grumman, and McDonnell Douglas to come up with initial "paper" designs. The latter two companies soon combined their efforts. Their design for the USMC version was unique in having a separate engine for takeoffs and landings.

In 1996, two of the three designs were "downselected" for the next phase, engineering and manufacturing development, or EMD. The McDonnell Douglas/Northrop Grumman design was not one of them, and, within a year, Boeing had absorbed McDonnell Douglas. The two remaining contenders were asked to build demonstrators (not prototypes) that proved their design could meet all requirements. Lockheed Martin opted to build two airframes, the conventional takeoff and landing (CTOL) X-35A and the carrier-suitable (CV) X-35C. The X-35A was then rebuilt into the short takeoff and vertical landing (STOVL) X-35B.

***Right:** A head-on view shows some of the stealth features of the X-35, like the alignment of intakes and fins, and the aerodynamic bumps ahead of the former.*

Boeing chose a slightly different approach. Its X-32A was built to demonstrate its suitability for both the "baseline" CTOL and the CV requirements, while the X-32B was the STOVL version. Boeing chose to create vertical lift on the X-32B by directing engine exhaust through swiveling nozzles as on the Harrier, with extra ducts for roll and pitch control in the hover. Lockheed used a vectoring rear exhaust and a shaft-driven lift fan behind the cockpit.

The X-32 was one of the most extraordinary-looking aircraft ever to fly. First proposed with tailplanes, it emerged as a tailless aircraft with a high-mounted, modified delta wing. This had little anhedral, unlike the Harrier, and the undercarriage was of conventional layout. Most striking was the giant forward-raked intake under the nose necessary to supply air to the Pratt & Whitney JSF119-614, which was rated at about 40,000lb of thrust (118kN) with afterburner. The X-32A first flew on September 18, 2000.

Lockheed's X-35 design was much more conventional in shape, resembling a scaled-down F-22. The X-35 had unusually shaped side intakes with "aerodynamic bumps" on the fuselage sides, rather than splitter plates or ramps. The tailplanes extended beyond the jet pipe, which swiveled downward in the X-35B's STOVL mode in a manner similar to the Russian Yak-141 "Freestyle" of the early 1990s. The engine was also a derivative of the P&W F119, named JSF119-611. In vertical mode, the X-35B's main nozzle generates up to 37,000lb of thrust (165 kN), the lift fan 18,000lb of thrust (80kN), and the roll control nozzles 2,000lb of thrust (9kN) each. These features made the X-35B about 3,968lb (1,800kg) heavier than the A and C.

Lieutenant Colonel Paul Smith made the first flight in the X-35A on October 24, 2000. The X-35C flew on December 16 that year.

Under the JSF EMD program phase, the X-planes were not expected to demonstrate mission systems, weapons employment, or stealth, although both were tested with representative weapons loads and exhibited many low-observable qualities. Both

PILOTING THE LOCKHEED MARTIN F-35 JSF

Above: *The X-35C first flew in California, but was mainly evaluated at the Navy's test center in Patuxent River, Maryland.*

The Lockheed Martin team concluded the X-35B flight test program with the so-called "Mission X" in July 2001. This was described in a contemporary press release:

"EDWARDS AIR FORCE BASE, CA—The Lockheed Martin Joint Strike Fighter X-35B completed one of history's most successful flight test programs on July 30 after achieving what no aircraft has ever done: a short takeoff, a level supersonic dash, and a vertical landing in a single flight.

"Test pilots Major Art Tomassetti of the US Marine Corps and Simon Hargreaves of BAE Systems each accomplished the unprecedented feat, which will be required of production JSFs for the Marines, Royal Navy, and Royal Air Force. Tomassetti flew 'Mission X,' as the operation is known to JSF team members, on July 20. Hargreaves followed up with a Mission X flight on July 26.

"'This completes the third and final phase of a concept demonstration program that has redefined the standard for flight test. The Lockheed Martin JSF team made a promise and kept it—including fielding a demonstrator aircraft that is representative of the one we have planned for production,' said Tom Burbage, executive vice president and general manager of the Lockheed Martin JSF program. 'That means fewer expensive development hurdles to clear and a more seamless transition into the program's next phase, Engineering and Manufacturing Development.'"

featured internal weapons bays and careful alignment of door edges and other parts.

The X-35 had many components from other aircraft. The main landing gear was derived from the Grumman A-6 Intruder and is built to cope with the stresses of carrier landings, so is over-designed for the conventional and STOVL versions. The nose gear came from the F-15E Eagle. For hover testing of the X-35B, a "dummy" gear loaded with strain gauges was fitted initially. The X-35's environmental cooling system came from the F/A-18E/F. The core of the Pratt & Whitney F119 engine and the auxiliary power system come from the F/A-22, while the engine-driven hydraulic pumps came from the rival YF-23. The accessory drive comes from the B-2 bomber. The ejection seat is the same one used on the AV-8B, and the two large multifunction cockpit displays come from the C-130J Hercules. Many subsystems and controls come from the F-16.

After demonstration of the conventional mode at Edwards AFB, the X-35A was taken back to Palmdale and rebuilt as the X-35B with lift fan and roll control ducts. It made its first hover tests in February 2001, followed by STOVL flights and transitions to and from the horizontal and vertical.

During its flight-test program, the X-35B completed 27 vertical landings, 14 short takeoffs, 18 vertical takeoffs, was flown by four pilots from the US and the UK, broke the sound barrier on five separate occasions, and completed five aerial refuelings.

"The best reward for this team's hard work over

Left: *The F-35C cockpit will have full-color displays and a sidestick. To the left of the throttle is the nozzle position lever.*

the years is a great success story like this. It was a privilege to be a small part of this history-making event," said Maj. Tomassetti, after becoming the first pilot to achieve a short takeoff, supersonic dash, and vertical landing in a single flight.

His mission included an automatic short takeoff at 80 knots, an in-flight conversion from the STOVL propulsion system to the conventional system, a climb to 25,000ft (7,620m), and reaching Mach 1.05. He then conducted a series of flying-qualities tests, converted back to STOVL mode, decelerated to a hover at 150ft (46m) above ground, and landed vertically. Hargreaves repeated the Mission X performance on July 26, adding a steep afterburner climb, 360-degree rolls at 20 degrees angle of attack, and an aerial refueling. He achieved Mach 1.06 at 25,000ft (7,620m). In a subsequent flight, he demonstrated a 60-knot automatic short takeoff (approximately 500ft/152m), then transitioned into a sustained hover, executed a 360-degree pirouette, and landed vertically with an aircraft weight of more than 34,000lbs (15,422kg)—double the hover weight of legacy STOVL aircraft.

"The ability to convert from STOVL to CTOL at full power ensures that no performance is sacrificed during the conversion and demonstrates the ruggedness and simplicity of the conversion process," said Hargreaves, also a Harrier pilot. In a flight later the same day, X-35 Chief Test Pilot Tom Morgenfeld expanded the X-35B's flight envelope with a full afterburner takeoff and accelerations to Mach 1.2 at 25,000 and 30,000 ft (7,620 and 9,144 m.)"

On October 26, 2001, the US Department of Defense announced the winner of the competition. In a press conference at the Pentagon, linked by video to Boeing and Lockheed Martin plants across the United States, Secretary of the Air Force James Roche said: "Both demo programs were very good. But on the basis of strengths, weaknesses, and degrees of risk of the program, it is our conclusion ... that the Lockheed Martin team is the winner of the Joint Strike Fighter program on a best-value basis." At the same time it was announced that the production aircraft would be designated the F-35. This was a further blow to the once-logical US designation system, under which the Lockheed product should by rights be the F-24, following the YF-23 as the last used fighter designation.

Below: *Behind the X-35B's cockpit is a lift fan driven by the main engine. This was a more radical than the vectoring nozzle system proposed by Boeing.*

The eventual value of the contract is a massive $200 billion, with a $4.8 billion going to Pratt & Whitney as main subcontractor. Despite lobbying in some states for Boeing to be allowed to build F-35s as a second-source supplier, the Pentagon insists that it is a "winner take all" deal. General Electric is developing the YF120 engine as a likely second-source powerplant for later production batches.

The system development and demonstration (SDD) phase will follow. This will see 22 aircraft built, 14 of them flying, and eight for ground testing to verify the product Lockheed Martin proposed. The first will fly in 2005, with production deliveries of the USAF's F-35A version in 2008.

The details of the actual F-35 will differ considerably from the X-35s, as will the performance specifications. An estimate of the relative costs puts the USAF F-35A at $40 million, while the X-35B and C will be $50 million apiece. So far costs have been kept in check, but the most complicated, risky part of the program has yet to be undertaken.

The JSF has always had strong export potential, particularly to replace F-16s, F/A-18s, and Harriers. Starting with Britain, other countries were invited to share the development costs and in return have their companies become eligible for competition as suppliers. British Aerospace (BAe), now BAE Systems, joined Lockheed Martin's JSF team in mid-1997. Rolls-Royce had a hand in the STOVL engines of both HSF contenders. By default, the US Department of Defense selection of the

***Above:** The first version of Lockheed-Martin's JSF to fly was the conventional X-35A, which validated the basic handling characteristics of the design.*

Lockheed Martin product became the United Kingdom's choice as well, although Britian had no actual say in the decision.

The British F-35s will replace the Harrier GR.9 aboard the Royal Navy's new aircraft carriers and on land bases. The exact British designation is not yet known, but the JSF is the Future Joint Combat Aircraft (FJCA) in British parlance. Britain's £2 billion contribution to the JSF's EMD phase gives it the only significant non-US voice in how it will develop and evolve, even if it does not buy a single example. More will be needed to get it through the SDD phase and into squadron service.

After a long period of uncertainty over what size of carrier to go for, which would largely dictate the British FJCA choice, the British Ministry of Defence made its decision in 2002 to essentially have BAE Systems build a carrier designed by Thales of France. It chose the STOVL (F-35B) version for both the Royal Navy (RN) and Royal Air Force (RAF) requirement.

Although the USMC is determined to acquire the STOVL version, there is still some doubt over this version, as it is the most complex option for which the requirement is the least. It could still fall victim to future technical difficulties or US budget cuts.

Manufacturers in the UK will build large parts of all F-35s, including the fully equipped rear fuselage and tail surfaces, and the outer wings of the CV variant. Rolls-Royce will largely develop the X-35B's lift engine. Martin-Baker will make the seats, Smith's Industries the data and voice input systems, and many smaller parts will also be sourced from manufacturers in the UK.

The other partner nations are Australia, Canada, Denmark, Italy, the Netherlands, Norway, and Turkey, all of which have contributed funds without necessarily committing to purchasing any aircraft. Singapore and Israel are the most recent nations to join. The latter is said to be particularly interested in a two-seat version.

Current plans call for production of 3,002 F-35s. The USAF requires 1,763 F-35As, the USMC 609 F-35Bs, and the USN 480 F-35Cs. The RAF/RN will take up to 150, although this is dependent to some degree on the final size of the planned aircraft carriers and the air wings they can carry.

The X-35C has already been retired for museum display in Patuxent River, so it is unlikely to contain many of the secrets of the production F-35C. Likewise the F-35B has gone on show at the Smithsonian Air and Space Museum. When last heard of, the X-32 was languishing in a hangar in Pax River.

***Below:** The X-35 prototypes had a USAF-style boom and receptacle refueling system, but British, US Navy, and Marine Corps F-35s will have a retractable probe.*

Index

Page numbers in **bold** indicate main entries

Picture Credits

All photos Aerospace/ Art-Tech except: **TRH:** 31 (TRH/R. Winslade), 39t (TRH/E Nevill), 43, 45t, 46b, 59b, 66t, 67, 68t, 69 (TRH/R Winslade), 69b, 71b (TRH/E Partridge), 74, 75t&m, 83t&b, 99t, 100b, 101t (TRH/RAF Museum), 114t, 117t, 119t, 139 (TRH/QAPI), 140t, 140b (TRH/IWM), 142t, 142b, 147t (TRH/ NASM), 147b, 154t&b (TRH /US National Archives), 159b, 162t (TRH/E Nevill), 188t, 193 (TRH/E Nevill), 196bb (TRH/E Nevill), 200 (TRH/ USAF), 206b (TRH/ E Nevill), 207t (TRH/US Navy), 211 (TRH/E Nevill), 225b (RAF/TRH), 226t, 230t, 232t (TRH/DOD), 235, 237t (TRH/British Aerospace), 238b (TRH/SAAB Scania), 239b (TRH/SAAB), 248t (TRH/USAF), 248b, 249 (TRH/Tim Senior), 250t (TRH/Tim Senior), 250b (TRH/USAF), 251t (TRH/ USAF), 265 (TRH/Hughes Aircraft), 266b (TRH/ DOD USAF), 269t (TRH/US Navy), 274t (TRH/BAe) 278t (TRH/BAe), 281t (TRH/ E Nevill), 282t (TRH/E Nevill), 284b (TRH/Dave Willis), 285b (TRH/E Nevill), 286t (TRH/ E Nevill); **Lockheed Martin:** 7, 312t&b, 313, 314 t&b, 315t&b , 316 317t&b; **US Dept. of Defense:** 8t, 11t; **Philip Jarrett:** 72t, 75b, 76, 77t; **Hugh W. Cowin:** 73, 76b, 77b; **Jim Winchester:** 51t&b, 236t (photo Robert Hewson); **Courtesy of Eurofighter:** 301, 304t

Acknowledgements

The author would like to give special thanks to Tony Holmes and Osprey Publishing for permission to quote from Osprey's *Aircraft of the Aces* and *Combat Aircraft* book series. Thanks also to Mick Oakey and Nick Stroud at *Aeroplane*, Rob Hewson, Austin J. Brown, Robert F. Dorr and Jon Lake.